ESSEX FARMING
1900–2000

by

Peter Wormell

We do not inherit our farms from our fathers,
we borrow them from our children.

For

STEPHEN

and his boys

Daniel and Guy

By the same Author

Anatomy of Agriculture
Called to the Classroom
Abberton and Langenhoe
History of West Bergholt

© Peter Wormell 1999

ISBN 0 9525903 2 8

Published by Abberton Books
Colchester CO5 7NA

Design Assistance: Waterside Graphics.
Jenny Deeks Desktop Publishing
Printed by The Lavenham Press Ltd, Lavenham, Suffolk

Contents

List of Illustrations

Help and Hospitality

Many people have given their unstinted, and enthusiastic help in the preparation of this book. I am most grateful to each and everyone of them, and whilst some have contributed more than others it would be invidious to draw up a batting order. The anonymity of an alphabetical order does not detract from the outstanding help which they have all given.

Prof. Michael Alder
Animal Health Trust
Hugh Baird & Sons Ltd
Roger Barker
Eddie Billington
Anthony Bonner
David Barbour
Lord Braybrooke
David Brook
John Brooks
Richard Brooks
Duncan Brown
Sir Richard Butler
Col. Local Hist. Centre
Stephen Chapman
Ashley Cooper
John Creasey
Robert Davidson
Ted Dennis
Alan Doe
Alex Dyke
Lt.Col. R.T.P. Earle
Essex Records Office

E.F.Y.F.C.
Tim Fagan
Antony Fairbanks-Weston
David Fisher
Ford Motor Co.
Roger Freeman
Geoffrey Gent
Paul Gooderham
Christopher Gosling
Patricia Herrman
Wendy Hibbert
Bill Holliwell
Michael Hughes
John Hutchins
Philip Hutley
Bernard Jenkin MP
Richard Lawrence
Malcolm Jones
Major B.L. Kentish
Simon Letherdale
Bernard Lewis
David Lipman
Pearl Lonsdale
David McMillan

Robert McTurk
Lt-Col.C. Manning-Press
Richard Matthews
MAFF (York)
Pat Morris
A.V. Muskett
David Naylor
Alan Nicholls
Francis Nicholls
George Nicholls
Prof. John Nix
Nigel Nott
Robert Orr
Ray Osborne
Tim Parker
Michael Parris
Bernard Partridge
Anthony Peel
Lord Petre
Andrew Phillips
R.A.S.E.
Lord Rayleigh
Reading University
Henry Ritchie

Peter Rooke
Eleanor Roper
Tim Roper
Tim Ruggles-Brice
John Sadler
Lilian Sadler
Philip Shaw
Janie Siggers
Pat Smith
Jeremy Squier
Tony Stevenson
Eric Stone
David & Faith Tippett
Tim Trenbath
Keith Turner
Barbara Watt
Hew Watt
Len Weaver
Tom Whirledge
John Wilkin
Peter Wilkin
Jeremy Wormald
C.R. Wright

To Dee Cole and the staff at Lavenham Press for personal dedication, eagle eyes and perfectionism.

I must give heartfelt thanks and appreciation to my indefatigable secretary, Jenny Griffin, whose enthusiasm, patience and cheerfulness have contributed an immeasurable part to this work. Her diligence and my never ending corrections have pieced together a tangled story.Mrs.Griffin's assistance is gratefully acknowledged.

P.W.

Awards of the Century

Most famous animal	–	Marthus
Greatest Disaster	–	Dutch Elm Disease
Most Innovative Machine	–	Doe's Triple-D. Salmons's Beet Harvester
Most Eminent Leaders	–	Hon. Edward Strutt
		George Raby
		Sir Richard Butler
Highest Accolade	–	Tony Clarke's Wheat Record
		Andrew Davidson World Championship
Demise of the Century	–	Horses and men. Essex pigs
Most Hated	–	The War Ag's
Greatest Rescue	–	Two World Wars
Greatest Survivor	–	The Essex Show
Most Progressive Newcomers	–	Young Farmers Clubs and Scotsmen
Most Influential	–	Writtle College
Most Famous Farm	–	Throws Dunmow
Most Joyful	–	Abolition of Tithes
Greatest Benefit	–	Myxomatosis
Most Famous Village	–	Terling
Most Famous Product	–	Tiptree Jam
Most Important Crop Demise	–	Mangolds
Most Successful new Crop	–	Oil Seed Rape
Greatest Loss	–	Eighteen markets
Saddest Story	–	Navy Beans
Greatest Changes	–	Tractors and Combines
Greatest Abandonment	–	Rotations
Breakthrough of the Century	–	Milk and Wheat Yields
Breakdown of the Century	–	New Village People
Worst Harvest	–	1958
Best Harvest	–	1984

Fame and Good Fortune

The fame of Essex farms and farmers gave the county a secure claim to be the leading agricultural county in England. This reputation was enhanced in the 20th century, and gained world wide recognition.

Arthur Young in 1807 said that Essex farmers were; "persons of enlarged and liberal minds"[1] whilst Thomas Wright in 1842 said unequivocally that; "the farmers of Essex are reckoned among the best in England".[2] A favourable climate, excellent soil and enterprising farmers became a powerful combination that no other county could match.

An arable county rather than a livestock one, the Essex breed of saddleback pigs were dominant in their day. Terling Friesians continued to be known world-wide and the Badley herd of Suffolk sheep from Great Bromley were avidly sought by sheep farmers all over North America, to such an extent that when the Essex flock was wiped out by disease, it was rebuilt from its original genes, re-imported back to their parent land.

Essex Red Clover was acclaimed throughout many parts of the world although its purity was jeopardized when the disastrous 1958 harvest destroyed the crop. Re-importation was required. Essex Pearl and Essex Conquerer were wheat varieties. Essex Crown a brand name for Matthews seed. The "Beauty of Essex" – a potato.

The villages and towns of the county gave their names to widely acclaimed products. Throws MS – beans from Dunmow, Rivenhall Giant – a variety of mangolds, Early Rainham's – cabbages, Kelvedon Glory – sweet corn whilst Kelvedon Wonder was the most durable pea variety and the most widely grown. D'Arcy Spice – apples had a long and distinguished history. Baddow Pippin and Essex Spice were also apples. Seabrook's Black was a variety of blackcurrant. Tiptree was famous for its jam.

The Dunmow Flitch was as famous as its bacon factory. Earls Colne for Hunts Rolls and Rayne for ploughs. Heybridge for coffee crushers used throughout Africa, whilst Goldhanger had given its name to a famous plough in the 19th century. Great Yeldham and Whitlock achieved national prominence, and Dagenham was the home of the most productive tractor plant in the world outside the USA. Tilbury became the second largest grain terminal in the UK.

The world wheat yield record was broken by an Essex crop and the first time the International Winter Wheat Championship left America – it came to an Essex farm at Wix.

Essex men achieved national prominence and three became presidents of the National Farmers Union. There were three Essex presidents of the Country Landowners Association and 10 out of 54 Masters of the Worshipful Company of Farmers. An Essex man, Sir Nigel Strutt, produced the most far reaching report on the effects of modern agriculture. It became the "Strutt Report on the Soil". Writtle College acquired a national reputation.

In every direction the fame and influence of Essex farming provided a contribution to the 20th century which no other county could equal.

CHAPTER 1

The Impetus for Change

Looking at the topography of Essex there are distinct bands of soils which dictate the nature of farming. Arthur Young divided the county into eight areas. By another criteria it would be possible to suggest that the A12 is a rough boundary with the northern sector predominantly arable whilst the land abutting the North Sea and the Thames contained a predominance of grassland.

In a county that is recognised for its arable farming and, is part of the three Eastern counties which form the Granary of England, it is surprising that in 1900 over one third of Essex was grassland and by the end of the century it was still 11%.

Not all the grass was in the coastal region. The county was criss-crossed by dozens of rivers and tributaries. Nearly three quarters of the parishes had a source of water running through them. Small rivers and tributaries created low lying land that was largely unploughable.

In 1900 the cropping and livestock balance of the county was largely traditional. When depression had been apparent, it was accompanied by unkempt farms, as farmers cut their costs, reduced their labour and reverted to a 'dog and stick' system of existence.

Despite these vicissitudes the area being farmed was at it highest in 1900. In earlier centuries the emphasis upon cultivatable farming had reduced the woodland area and increased the productive acreage. Enclosures had contributed, although Essex was a county which was enclosed from Tudor times and was not subject to the enclosure movement which took place in the 18th and 19th centuries. There were some enclosure Acts relating to the county but they were, in general, annexing common land, or common grazings to the Lord of the Manor, and were often expensive to convert to farmland. In most cases they were small parcels of land.

After centuries of increasing the farmland, the 20th century saw a dramatic reversal. Nearly 25% disappeared.

To what extent was the farming regime in 1900 dictated by soil and climate? There had been a 20 year depression and farmers had turned to livestock, mainly cows, actively encouraged by the influx of Scottish settlers. As the livestock increased, and in consequence of the unprofitability of cereal crops many acres were devoted to ancillary crops required for feeding animals.

This was accompanied by a decrease in arable crops. In the 19th century hops had declined as an important Essex crop but they remained traditional in Kent. This was promulgated by the lack of facilities for manufacturing malt from hops, and the decline of the brewing industry in the county. In the 20th century the livestock and grassland diminished and arable farming took over.

The climate of the county placed it in a premier position for the production of seed, and Essex crops became 'exported' throughout the British Isles. The germ of the seed was not normally destroyed by wet harvests, which occurred to the west of London and in the midland counties, but Essex seed could produce high yields of good quality and it

1 1920s. Steam Ploughing at Tiptree Hall.

became renowned for this. The Marks Tey/Kelvedon area with its easy working, well drained soil and its abundance of sunshine, became a centre for seed production.

Along the northern belt of the county the clay/loam soil produced heavy cereal crops yet when fields were sown down to grass they often dried out in the summer months. As a grass growing county Essex could not compete with such places as Leicestershire. But it did not have the light, blowing sand of the Newmarket area in Suffolk or any of the sandy soils found in Norfolk. This may seem contradictory when the aggregates industry found so many sites in Essex. Most of the sand and gravel diggings were to be found in small pockets and were underneath a layer of top soil that was producing useful crops until it was excavated. Restoration, which was embodied by law in the later part of the century, returned erstwhile diggings to crop producing fields.

In the early part of the century the pattern of farming was dictated by economic and political events. The swings of depression and prosperity were stimulated from political decisions and Essex was not immune, or isolated in the effects of these events. Farmers were forced to change their farming systems.

There was another constraint that was important. The ability of the workforce to acquire the professional skills which would be needed if a farmer decided to buy a flock of sheep - and did not have a resident shepherd. Towards the end of the century, when mobility was less of a constraint, many farmers with flocks of sheep employed a shepherd from Wales at lambing time, and shearing was normally done by a gang of contractors. This was not possible to the same extent in 1900 and thus by long tradition farmers were unable to make radical changes to their systems.

The introduction of sugar beet required lessons for farm workers to learn how to single them. It was an art they had not previously deployed although mangolds had always been hoed by hand and thinned out to allow each plant room to grow.

If political trends were responsible for changes, the twin events; the increase in the population of London and secondly the increased feeding standards of the whole population, gave Essex farmers, although at first only in the close proximity to London, the opportunity to develop crops such as vegetables which could be quickly transported to the metropolis. Fruit was prone to the delays on the railways which encouraged the establishment of jam making.

The changes throughout the century were slow until after 1950. Any improvements during the First World War were lost in the aftermath although, as a side-effect, an increasing number of specialised poultry farmers and fruit growers were established.

The land losses were unprecedented when compared to previous centuries. The most extensive developments being the new towns of Basildon and Harlow although the spread of London in a wide band, despite the green belt policy, created housing estates where fields had been. Most of these developments took place in the second half of the century. As the towns became overgrown they spread their tentacles until they reached saturation, after which the planning authorities decreed that villages should be rejuvenated with development. An injection of new people was expected to bring life back to moribund villages. This did not occur because there was little employment in the countryside.

The new village inhabitants commuted to the nearest town and throughout the whole county a large number travelled daily to London. Many did not contribute to village life and were hardly ever present. Villages became dormitories. The farmer became isolated. He was a quaint relic of the past whose activities were not suffered without indignation and opposition.

Whilst development money was responsible for large injections of cash into farmers' pockets there were often adverse repercussions. A farmer selling a plot of land at an enhanced building price was warned that it might create an awkward shape to his field, or that his activities would be constrained with problems such as spray-drift from agrochemicals, dust from combines, headlights from tractors at night, and noise. Factors which influenced both farmers and planners to keep the new developments into segregated estates. The ribbon development and the substandard 'jerry-building' in the south of the county in the 1930s was not repeated in the 1970s. The injection of capital gave farmers the opportunity to combat rising inflation and to finance the extensive changeover from men to machinery.

2 1930s. River Blackwater. Essex had 220 mills along the many creeks and rivers.

3 Copford Green. Typical Essex open wagon shed with hay loft above and neatly thatched.

The farm labour force declined to a miniscule level. No longer were farm workers the predominant voice in the village pub. There was no need for them as machinery took over their work. As wages rose it was undeniable that farm businesses could not have afforded to keep the same numbers of men employed, an argument always advanced by farmers when arguing against wage increases.

The second reason was the change in society which abolished manual tasks in every direction. The village road sweeper was supplanted by the lorry with its rotating brushes and flashing light, an innovation that was unheralded. The laborious tasks on a farm were replaced by machines and the farm workers learnt new skills. This reduced the influence of farming in village affairs.

Farming was constrained and directed by the manipulations of politicians to the extent that price increases or decreases were used as a carrot rather than a stick. Oil seed rape and linseed would not have been grown in the county, and cows would not have reduced so dramatically without the impetus of the E.C. Dairy Conversion Scheme. Fruit growing would not have declined so rapidly without grubbing-out grants. Sugar beet in the county, and the closure of the Felsted factory would not have occurred without 'sugar-politics'. Potato growing was strictly controlled by the Potato Marketing Board.

Despite these constraints there was an unmistaken policy of co-operation. Farmers welcomed most of the changes. Dairy farmers, for instance, gave up their cows and opted for the easier life of arable farming. Pigs became a specialist industry and the story of the century revolves around creating islands where the owner was an expert and had the requisite staff, and back-up facilities to improve his efficiency. Farms; from a hotch-potch mixture with a little of everything became victims of monoculture. There were many that grew continuous wheat for upwards of 20 years in the face of all the old edicts about rotations being beneficial for the soil, and there was a movement towards putting live-stock indoors, such as pigs and chickens, which produced more eggs per bird, liveweight gain per pig.

This rationalisation was created by economic pressures yet the second half of the century was generally a prosperous time for agriculture. Why then, did farmers follow this route? It was partly engendered by the reduction in the farm staff. A tractor driver did not easily translate into a stockman for the first and last hours of his working day. It impaired both. The stock did not get the requisite attention and the expensive tractor did not work the maximum hours. There was always a conflict between the needs of the animals and the needs of the crops, sometimes overlapping - to the detriment of both. The general prosperity was only evident when farming increased its scale and the avaricious neighbour annexed every possible piece of land to increase his business. It made the acquisition of machinery more viable and gave better employment to his arable staff. Many farms could have been regarded as one and a half man units. The half became an expensive luxury and the system was trimmed downwards. Although change was stimulated by solvent conditions it was also rapid, and farming practices could not afford to remain static. New varieties of wheat and new rations for livestock were introduced at a vigorous rate. The farmer who did not employ them soon found himself falling behind his neighbours.

The changes were catonic. Nothing was sacrosanct. Hedges were swept away to create sizeable blocks of land to facilitate the new monsters of the fields. In reality much of the patchwork pattern of the countryside owed its origins to the Victorian period when, with a surfeit of labour, men were employed to dig ditches and plant hedges as a method of draining the land. The natural vista of the Essex countryside, and particularly along the coastal areas, was of an open area where few trees had ever successfully survived. The harsh winter winds and the dry summers were not conducive to natural afforestation. Many of these areas had never been covered with woodland and where hedges were bull-dozed farmers were given grants to hasten this process. There was active encouragement to change the face of the countryside.

As the new style of farming spread it necessitated a vast building programme of grain stores and machinery housing which, again, created a changing scene. A major encouragement to change the system of a particular farm was undoubtedly the flexibility of farming families. The influx from other counties brought new ideas with them, but before newcomers could take these farms the old established families had to vacate them.

As a measure of the swing throughout the century it is difficult to find more than a dozen farming families in situ who were there in 1900. There are more whose descendants farm although they may have moved from one farm to another. Most of the Scottish settlers from the 1880s had descendants in the county and a few continued in the same farm. A larger number moved to a better, or larger, farm when the opportunity occurred.

What happened to the families who disappeared? There was always a natural wastage where there was no male heir, or the sons were not interested in farming. There were those who became disillusioned, particularly during the inter-war period that they were forced out by debts and bankruptcy. Others advised their children to train for another occupation. They had little confidence in farming future, little trust in the politicians, and regarded their own lives as little more than slavery for a pittance.

There was more stability from 1950 onwards and particularly when working farmers became the predominant landowners. In the days of an active tenantry some families moved because they fell behind with the rent and simply decided to give up. There was little evidence of tenants being ejected on religious grounds, or for bad husbandry. The emphasis lay in the other direction. Before 1950 landlords were pleased to get tenants for their farms, and by rent reductions when necessary, were keen to keep them.

The movement in the second half of the century was a story of amalgamations. Land was annexed by avaricious neighbours. Farms were added to create farming empires. It was usually the older, more backward, and subsistence living farmers who were replaced by their neighbouring agri-businessmen. It brought a new and vigorous approach and an injection of much needed capital. It was the changing attitude of farmers, and their aspirations to a better life-style which was a major factor which induced change.

In the midst of this crescendo of indecent change there were many false starts. The story of the century is one that embraces both successes and failures. It is a story that is enveloped and encapsulates change on a scale that had never been seen before.

This study examines the changes in the various sectors of farm life.

CHAPTER 2

A Truly Rural Landscape

As the 20th Century dawned the inhabitants of Essex could look back on a hundred years that had seen considerable changes, but had not fundamentally altered the pattern of either village life or farm work. The countryside still looked the same. A landscape of small fields and hedges, hay and corn stacks punctured the sky-line, farmsteads and barns still nestled on ancient sites, and church towers stood as rock solid reminders of timeless stability.

Country lanes still meandered in shapeless confusion, rutted in winter, dusty in summer. The ring of the blacksmith's anvil echoed in every village street. Horses trudged towards the markets with heavy loads. Cattle grazed the marshes and meadows, sheep folded the arable fields, and grazed the pastures. There were cows in the fields. A mixed variety of breeds with myriad colours and shapeless configuration. The cottages were unsanitized, water came from the village pump. Tallow, candles and clothes pegs, from the itinerant gypsies. The major addition to the village scene was the appearance of a school in nearly every parish, and a greater number of shops for the labourers' wives to spend their meagre money in, albeit that the shop consisted of the front room of a cottage that had stood for centuries.

The fields were ploughed with horses, and had been so since 1800 when Arthur Young reported:[1] 'scarcely any common farmers use oxen; there are such cases, but they are very few; some gentlemen have them'.

The fields were hoed by men and women, the harvest carried by wagons, the hay made into cocks. The whole village was involved in getting the crucial harvest home, an annual event that had not changed for centuries. A 19th century innovation was the advent of annual harvest thanksgiving services in the Anglican parish churches.

The whole village was agriculturally orientated although by 1900 fewer men worked on the farms, but those in allied trades, such as carpenters and blacksmiths, still relied on local farmers custom.

This rural idyll could have equally applied to the 18th century and beyond. There had always been progress but the rate was slow. During the 19th century many changes took place yet the visual and aesthetic change was ephemeral. Life went on as usual.

The outward tranquillity of the typical Essex village disguised some important changes. The squires largely remained, certainly the structure of squiredom, and the farm workers were mostly indiginous, but 20 years of depression had forced out many of the farming families, yeomen (or owner occupiers) had become fewer, and there had been an infusion of new blood – with unfamiliar accents. Mainly from Scotland but also from the West Country. There were greater numbers of animals on farms and fewer arable acres. Dairying, market garden and vegetable crops as well as fruit, were more prevalent.

The village still fed itself. Practically everything that was eaten and drunk by the inhabitants was "village-grown". There were bakeries using flour that came from the local miller, either wind or water, the discarded bran and middlings from the milled wheat went back to the farm for animal feeding. Milk was produced from grass, mangolds, turnips, hay from the nearby fields. Straw was turned into muck which returned to nourish another crop.

There had been a maltings in almost every village, hence the prolification of "Maltings Farm", to be found throughout the county but by 1900 many village maltings had ceased to operate and the business was being concentrated into larger breweries in the towns. Hops were still grown in Essex and, at this date every farm had a brew-house. "Home-brewing was carried on, almost as a matter of course, in every country mansion and large farmhouse in Essex. Malting was a very important industry in the county"[2]. Local beer was as indigenous as the timbers that roofed the church.

Vegetables were home grown, most labourers had an allotment, sometimes run by the parish, or the farmers allowed them a field corner to grow potatoes. There were reservations that the worker might expend more energy on his own patch to the detriment of his master's demands, but every family relied upon its man to provide food. Growing potatoes, snaring rabbits – an occasional pheasant!, whilst gleanings from the harvest fields fed the chickens and produced eggs. The potato peelings, apple cores, kitchen scraps, fed the occasional pig.

There were the wild fruits from the hedgerows, blackberries flourished on the heavy clay lands of Essex. Damsons, sloes, meddlars, wild plums and crab apples were all gathered by the mother and the children. Every farmstead had a small orchard attached with knarled unpruned apple trees, greengages and plums were grown. Chickens scratched the grass beneath the trees and injected nutrients into the soil. The circle of self sufficiency was complete. The village needed very little imported food to sustain it's population.

Some chroniclers have suggested that the village culture of independence was breaking down. True; shortages were smoothed out by the demands of a wider community and seasonal fluctuations played an inevitable role. The blacksmith had been encouraged to buy ready-made horse shoes which he could customise for individual animals, the cobbler bought large sheets of ready tanned leather for his craft. Imported timber was coming into Essex ports, and village carpenters might well be using it. But this did not exacerbate a situation that existed. To suggest that 'the self-supporting character of the villages is gone'[3], was to anticipate a village economy by over 50 years.

The farms existed to support and feed the village which they served. The surplus from the harvest went to the towns. Bullocks, sheep, pigs, eggs and poultry, the Michaelmas geese and turkeys had always been reared for sale, but the priority of avoiding village hunger came first. The interdependence was exemplified by the goods which were purchased from the sales in the market. A century earlier, in 1800, a Fingringhoe farmer[4] was buying cotton for dresses, silk handkerchieves, chocolate, a looking glass, a gun and ammunition. But these were the purchases of the farmer. They were not the items that a labourer would buy. He assisted in driving cattle to market, and would drink beer in the hostelry before walking home again. He was not a rabid purchaser of town or imported goods.

Dr.Stephen Hussey charted the decline of self sufficiency; "a myriad of new cultural forms touched the market towns and villages of the countryside... so that by 1900 in an ordinary market town such as Colchester it was possible to buy

4 1910 Romford Market. Occupied the whole street.

Devon Cream, Welsh Cheese, Argentinian Beef, Danish Bacon, Dutch Vegetables, Cuban Cigars, Indian Cloth, a bicycle made in Nottingham and a piano made in Germany".[5]

Sugar had always been purchased but jam preserved the summer fruit and pickling eggs stored the summer flush. The essence of the summer larder sustaining the populace in the barren winter was an ethic that had existed since hunters had roamed the county. The principles remained strong in 1900.

Numerically the agricultural interest dominated the village. The pub was punctuated with farming arguments. Rivalry and loyalty between one farm and another, pride and boasting became hopelessly entangled and hotly discussed. The straightness of the furrows was a matter of supreme importance. It was a community that revolved around its social centre and a community that was bound to the soil. In this social structure the farmer was both aloof, respected and feared. His power over the lives of his labourers, and the reputation of a dishonest worker would preclude his employment by any other farmers, was more relevant than the sermon from the pulpit or even the squire. It was a closer contact. Economically the inhabitants relied on the success of the farmer to survive, and farming was sustaining a severe downturn. There was little agitation amongst farm labourers in 1900. There had been lock-outs and mutterings up to the 1880s, and a resurgence in 1907, but with farmers solvency under question it was not a propitious moment to make demands.

The parishioners recognized that they now lived in a modern world, that change was irreversible and usually for the better. The stability of life was enshrined by Queen

Victoria herself whose indestructibility spread a quality of placidity that was self evident in the timelessness of the countryside. Napoleon and the dissolute Hanovarian kings were now beyond the memory of the oldest inhabitants. They were history and hearsay. There had been no major wars since the Crimean nearly half a century earlier.

The modern world was exemplified by cottage, farmhouse and barn rebuilding, by the binder which now cut the harvest, the horse drawn mower which cut the hay and the threshing machine which now threshed out the corn in winter. More corn was planted in rows. Broadcasting had almost disappeared with the widespread availability of the Smyth drill[6]. The smallest farms could hire a "drill Man", who came with his horse drawn machine and drilled the fields. Corn in rows meant that a hoop-hoe and a cottis hoe, could help to keep the crops weed free, yet it was the corn fields that were the dirty ones.

There had been a spate of cottage building in the middle of the century. Farm houses had been expanded, with brick built additions, in the years soon after Waterloo. The common red bricks, often made in the same village and the more expensive "Suffolk whites", which adorned the grander houses such as the Rectory. The cottages had no main water but more now had individual wells, or a community pump that served a small number grouped together. The village street was open and devoid of the furniture that would bedevil it in the coming century. Electricity poles and infilling with bungalows would transform the scene in the 20th century, and introduce more changes since the village itself had become established around a pond, a clearing or a green.

The cattle still went trudging along the lanes to market, goaded by the drovers, excited boys with sticks, much shouting and often clouds of dust. The bleating of sheep, the mooing of cattle and the snorting of pigs heralded the approaching cavalcade before it came into sight. The cart of pitiful furniture pulled by a skeleton-like pony witnessed the removal of a family from one place to another. The pub provided a resting place and it was also the village gossip shop. Newspapers were now in mass circulation and news of events arrived faster.

The railways had carved an iron road across the county. reaching Chelmsford in 1840, Colchester in 1843 and Braintree and Maldon in 1847. They soon stretched beyond Essex to Ipswich and to the fashionable watering spa at Walton-on-the-Naze. The railway and the rivers brought coal for the first time to Essex villages far removed from the coal fields.

They also opened up the farmers markets. Milk now went to London daily, the hard grind of farmers' wives and village women making cheeses and butter, for which Essex had been famous, was now supplanted by the distribution of liquid milk. Vegetables could arrive at Covent Garden in time for the maids from the mansion houses of Belgravia to take their pick for their mistress's approbation. At the turn of the century the branch line from Kelvedon to Tollesbury had been financed and planned. It was the "crab and winkle" line which served Wilkin's jam factory at Tiptree. Another new market was opening and it would require locally grown fruit to provide the raw materials.

Majestic viaducts had arisen at Chapel and Lexden, cuttings had been dug by Irish immigrants at Audley End and the whistle of the engine accompanied by a trailing cloud of white smoke had become a feature of the landscape, yet it's impact was minor covering, as it did, a very small area of land and visible only from a fraction of the fields where farm labourers worked. They might hear it's whistle if the wind was in the right direction.

5 1906 Littlebury. A load of flour from the timber built water mill.

The effect on the aesthetic view of the countryside was minimal. The bulldozers, motorways, airports, parking lots, factories and New Towns were not yet on the drawing board. In the 20th century there would be a revolutionary change in the appearance of Essex.

Steam had been the great invention of the century. It had spawned the first railways and had translated it's power into farming. Thomas Darby born at Sheepcotes Farm, Little Waltham, who later moved to Pleshey Lodge had pioneered steam digging the fields with his "walking diggers" in 1880. Davy Paxman produced a 10 ton steam engine and digger which could enter 8 feet wide field gateways. Called the "Colchester" it was produced between 1888 and 1894. It also had a winch to pull itself out of swampy ground. The horse replaced the oxen, but the steam engine did not replace the horse. Factory-like chimneys sprouted on many farms as steam boilers were installed and a complexity of shafts and belts radiated to drive farm and barn machinery. They were not, however, widespread.

The population of Essex had gone from 252,473 in the census return of 1811 to 1,083,998 by 1901. It might have been supposed that this would have swamped the villages beyond recognition. The increase had been absorbed in ribbon development towards a countryside which they had not yet reached.

Essex was predominantly agricultural, but not necessarily an agrarian economy. The service industries such as the fledgling gas, water and electricity undertakings, shop-keepers, textile workers and the thousands of professional and white collar workers who lived in the metropolitan area combined to distort the figures. The population had risen by 476% in the 19th century but 54% of the people lived in 2% of the county in West Ham. The urban population occupied 17% of the county and the agricultural rural area amounted to 83%. There were rivals for the agricultural crown. The building and construction industry employed only 274 less than agriculture in a county of over one million. More people than ever before were employed in domestic work and transport and communications.

The number of people in the villages of Essex had diminished. The decline of all forms of craftsmen had been exaserbated by the advent of factory production. They could not compete, and fled to become factory workers themselves. Thaxted went down by 235 persons in the century. The three Laver villages, High, Little and Magdalen had a combined population of 664 in 1801 which had dropped to 626 one hundred years later. Dedham had a smaller population than 100 years earlier. Over the whole of Essex 83 parishes saw a decline in their populace but nearly 200 had passed their peak just after mid-century and were on a falling demographic graph. There were new village industries such as Hunt's Ironworks at Earls Colne, Mr.Bentall's factory at Goldhanger, Sir Walter Gilbeys jam factory at Elsenham and Wilkin at Tiptree.

There was a reputed 142,585 employed in agriculture in 1811 which was 56.4% of the population of the county but by 1901 over 100,000 farm workers had gone. They now only represented 3.81%. These figures, however, cannot be relied upon as totally accurate. The 41,306 employed in agriculture in 1901 can be taken as a reliable starting point for the 20th century.

Farm workers had started the century in a state of poverty and ferment. The Napoleonic wars had pushed up food prices but not wages. The misguided system of poor relief imposed by parliament did not alleviate the problem. By the latter years of the century farmers and landowners were in a parlous situation but the labourers were better off. Their wages throughout the whole century had only risen from around 10s.0d. per week to 13s.0d. per week, but the price of food had dropped dramatically and with this imbalance of economics the labourers could now afford to eat meat that was purchased, not poached, they bought coal and were better clothed. Their children no longer contributed to the family budget because they were confined in the school room. As the century ended the labourers could consider that their lot was not as bad as their grandfathers had been.

The same could not be said about the landowner. The concept of the squire in every village still remained. Essex had never been a county of large estates. Arthur Young had remarked "going north from Skreens (Roxwell), twelve miles, as the crow flies to Lord Maynard's (Dunmow) there is not a trace of a gentleman's house; yet there are parts of the country that offer fine scenes of woodland landscape with bales and brooks admitting every sort of decoration".[7] There were a large number of modest estates around the 2,000 acre level. It was a county with a strong backbone of gentry, but not nobility. In the last quarter of the century, estate income had plummeted as rents were continually revised downwards. Despite this, most estates survived and were probably larger than they were in 1800.

6 1925. Burnham Hall. Workers pulling rhubarb.

The Terling estate was 5,835 acres in 1816 and 8,632 in the 1883 survey.[8] The Birch Hall estate saw a continuous programme of expansion throughout the 19th century. As adjoining farms came on the market they were purchased and the estate more than doubled to 5,266 acres. This pattern of expansion was common throughout the county. The estates were larger. Those that were sold for lack of an heir, such as Berechurch Hall, had been sold in their entirety. This property passed through three owners before 1900 yet it retained it's historical area, despite the fact that at one sale it was lotted in 36 separate parcels. The squires had not indulged in a massive wave of mansion building. Easton Lodge (Viscount Maynard),Stisted Hall, Birch Hall and Berechurch, rebuilt by a wealthy brewer were isolated examples rather than a trend.

Although there had been some changes, the tenants and workers on the majority of estates could look back on an uninterrupted period of family ownership. There had been Bramston's at Skreens (Roxwell) since 1635 and they were there in 1900. The Braybrooke's were at Audley End. Ruggles-Brise at Spains Hall. Lord Brooke at Easton. Buxton at Warlies, Waltham Abbey. Capel Cure at Blake Hall, Ongar. Du Cane at Braxted. Hanbury at Holfield Grange, Coggeshall. Honeywood at Marks Hall. Barrett-Leonard at Belhus (Bell House). Saville-Onley at Stisted. Strutts at Terling. Round at Birch. Raymond at Belchamp Walter and many others. There was a stability induced by continuity. The old families had always been there – and they always would, was a common belief as the 20th century dawned.

There had been a disastrous 20 year prelude as rents had tumbled in the wake of the acute farming depression. Landowners found opportunities to buy farms cheaply during depressed times when smaller yeomen were forced to give up. There had been a shortage of tenants but by 1900 this was a reducing problem and by 1906 the 'in hand' farms on the Orsett Estate had been re-let. Tenants from Scotland, Somerset and Devon had been attracted to take vacant Essex farms.

Farmers too had seen a disastrous drop in prices. The price of wheat had inexorably fallen throughout the whole century. Arable land had declined, pasture had increased, but derelict and unkempt land had also increased. The 19th century had produced great advances in agricultural knowledge. The motto of the R.A.S.E. adopted in 1844 was "practice with science", and farmers knew the principles to produce better livestock and better crops. The problem was that they could not afford to invest in these improvements when they adopted a policy of retrenchment – or went out of business completely.

The preponderance of squires, farmers and labourers as the true heart of the county, was partly engendered by historical habits and partly as a mark of the visual impact which farming had upon the county as a whole. Farmers were not a homogeneous group, ranging from the architypical John Bull character with his waistcoat and gold fob watch, to the unkempt, grizzled and sinew handed son of the soil whose lifestyle, and income was close to the labourers in the village. Farming had a purchasing power in the towns but times had been bad for over a generation. There was an intrinsic, even romantic attachment to the countryside. The downtrodden and poverty stricken villagers had willingly departed in favour of what turned out to be the slums and slavery of factory work. A generation earlier there was another reason;

> 'The countryside became the barometer to the morale and thinking of the nation. It is the early twentieth century when the countryside becomes the chosen emblem shared by artists, composers, writers, poets and politicians when they want to capture the essence of Englishness. Nationhood and the countryside became inextricably bound together'.[5]

The power and influence of the farming lobby was not all pervading. They were in a minority position on many public bodies – but they were the largest single group. This applied to Essex County Council in 1900, the Rural District Councils, Boards of Guardians and including all those with an agricultural interest the Justices of the Peace. It was at the parish level where farmers had an overall majority. They chaired most of the newly formed (1894) parish councils. They invariably occupied the positions of church warden. Where their own economic interests were centred they took an active part in the administration.

In 1900 the depression had lasted for a generation. Buildings that had once been tidy had become unkempt. Weeds flourished and hedges were overgrown. A air of dereliction hung over the county. This was then the scenario that existed and there was little to suppose that there would be any change in the foreseeable future. A pundit, if he had been writing at the time could not have argued otherwise.

There was no hint that farming practice, and village life would be transformed during the century to come. It had always been thus, and everyone expected it to remain so.

They could not have been more mistaken.

Beyond All Recognition

In 1900 Essex farmers could look back on a century with only 35 good years. The last 25 years had seen unprecedented depression. In the 20th century the figures were reversed.

There were 66 good years and only 34 years when farming was in serious trouble, and in the years before 1914 there had been a slow, but inexorable measure of improvement. Coupled by the fact that farmers, with a generation of subsistence farming to remember, had forsaken arable farming for dairying. The 20th century was to reverse that policy.

This new century was to see inflation at a faster rate than ever before, as wages, crop values and land prices escalated. The bouts of uneconomic farming were sectionalised with pigs, dairying, cereals all suffering short-lived periods of depression – but not simultaneously. The adage of "up corn, down horn" still prevailed

In the daily life of a farmer and his employees, (no longer labourers) the changes were fundamental and far reaching. Every facet of farming and farm work changed. The farm worker at the beginning of the century would be seen in corduroy trousers and a bowler hat. By the end he was wearing a boiler suit and a baseball cap. The cottages were modernized in keeping with modern demands and rural housing caught up with it's town cousins. Village life lost its character and the village shop declined. Gone were the butchers, lace makers, saddlers, bakers and coal merchants of which there was often more than one in nearly every village. Despite the attraction of supermarket shopping, in nearly every Essex village at least one shop existed and in many a Post Office, often the two combining. In spite of the prophets of doom the village shop tenuously survived in reduced numbers. Bus services, unknown in 1900, came and went again – but not all of them.

The blacksmith disappeared and the filling station, or used car lot took it's place. The pub mostly survived albeit that it lost it's sawdust image, embarked on providing cooked meals from the 1970's onwards and attracted it's customers from a wider area, many coming from the towns to sample it's culinary delights. The pint of beer was replaced by the glass of wine or the gin and tonic. The facade still resembled it's ghost but the average interior was improved and usually in a tasteful manner.

Most of the churches remained but the presence of a parson was supplanted by the amalgamation of benefices, a harking back to the days of "plurality", in the 18th century when parsons enhanced their incomes by gaining two livings and paying a curate a small sum to "mind the shop". The 20th century ecclesiastical reorganization was forced by the poverty of the Anglican establishment, rather than it's prosperity. The roads became tarmacadamed from the 1920's onwards. A rash of 30mph signs, concrete kerbs and footpaths, electricity poles and, perhaps strangely, a heightening of village hedges. It became a less open village, but a more open countryside.

The field hedges that survived became mechanically trimmed but the gardens of the new village commuters were planted with pink flowering cherries and other incongruous species. It was the changing source of energy which allowed trees to flourish.

Until the railways brought coal to the most remote parts of the county, and only if the labourers could afford it, the staple fuel was wood. One man calculated that he had cut down four sizeable oak trees every year since he had been married to keep his family through the winter. The prudent labourer spotted his likely targets for the next winter's avaricious appetite.

The universal acceptability of coal and, later, oil coupled with electricity, and in many villages north sea gas, provided alternative fuels – and allowed the oak trees to mature. Unfortunately the elms succumbed and became a rarity in a county where they had been romanticized by painters through the centuries.

*7 1966 Ardleigh. Cabless tractor and one-way plough after spring barley. Working for J.W. Curtis &
Sons who later emigrated to Australia.*

The labourer of yesteryear braved the elements. As he stood on the lee side of a stack to avoid freezing winds on a winter's day whilst he had his "bait". He worked out in all weathers, without the benefit of a plastic coat. His weather-beaten face displayed the outdoor life that he led. It was, until mid-century, a physically demanding job; forking muck, pitching sheaves, threshing the stacks and digging the ditches etc. was a manual operation.

But in the second half of the century mechanisation rapidly stepped in to take over all these jobs. By the end of the century the farm worker was ensconced in an air conditioned cab on his computer orientated tractor with his radio keeping him in touch with the whole world, and a communication link with the farmer on another tractor.

The first tractors were cold and wet, combine driving was dusty. The advent, and quick acceptance of air conditioned meant that the farm worker could wear clean clothes, and have clean hands whilst achieving his daily tasks. His life, both in the field and at home improved immeasurably. Livestock farming saw such innovative introductions as the automatic milking machine and electronic pig feeders. Bulk transportation of milk, feeding stuffs, fertilizer and cereals, took the physical labour out of the job. Fork lift trucks became vital as a piece of farm equipment.

The farm worker was no longer tied to the farm all his working day. His hoe and sickle was replaced by the pen and the calculator! Farm workers no longer went to the Essex Show but many to the Doe Show. Another calendar spot that became a permanent feature on the Essex calendar.

The farmers' daily life was exchanged from the field to the farm office. Financial planning, form filling, the advent of mobile 'phones and the necessity to keep up with rapidly changing developments meant that from around 1960 farmers started to convert a room in the farmhouse specifically for an office, or to a conversion ensconced in a handy farm building.

His daily life changed considerably when reps became motorized from the 1930's onwards, but more from 1950 when petrol became more readily available. The merchant's representative was truly the representative of the merchant. In the '80s and '90s as the labour force changed to a one-to-one ratio with farmers, they were forced back into the tractor or combine seat, and the mobile 'phone put the farm office into the tractor cab.

Farmers ceased going to market as they had done for centuries. The farmer's wife no longer needed to be taken to the town for her shopping. She had her own car, visited the supermarket and stocked up the deep freeze. For the arable farmer the death knell to the Corn Exchange sounded when corn was no longer valued on it's physical appearance or between the teeth of the merchant, but became a subject of laboratory analysis. The merchant became a messenger boy for the technician. Corn Exchanges gradually closed and only two livestock markets, Colchester and Chelmsford survived to provide an outlet for cattle, sheep, pigs etc. Many other products did not pass through a market but were transferred direct from farm to food processing. The importance of the livestock market, a centuries old necessity of life declined almost to the point of extinction. There were 20 markets in the county in 1900.

New crops came, some went almost as quickly. Sugar beet, hailed as the salvation of Essex farmers in the depressed pre-war days, reached its zenith and declined. The county factory at Felsted closed. The bright yellow fields of oil seed rape in late spring became as much a feature of the landscape as the golden fields of harvest, or the green meadows and grazing cattle. Fruit growing went into terminal decline, both orchards and soft fruit. Turnips were no longer grown, oats were never seen. Mangolds, rye, Essex red clover were all consigned into the history books.

Farms were amalgamated. Farm houses were sold off to professional men. Redundant farm cottages, were sold to "outsiders".

Perhaps most fundamentally the countryside and the village was no longer ruled by the agricultural community. It may not have become a playground for urban people but the influence of lobby groups withered away the farming authority. The tide of urban based pressure dictated farming methods and practices. This was more apparent after 1970, when food production was not geared to a memory of war-time rationing.

Farmyard smells were obnoxious to new village dwellers who had little connection with the village. The erstwhile farm houses provided a neat opportunity for this transference as well as an injection of capital. In the period from 1950 onwards, but escalating as the towns were built to capacity, villages saw a massive building programme and an influx of new people. In the last century they fled from the villages. In the 20th century they flooded back but it was not the village romanticised by T.V. – or the life their grandparents had left.

Essex farm buildings, from a visual appraisal, fell into three distinct periods. The few Elizabethan barns that survived, the spate of building with red bricks and pantiles in the 19th century, and the activity which took place from 1950 onwards. The advent of hollow concrete blocks, steel stanchions, asbestos roofs and asbestos cladding. The popular materials of the day will help future historians date the progress.

The changing demands of agriculture, particularly larger machinery, negated the old fashioned cart lodges, which were too low to accommodate tractors with a drivers cab, the narrowness and height of barns made them unsuitable for modern combines, This cumbersome machinery needed new buildings to house it. Silos for silage making were erected. Tall feeding storage for poultry sheds and larger buildings for implement repairs were built to satisfy a demand. Very few of the existing buildings, mainly of Victorian origin, proved suitable. Some were retained for storage purposes, an occasional shed proved useful for a chemical store, and in many places throughout the county, farm buildings achieved a new lease of life when converted for small industrial purposes. It saved some ancient buildings albeit that they hardly resembled their previous role. Agricultural repair shops in country villages became a rarity. They could not exist on farming customers alone but relied upon precision engineering and other activities. One at Fingringhoe produced the machinery for animated figures at Theme Parks although still engaging in repairing farm machinery.

It was not only the rural villages that introduced industrial style units into erstwhile and redundant farm buildings. At Hatfield Broad Oak, Roger Simons purchased a derelict set of farm buildings in 1981 which were threatened with demolition. It became the centre of operations for a sausage company. Broad Oak Farm Sausages originated in 1927 as a pig and sausage enterprise run by a local doctor. The butcher's shop was bought by Mr.Simon's father in 1966. The range of activities were legion – few of them connected with farming.

CHAPTER 3

Before the War. 1900–1914

In 1900 farming had been in deep depression for 20 years, but during that time Essex farmers had learnt to adapt. Led by Hon.Edward Strutt and followed by the invasion of Scottish farmers into one of the driest corners of England it had been proved that keeping cows was a viable alternative – if not a salvation. Market gardening had spread eastwards along the Thames as urbanization had forced it further away from the centre of London. There was a good market for both milk and vegetables. Fruit growing expanded but most importantly the expensive, and loss-making wheat and barley crops had declined.

From being a cash generating business farmers had become more self sufficient purchasing less and selling less – but keeping solvent. It was a siege economy but it was the only route to take. The metropolitan area of the county with it's teeming millions of customers provided a ready market and whilst imported food was the real challenge, Essex farmers had better opportunities with the proximity of London.

It had always been a panacea of good times that multiple holdings increased as farmers found the confidence to take more land. In bad times retrenchment was considered a sound policy, but as farmers succumbed, and there were few brave enough to take their places, the farms were annexed, sometimes rent free, to a neighbour. George Wordley of Orsett increased his holding from 89 acres in 1880 to 229 acres by 1905. There was a surfeit of farms, few farmers willing to take them, yet, as in every depression, there were opportunities for the enterprising man. That Essex was in a parlous state is apparent from accounts of the time. Thomas Whitmore [1] gazed out from Rettendon church tower towards Raweth, North Benfleet, Thundersley and the Thames estimating that there was over 22,000 acres of vacant land fast returning to it's wild state. 'A few years later his son [Francis] rode from Orsett Hall to Chelmsford and saw not a single field of wheat'.[2] It was on the heavy clay in the south of the county that the greatest problems lay, but the effects of a quarter of a century of depressed agricultural prices spread wider. A Felsted farmer on heavy boulder clay, not the undrained grasslands of the southern part of Essex wrote:

> "There are farms without sheep, farms without cattle or pigs, farms that are undermanned and underhorsed, with overgrown hedges, and ditches filled in, and arable lands chiefly remarkable for their splendid clots of twitch and thistles... farmhouses, buildings and cottages are rapidly going to pieces. Many have fallen down, and will never be rebuilt; and as the buildings and cottages with their inhabitants disappear, the church goes out of cultivation ...Agricultural land is regarded as the worst possible investment for spare capital; landlords advertise their farms in vain".[3]

In 1897 Francis Whitmore was advertising for tenants in the North Devon Herald, Leeds Mercury, Preston Herald, Yorkshire Post, North British Agriculturalist, Kilmarnock Standard, Glasgow Herald and many others including The Times.

8 *1910 Gestingthorpe. Ten men with a variety of rakes and forks. Was it hay or barley?*

The southern half of the county with its islands, marshes and extensive grazings was a better place for dairy farming than the upland central region of the county. But it was at Terling, that the greatest impetus was given. The malaise of unprofitable farming spread throughout the whole county but some sectors were more easily adapted for structural changes than others. There was little doubt about the general condition of the county. It "floundered in a state of chronic economic depression...especially the north of the county with its clay belt and low rainfall made for corn growing. Subsequently the county was made to suffer in cruel fashion".[4]

But the depression had not been one long continuous downhill path. Lord Ernle wrote; "the nadir of the great depression came in 1894–95, when the price of wheat per imperial quarter fell to 22s.10d. and 23s.1d. The lowest figures recorded for 150 years"[5] and it fell unequally on various farms. For those in the market garden areas nearer London but spreading as the train services improved, and those who adapted their farming to suit the times, there was the possibility of remaining in business.

The other major factor was a change from the fox hunting Essex farmer to the hard-working son of the soil, who toiled beside his labourers, or did not employ any at all, many also like the Scots had large families and made their children work on the farm for the family good. It was a combination of a lower expectancy in living standards, a propensity to work hard and an ability to follow a flexible stocking and cropping policy. By these criteria some farmers survived. Many did not.

From 1900 the tide had started to turn, imperceptibly at first but farming had come to terms with its position in the economy, farmers had come to terms with their position in society and war clouds were already showing on the horizon. Nothing much happened for the first few years yet the previously defunct Orsett show was revived in 1895, the Tendring show similarly, the prize list in 1902 offered £30 to the winners and at a meeting in Colchester the Tendring Farmers approved the tax on corn and flour, although they regretted that a higher duty was not put on flour. They applauded the greater interest which the government were showing "to the agricultural interest".[6] But in the same year Rider Haggard visited Essex and was told by a farmer at Ardleigh that he would "give up the following Michaelmas as he was tired of it and ought to have left 20 years before".[7] He also commented:

> "The impression left upon the mind by my extensive wandering is that agriculture seems to be fighting against the mills of God. Many circumstances combine to threaten it with ruin although as yet it is not actually ruined".

Whilst Scots and West Country farmers were being lured to Essex, Essex farmers were being lured to Canada. Farms of 160 acres each, being one quarter of a square mile, neatly parcelled by the Canadian land authorities, were offered free. The advertisements said:

> "Western Canada is the land of the Contented Farmer – the land where crop failures never occur; the land that gives splendid returns for labour. An excellent climate, perfect health, the best social and religious advantages, well-conducted schools, convenient markets, good roads and exceptionally low railroad rates are advantages given to settlers on the ranching and grain farms of Western Canada".[8]

Wheat prices were always used as a barometer for the swings in farming profitability. Since the major receipts for Essex farmers, and elsewhere, was from livestock, particularly milk, the contribution from cereals sold off the farm as a cash injection was of less consequence. Never-the-less in the period 1905-14 average wheat prices were 14% higher than in the previous decade. It resulted in a renewed interest in corn growing

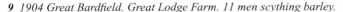

9 *1904 Great Bardfield. Great Lodge Farm. 11 men scything barley.*

10 *1910 St.Osyth Marshes. 17 men with scythes cutting hay.*

which had always been the historical attribution of Essex farming. Frederick Findell, Howses Farm, Gt.Sampford with 220 acres was making an annual profit of £156, or 70p per acre. He was struggling to maintain a largely arable system. His livestock consisted of 10 working horses, five nags and colts, 23 bullocks, a total of 260 sheep, 18 store pigs and only five cows. His receipts for 1905 show no return from milk. In that year the average prices of wheat and barley were (converted) £6.90 per tonne. They had been double in 1874.

On the Terling estates of Lord Rayleigh the profits in 1900 were also 70p. per acre. By 1914 the Terling farms of over 6,000 acres were showing a profit of £1.55p per acre. This had already risen to £1.05p in 1905 when Frederick Findell was making only 70p. As Gerald Curtis observed "but he left Essex at the wrong moment. From 1907 onwards wheat prices never fell below £7.16p for many a long year. Sampfords wheat acreage rose at once from 636 acres in 1901 to 929 acres in 1911".[9]

Over the whole county the average annual reduction of corn crops in the 24 years prior to 1900 was 4,336 acres. In the 14 years before the First World War the Essex acreage rose by an average of 626 acres p.a. Sheep numbers were dropping rapidly due to the uneconomic price of wool and the competition from meat imports. In 1897 70,000 cattle were imported through Tilbury.

Findell was slow to change and his emphasis upon keeping sheep was contrary to the county picture. In the previous 24 years there was an average annual reduction in the

sheep population of 3,349. Essex farmers were still aware that deep rc
changes were needed after 1900 and in the first 14 years of the century
population went down by an average of 8,784 p.a. Permanent pasture which had risen
3,624 acres p.a. escalated to 12,703 acres p.a. The increased numbers of cattle, and cows
in particular, were responsible for the grass acreage, although some of this reverted by
natural regeneration. Many fields were ungrazed, although hay was a lucrative crop near
the coast where transport to the Great Wen could be accomplished by sea. The number of
cows had been increasing by 559 pa before 1900 and 714 p.a. afterwards. Essex farmers
were still swinging to a milk market that offered a satisfactory return. Essex farmers,
however, did not like cows.

> "Cows are very large consumers, and the daily supply of milk which the public are
> enjoying is now being made at very great expense, when we take into
> consideration the high standard which is now compulsory, and for this reason,
> combined with the stringent sanitary measures now in force, many are turning out
> of the business altogether and selling off their cows".[10]

As the war got closer there was increasing anxiety about the dangers of submarine
warfare. A greater emphasis was placed upon a healthy and prosperous home agriculture
– not that it translated itself into tangible rewards. It was much more a promise of things
to come, but it created a sense of subdued optimism amongst Essex farmers. Not quite a
revolution, but some improvement as Sir Daniel Hall noted:

> "I no longer saw the derelict Essex which was once the type of ruined English
> agriculture. The land is cheaply worked and not as clean as formerly but the

11 1910 Stapleford Abbots. Horse rake and hay wagon, with supports to facilitate good loads.

countryside seems to smile with a quiet unexcited prosperity. It is providing bread and butter, at all events, for it's occupiers".[11]

Gerald Curtis lamented that Sir Daniel had not visited Sampford.[12] He apparently toured the Rodings, Tiptree and Ardleigh. Curtis stated that although the crops in the 8 Roding villages [13] were satisfactory but he noted the profusion of wild oats and the luxuriance of the thistles. He wrote "had he visited the parishes on the bolder clay he might not have found all as radiant as elsewhere".

Farmers were beginning to co-operate and not to defend the strong independence that had always been part of their nature. It was not only the larger farmers who led the vanguard in this movement. A Tendring Hundred Farmers Co-operative was formed just after the turn of the century to help smaller farmers in their purchases; insurance rates, and other commodities. The embryonic principles of bulk-buying. The larger farmers were happy enough to join in this co-operative and reap the benefits.

In 1897 East Anglian Farmers Ltd. had been formed with the support of Lord Rayleigh, Lord Petre and Captain Whitmore to enhance the sales of farmers' produce. They concentrated upon market garden, poultry and dairy products. They bought a warehouse at Stratford and had stalls at Covent Garden market. By 1911 total sales had exceeded £160,000. [14] The Eastern Counties Dairy Farmers Society was formed before 1900 and was affiliated to the Central Association of Dairy Farmers. In 1902 they were concerned about the price of milk and the objectives of the Society, outlined at a meeting in the Corn Exchange, Chelmsford were to press for better milk prices. "The Society has virtually raised the minimum figure which it recommends to members year by year".[15]. At the annual dinner afterwards at the White Hart Hotel Hon.Edward Strutt, Chairman, proposed the toast, "success to dairy farming". Eight years later the dinner was held in the Picture Room at the Shire Hall and the toast was, "success to the co-operative movement". The emphasis had changed and a long list of manures, feeding stuffs etc. which had been negotiated by the Society were mentioned with pride.

The Eastern Counties Dairy Farmers Society received an invitation to amalgamate with Eastern Counties Farmers Co-operative Association which had been formed at Ipswich by seven farmers in 1904 with the objective; "to provide a continuing independent force strong enough to exert an influence on the market".[16]

In 1908 a meeting in the Town Hall at Dunmow decided to set up the 'Dunmow Flitch Bacon Factory'. It was another farmer inspired enterprise launched by William Hasler and had a capital of £20,000 to build a factory with modern machinery and produce bacon of the highest quality.

By 1901 Sir Walter Gilbey Elsenham Hall was dispatching jam to 50 retail outlets. In 1904 an extension of the line from Kelveden to Tollesbury included a station at Tiptree to facilitate the movement of jam from the then Brittania Company.

In the Lea Valley the glasshouse and market garden production increased as newcomers arrived to expand the activity. Lord Rayleigh's Dairies was formed in 1900 to retail milk. There were many innovative enterprises launched during this period. They were partly born of desperation but they exhibited a faith in the future.

The Ivel tractor, the first successful petrol driven tractor was invented. Milk recording began in 1914. Those who joined the Essex Milk Recording Society were in a favourable position to increase the efficiency of their cows. The first importation of Dutch cows since 1892 took place when 40 bulls and 20 heifers arrived at Tilbury docks 3 days before the outbreak of the First World War. The importation of Dutch Holsteins later better known as Freisians was to have a major effect upon dairy production throughout the whole country, and throughout the century.

In 1912 a sugar beet factory was built at Cantley, Norfolk and some farmers in Essex experimented with this new crop, which had already had a chequered and unsatisfactory launch in the 19th century. The 1912 experiments largely failed and the crop was not taken up until after the war.

Branches of the National Farmers Union were in existence before the war at Braintree, Dunmow, Colchester, Chelmsford, Ongar and Romford and in 1913 a county organisation was created with George Raby, Tillingham Hall, Southminster, as the first chairman. A branch of the then Central Landowners Association was formed in 1909, and the workers set up an Essex branch of the National Agricultural Labourers' and Rural Workers' Union in 1912. Jesse Collin's Rural Labourers' League had campaigned earlier for an England of yeomen peasants with 50 acres each. It was, perhaps, a pious ambition but the 1908 Smallholdings Act gave the county councils the power to buy farms and divide them into smaller units with the opportunities for a ladder for farm workers. The Essex County Council quickly embraced this Act and created a Smallholdings Estate.

The pre-war period saw many changes but most importantly it was laying down the foundations for a new type of farming business. There was co-operation, a more scientific approach and a degree of confidence. During the next six years, until 1920 the foundation stones that had been laid brought home a bountiful harvest.

Table showing how Essex farming changed from 1876 before the depression became acute. 1900 when the surviving farmers had adapted and 1914 before the First World War had forced more changes:

<u>HOW ESSEX FARMING CHANGED DURING THE DEPRESSION</u>

	Total Acres	Total Corn	Arable %	Cows	Total Cattle	Perm Pasture	Sheep
1876	825,835	406,976	62	22,205	75,832	184,910	373,300
1900	801,768	302,892	49.3	35,636	90,807	271,907	295,334
Change Since 1876	(24,067)	(104,084)	(12.7)	13,431	14,975	86,997	(77,966)
1914	791,203	311,669	51.9	45,643	96,555	284,610	172,352
Change Since 1900	(10,565)	8,777	2.6	9,827	5,748	12,703	(122,982)
Change 1876-1914	% (9.6)	(23)	(10.1)	205	27	53	(217)

Summary: Farmland down by 10%   Arable land down by 10%
            Pasture up by 53%   Cereals down by 23% wheat by 34%
            Cattle up by 27%, Cows by 205% and sheep up by 21%
            A clear substitution of crops for stock.

CHAPTER 4

The Wartime Boom

The preparations for war included a half-hearted policy to increase food production. Britain had not faced a European adversary since Napoleon, although the Crimean War had blockaded the grain ports in the Baltic, creating disruption of supplies. That was nearly 60 years earlier but the bulk of Britain's grain and meat imports came across the Atlantic.

When war was declared in August 1914 the harvest was ready and wheat plantings in Essex were up by 5,000a from 1913, barley by 600a, beans nearly 2,000a, and turnips up by 617a. The acreage of oats, peas and clover had gone down, clover by nearly 6,000 acres. The area of arable land had risen by a minuscule 793a (1%). The small swing was precipitated by the weather in the previous autumn which had allowed winter wheat to be planted, rather than any expectations of enhanced prices or to stock the wartime larder. Most farmers were oblivious to the effects that the war would have, and apparently the government was as well.

By 1920, and with the benefit of hindsight, farmers could look back upon an unprecedented boom. In 1917 the price of wheat reached it's highest level for 99 years. Wartime farming became what J.A. Venn called; "the abnormal war years when there was currency inflation. The government manufactured paper money and got away from the linkage with gold, and prices soared".[1] Mr. Venn was speaking to Essex farmers 10 years after the war, and his conclusions were not made without due consideration.

The interruption of imported meat by the German submarine campaign precipitated the rise in livestock prices that commenced in 1915. Two years later meat prices had doubled and fatstock had followed suit. The army was being fed on home killed beef of which there was a scarcity due to inadequate imports. The extra demand by giving soldiers, who were generally unused to eating beef added to overall consumption. From September 1917 and throughout the following winter the government imposed maximum wholesale prices. In January meat rationing was introduced. There was turmoil by the Authorities. Farmers seemed to sail along on a tide of oblivion accepting the boom in prices without question. Edith Whetham wrote;

> "Scarcity of imported cereals and all cakes, the ploughing of grassland for wheat and potatoes, and the growing scarcity of men on the farms were further reasons why many lowland farmers disposed of their flocks of sheep in the last two years of war, while dairy farmers reared fewer calves and sold a higher proportion of the reduced output of milk".[2]

Gerald Curtis was less restrained in his comments upon the situation written 65 years later:

> "It had not yet been realised that increased agricultural production was vital to the country's survival, but by the end of 1916 it was clear that the Navy, in face of

unrestricted submarine warfare, could not guarantee the arrival of food imports; and the nation was on the brink of starvation".[3]

Sir William Gavin echoed the same sentiments:

"In 1914 British farming was in no condition to respond to any demand for increased production...It seems incredible today that at the outbreak of war in August 1914 this appalling flaw in our armour was not instantly recognised...In February 1917, when the Germans launched their unrestricted submarine campaign, our wheat stocks were so reduced as to represent only One Week and Five Days bread supply for the nation with no substantial home supplies in prospect until the following harvest in September".[4]

The strategy that evolved was the policy of continuing large scale imports which, it was supposed, the Royal Navy could ensure, rather than a realisation that the starvation, or otherwise, of the British public rested upon the efforts of British farmers. A fatal flaw in the projected philosophy which was not repeated in the Second World War. By that time the lesson had been well and truly learnt, Meanwhile prices rose to new levels. Essex farmers were now traditionally, if not historically, dairy farmers, cows had been the salvation of many farming families, and had become the main cash generator for Essex farming. Yet behind this thin facade, and they were still traditionalists at heart, there was a feeling that cows were not indigenous to Essex – but wheat was!

Given adequate remuneration most farmers would have joyfully sold their herds and become arable farmers. The production of crops was inherently more natural to the Essex climate that trying to grow grass in such a dry county.

There had been no impetus to plough up grassland and the substantial wheat increase had been largely at the expense of the barley crop. Since wheat was essentially autumn sown, and most barley varieties at that time were not winter hardy, the conclusion must be drawn that the open autumn was more responsible for the increased wheat acreage – than the cajoling of politicians, or any threats of food shortages which by this time had not materialised.

The disorganised attempts to co-ordinate the war effort had lacked direction in every sphere as well as in farming. The Prime Minister was deposed and Lloyd George became PM. His new Minister of Agriculture R.E. Prothero [5] immediately appointed the leading Essex farmer, Hon.Edward Strutt, as his Chief Agricultural Advisor. It was an immense task to convince farmers that they must change their farming systems and increase productivity, when they were still licking their wounds from the previous 40 years of deprivation. The cash that was flowing into farmers' pockets was utilised to reduce indebtedness, pay for the inadequacies that farms presented, such as re-digging ditches, and there was little confidence that the boom would last.

Prices at Essex markets continued to spiral upwards. Fat cattle of which a 12cwt. beast was fetching £23 15s. (£23.75p) in 1914, not much more the following year, jumped to £38 10s. (£38.50p) in 1916 and the pre-war value had doubled to £47 7s.(£47.35p) by 1917. Meat was desperately short and whilst a high proportion of the live weight gain per beast at this time was from grass feeding, many permanent pasture meadows and marshes had a greater concentration of stock. They had been understocked due to the shortage of capital. There was an expansion of meat production without any commensurate reduction of cereals.

12 1915 Terling. Womens Land Army workers. What were they digging?

An acre of wheat would produce three/four times as much fibrous food for a hungry nation as protein rich meat The output of wheat, therefore, made economic sense. Livestock when fed on concentrated food, which few were at that time, were bad food converters. The protein level was little compensation against the satisfaction of thick sandwiches!

Wheat prices followed very much the pattern of fat cattle. When allowance is made for the variations in the average yield from one harvest to another, and the worst harvest of the war was in 1916 when the production of wheat nationally was below that achieved in 1902, and the other staple food, potatoes, was the lowest since 1912 showed that the weather conditions each year had a severe effect upon the productivity of farmland. For farmers, however, increased prices until 1917 produced an enhanced gross return per acre which had been £6.51p in 1913, was £7.39 in 1914 jumping to £10.66 in 1915 and a peak of £14.39p in 1917. Thereafter it settled down just below £14 per acre. It gave farmers a healthy turnover.

Costs rose in roughly the same percentages as end product prices. Farm workers at Helions Bumpstead and other villages along the northern boundary of the county had been involved in a "lock-out", in early 1914. In June a Union conference at Saffron Walden decided to call out its members all over the northern half of the county. Farmers' sons and other non-involved people drove motor cars to Helions Bumpstead to help gather the hay in June/July. They were confronted by 150 labourers but were not deterred. Strikers attacked cottages and there was a considerable degree of disharmony in the villages. Wages figures of 13s. 0d to 14s. 0d were normal. The union asked for 15s. 0d and were unsuccessful. The average national weekly wage in 1914 was 18s. 0d. This included the northern counties of England, which were always higher.

During the war years wages increased rapidly so that by 1917 they were 25s. 0d. (£1 25p) per week, 30s. 0d (£1.50p) a week in 1918 and the spiral continued until 1921 when they reached 44s. 5d. (£2.22p), nearly two and a half times higher than pre-war. "Costs of production went up very much, prices were high, but those who got heavy crops found that a very useful profit was left. On the other hand, small crops meant a possible loss".[6] A greater problem faced Essex farmers. It was not the cost of labour, but a shortage. More than a third of those employed on farms were called up for the services, or transferred to more direct war work such as munitions factories. Prisoners of war were drafted in to help with the harvests, women were recruited and "public-school boys were employed during their holidays".[7]

A Sampford farmer was criticized by the Ministry officials because he only employed seven men, when according to their standards he should have had nine. A Stansted pig buyer appealed against the call-up papers of his working manager on a 26 acre farm. He was the only employee and claimed he had a large herd of stock.

> "The Military Representative said the applicant was given three months to get another man. Applicant said he had advertised for a substitute and only received one reply, and that was from an insurance agent who knew nothing about farm work".[8]

On this farm there were eight breeding sows and four cows which supplied the milk for the village. If he lost the last man he would have to close the farm and sell out. Conditional exemption was given! Other attempts were made but the shortage was exacerbated by the fact that the more able bodied and skilled farm workers had been drafted leaving only the old men and children. At Sheering, Miss Merry, an approved teacher, was drafted into the local school by the Essex County Agricultural Committee. She was given the task of instructing the older children how to milk a cow. Starting with a dummy the lessons were followed up by practising on the herd at Sheering Hall. "Great interest has been displayed by the children".[9])

Although livestock care was a daily business, the labour requirement on a per acre basis was greater for arable crops than for keeping stock. A cow at that time required three/four acres to support it with it's summer pastures, winter grazing, mangolds, turnips, chaff and straw not being counted, and an area per capita for growing and making hay. On this basis a cowman milking 10 cows was providing most of the labour requirement for 35/40 acres. A further modest input would be required for seasonal work such as hoeing the roots and making the hay. But on an all arable situation the ratio of men per acre would have been around 15/20 acres per man. In vegetable, fruit and market gardening cases the labour requirement was higher. There was an inbuilt objection by farmers to plough up pastures. They remembered the old adage that; "to plough a pasture doth make a man, but to make a pasture doth break a man".

Ploughing pastures was akin to cashing in hard won savings. The value of a pasture was not so much in its productivity or cash return but in the capital which was invested. Grass seed apart there was a further requirement for hedges and fencing to be of a high standard; gates to be maintained; a water supply to be arranged. Whilst a ploughed up pasture could give a return the following year, it was a much longer process to get a newly sown pasture into a state where it could be rightly called "established".

13 1914-18 Thorpe-le-Soken. Ladies hand dibbing

There were numerous cases where the War Ag's ordered grass paddocks to be ploughed up. Thomas Bradridge of Green Farm, Sampford was ordered to plough up 20 acres. He appealed, lost his appeal and was forced to obey. A neighbour, Sam Furze, of Hempstead Hall refused to plough 45 acres, was taken to court, prosecuted and fined.

"I remember most distinctly the large number of crop failures when heavy clayland was ploughed up late in spring and put in with oats. In many cases hardly as much crop was obtained as was sown as seed".[10] Wire-worm and leather-jackets were a common cause of failure when cereal crops were sown on newly ploughed pasture. It was often reckoned that it took until the second or third year before the long accumulation of fibrous root material had decomposed and that the inherent pests which had lurked in the grass were eliminated. Better crops were certainly achieved after a few years ploughing.

Although the War Ag's used their dictatorial powers, they were mild compared to those used in the Second World War.

The powers of the committees which embraced controlling cultivations, ploughing up pasture, and in extreme cases taking over farms that were incompetently managed, were strongly resented by farmers at the receiving end of these orders. In the early years of the war farming did not have official directives. The war was not hurting, shipping losses were counterbalanced by new shipbuilding and a cautious approach by the Kaiser who ordered his commanders not to sink neutral ships. Shipping losses were reduced, and 12 U-boats were sunk. It was also confidently expected that the excellent harvest in both North and South America in 1915 would supply all of Britain's needs.

There was little shortage until summer 1916 but within a few months foreign wheat markets were disrupted, the American harvest was lower than the previous year and equally bad for Britain's allies on the continent. Shipbuilding was not keeping pace with losses and there was a failure of the potato crop. There were fears that land could become derelict, that yields would decline and livestock diminish. The impetus of unrestricted submarine warfare in 1917 and the realisation of the gravity of the situation, and a new Minister of Agriculture gave a stimulus to the formation of the County Committees.

In Essex the wheat acreage in 1915 (162,201a) was the highest achieved during the whole war and a rise of 29,131a over the previous year. Since this crop was planted in the autumn of 1914 before the full impact of the war was felt, it was stimulated by the promise of better prices. It was also a favourable autumn for planting. The barley acreage went down by 18,983a, oats up by 8,222a. In total the cereal acreage went up by 18,393a. By the end of the war it had risen by 28,762a. The bulk of the swing had occurred without the impetus of war – or the War Ag's, and the swing to cereals was achieved, not by a massive pasture ploughing programme, but by a reduction in other crops. Although the cereals area went up by more than 28,000a, the arable acreage of the county only rose by 23,000a.

Permanent pasture had gone down by some 25,000a, almost a direct substitution. A proportion of the permanent pasture was unploughable being undrained marshes, river valley meadows prone to winter flooding and parkland studded with ancient oaks. The Army expanded its land requirements for training ground, particularly around Colchester and Foulness where the War Department bought the Lordship and Manor in 1915. By 1918, thousands of horses destined for France were grazed on the coastal marshland.

The peak of wheat plantings in 1915 could not be sustained. It was bad farming practice to plant wheat twice in succession, and contrary to tenancy agreements. Wheat was normally the first crop after a pasture, thereafter entering into a rotation that included barley and root crops. Some of these were required to feed the additional 5,000 head of cattle, although the number of cows in milk dropped from 33,440 in 1914 to 29,629 in 1918.

The numbers of sheep fell by 43,000 in the period. At 10 sheep per acre this released 4,300a. The cow population required about 60,000a to provide its fodder for the winter months, apart from the summer grazings. Beef cattle similarly required grass. The demands of the livestock sector precluded any greater ploughing up programme and gave farmers a strong reason to resist. Essex was one of five counties with more than 100,000 acres of wheat. The encouragement to plough up old pastures amounted to 25,000a but did not show a commensurate increase in the total cereals in the county which only increased by 895a.

At the end of the war the arable acreage had risen by 3.5%. Since Essex covered 2.5% of the farmland of England and Wales it would seem that it achieved more than could be expected. But it was already a largely arable county and the scope for conversion was more limited. In England and Wales the increase in arable land during the war was 5.2%. By this criteria the Essex increase was below the national average but this disguises the point – that many other counties had greater scope to increase their arable quota.

The armistice was declared in November 1918 when the autumn sown crops were already in the ground. The ending of hostilities was anticipated but farmers faced the future with equanimity. The Corn Production Act (1917) had guaranteed minimum prices for wheat and oats and a minimum wage for farm labourers. This solid support gave Essex farmers little cause for concern. Planning for the future was unaltered. With the escalation of war time prices farmers had done very well. The changes in the balance of enterprises was comparatively small.

Farmers discovered that they could make better profits by doing the same as they had

14 *1914-18 Tiptree. Soldiers hoeing*

always done. In farming terms it had been a "short" war. By the time there was an urgency for food from home agriculture it was already 1917. And with the traditional delay between planting and harvesting there was little scope to make massive changes.There was unusually bad weather in the early months of 1919 followed by a wet spring and a drought in May/June. Not the most propitious scenario for a good harvest. In the event it was a poor one.

The yield of barley was the lowest since of 1898. Oats yielded their lowest return for 35 years and wheat at under 15cwt., the lowest since 1912 and 2.4cwt. per acre less than in 1918. There was a high death rate amongst lambs and the cattle population also suffered. The last factor influenced a peak of nearly £5cwt., or £60 for a 12cwt fat beast in 1920. It plummeted thereafter. Potato yields showed a decrease and the production for the year from Essex farms was 80,000 tons – 53,000 tons less than the previous year. "The yield per acre was, however, almost normal, and the drop is explained by a great decrease in the acreage".[11]

The swings in agricultural production were influenced more by the climatic conditions of the season, rather than a pre-planned swing to capitalise on enhanced prices. The 1919 harvest, the first in peacetime, but sheltered under the auspices of a government guarantee, did not give farmers any reason to change their tactics. They had always realised, and accepted that the behavioural patterns of the weather, from one year to another would have a profound effect upon how much they had to sell – and these swings were a natural part of the gamble that was farming. In 1920 wheat prices hit a high peak that was not to be achieved again for another 28 years.

In 1920–1 the price of barley was higher than wheat, "a strange and unprecedented phenomenon".[12] Barley was £7.50 ton pre-war, it averaged £15 from 1915–8 but in 1919 reached over £21 and £25 in 1920. The following year it was down to under £15 and only £9 by 1923.

The Corn Production Act was perfunctorily repealed just three weeks before harvest was due to commence in 1921. The promise of continued farming support was summarily withdrawn. It was also one of the driest years of the century. In some places the driest June since records had been kept. It was not a good year for the crops.

The boom had been short-lived. The depression that followed was to be deeper and more severe than conditions at the end of the 19th century or the run-up towards 1914. Average profits were slightly better just after the end of the war than during it. Enhanced cereal prices helped. The Terling Estate quickly plunged into losses although Strutt & Parker farms managed to maintain a small profit. When such large and efficiently managed farming enterprises like this could not make a profit there was a worse outlook for the backward thinking, smaller farmer who represented the large bulk of Essex farmers. The boom was over and the next period was to be a catastrophic one.

HOW ESSEX FARMING CHANGED IN WARTIME

	1913	1914	1915	1916	1917	1918	1919
Total Area Exc. Water			976,125	976,125	976,125	796,125	976,125
Total Acreage crops & grass	790,436	791,203	789,599		789,508	787,539	783,367
Arable Land	505,800	506,593	507,034		511,312	528,373	526,751
Perm. grass	284,636	284,610	282,565	281,079	278,196	259,166	256,616
Wheat	128,324	133,070	162,201	133,697	135,307	155,707	122,941
Barley	61,012	61,681	42,698	53,623	65,999	56,920	59,653
Oats	63,004	59,400	67,622	66,280	72,303	67,927	70,700
Rye	1,144	1,087	1,110	1,442	1,162	1,688	2,703
Beans	29,986	31,620	30,725	26,989	19,261	25,517	30,899
Peas	25,059	24,811	22,151	18,974	19,208	17,450	20,068
Potatoes	12,659	13,770	13,773	12,537	13,208	20,586	13,333
Turnips & Swedes	12,649	13,266	10,460	10,930	14,349	11,849	11,732
Mangold	26,180	26,825	22,204	18,642	18,876	20,690	18,438
Cabbage	4,900	4,698	4,871	3,917	3,928	3,212	4,249
Kohl-Rabi	3,785	4,274	4,676	3,577	3,891	3,474	2,507
Rape	692	952	760	510	799	788	742
Vetches	7,793	8,837	8,659	5,788	5,075	3,633	4,540
Lucerne	14,721	14,183	13,675	14,043	12,569	10,203	8,798
Sm. Fruit	2,013	2,134	2,094	2,262	2,194	1,945	1,813
Clover & Grasses	70,190	64,261	63,510	65,787	70,362	64,535	72,171
Other Crops	13,804	12,163	11,572		11,723	15,071	15,426
Bare Fallow	27,840	29,561	24,273	41,087	41,098	45,683	59,517
Horses for Agriculture	26,685	26,233	23,894	24,829	25,309	25,384	25,472
Stallions	212	204	199	231	241	223	239
Others 1 & over	5,050	5,078	4,630	4,687	4,991	4,935	5,059
Under 1 year	2,492	2,242	2,110	2,251	2,083	1,999	2,191
Other Horses	7,304	7,767	7,633	7,377	6,813	6,424	6,519
Total Horses	41,524	41,321	38,466	39,375	39,437	38,967	39,480
Cows in Milk	30,757	33,440	32,038	31,250	30,415	29,626	30,250
Cows in Calf)	11,266	5,460	5,181	4,807	5,446	5,973	5,432
Heifers in Calf)		6,743	5,999	7,532	7,492	9,585	7,406
Others 2 & Over	15,528	12,260	12,554	13,000	13,270	12,583	15,175
1 and under 2	16,759	17,826	19,244	21,627	21,428	19,655	20,322
Under 1 year	17,830	20,826	21,621	22,521	20,891	19,744	19,100
Total Cattle	92,140	96,555	96,637	199,737	98,942	97,166	99,202 (Inc. Bulls)
Ewes	70,045	69,127	62,708	66,274	62,950	52,993	42,843
Others 1 & Over	35,444	28,613	30,878	32,660	32,454	29,323	45,603
Under 1 year	78,679	74,612	67,284	71,625	65,610	58,905	47,630
Total Sheep	184,168	172,352	160,870	70,550	161,014	141,221	136,699 (Inc. Rams)
Sows	9,407	11,574	9,818	10,125	8,849	8,966	8,489
Other Pigs	61,164	69,996	65,476	67,359	55,070	45,452	48,816
Total Pigs	70,571	81,570	75,294	77,484	63,919	54,418	57,966 (Inc. Boars)

© Crown Copyright; MAFF Returns.

CHAPTER 5

The Black Spot of the Century

After 1921 farming went into sharp decline. Prices of all products fell sharply. Wheat dropped from £16.65p in 1921 to £11.10p in 1922 and to £9.85p the following year. From the good times in 1920 British farm prices had dropped 50% by September 1922.

The situation was compounded by the acute drought which occurred in 1921. "No rain fell in Thurrock from March until after harvest".[1] At Maldon Hall William Brown reported that there was; "no measurable rainfall from St. Valentine's Day to 24 September. The sheep roamed over the barley in search of food".

The Brown family had moved from Wyfields Farm, Orsett to Maldon Hall in 1919. The price of wheat was then 66s.0d.qr. The following year it was down to 18s.0d. "I sold wheat at Newbury for £1. That was murder".[2]. The collapse of wheat prices was accompanied by a general decline of all farm commodities. Farms which had made a profit in 1921/2 recorded losses the following year.

This went right across the whole range of output. Cereals, beans and peas, potatoes, carrots, hay. Livestock which had been losing money in 1921/2 made some slight recovery. Pigs and sheep showed a modest return and cows, although profitable at 24p per acre dropped to only 7p per acre. Gone were the pre-war days when Hon. Edward Strutt had shown 10s.0d. (50p). Cattle and sheep continued to be unprofitable throughout the whole period but poultry showed modest margins. In the initial years of the depression many farmers were losing £2 per acre every year.

After having fed the nation in its hour of need, and been promised continuing support, enshrined and guaranteed by parliamentary promise; farmers felt a sense of deep betrayal. The economic chaos into which the whole country was plunged left no room for support from politicians, even well meaning ones. The promise to returning troops of a land fit for heroes could not be sustained. Mass unemployment highlighted by the Jarrow Hunger March. The withdrawal from the gold standard and industrial unrest did nothing to assuage the rural depression.

Milk prices dropped catastrophically. Under the first contracts in 1922/3 the average price for liquid milk was just under 7p per gallon. In March 1922 the buyers only offered 3.3p per gallon, a price that was below the cost of production. There were similar decreases for manufacturing milk. It had been the mainstay of Essex farming since the 19th century and with its proximity to the mass market in London Essex farmers expected to capitalise upon their geographical advantage. But they were in a weak position.

Milk wholesalers in London often refused to pay for milk claiming that it was "off" by the time the train arrived. The far away farmer was easy game for less honest dairymen. In times of flush farmers tipped the milk down the drains. Prices of pedigree Freisians at the Terling sales in 1921 were £204 per head. £106 in 1923 and only £51 the following year. The top priced animal in 1923 fetched £1,680 but six years later the highest price was only £250 and from 1931/3 6,000 Freisians were sold at an average price of £28. In 1921/2 the depression was still in its infancy.

In the Dengie/Maldon area "there were either seven farmers in a nine mile radius or nine farmers in a seven mile radius who committed suicide".[2] Farming bankruptcies rose from a mere 44 in 1920 to a peak of 600 in 1932. Farm rents dropped from around £2 an acre to less than half that figure and landlords, faced with ever increasing costs, adopted a policy of selling their estates. There was a mass exodus of Essex landowners at this period. Some farms were offered for as little as £5 per acre but farmers had no confidence to buy their farms, and investors saw no future in agriculture. There was virtually no market and when tenants vacated it was difficult to find men to replace them.

"It was often the biggest farmers with the largest overheads who went under first...the smaller farmers were able to get by with the help of their wives and children. But you could always tell. Once you started to see the horses going thin, then you knew the end was pretty near".[3]

Frank Pertwee launched a merchanting business as a break away from farming. With 750 acres at Morehams Hall, Frating, Cold Hall Great Bromley and other land south of Colchester; "it failed to bring in a living"[4]. Diversifying out of farming, but dealing with farmers had its inherent risks. "There were, alas, many failures and sometimes we just had not the experience to see them coming. Sometimes we tried hard to keep a poultry farmer afloat, but would have done better to cut our losses (and his) earlier".[4] His son, Norman had no doubts about the differentiation between those who survived, and those who succumbed.

"it has been sad to see the Essex men themselves having to sell, but in most cases they were farmers who had been brought up to manage, but not to labour and the Scots who came down, sometimes with quite large families, got through because of their ability to do the work themselves at a low cost".[4]

Established farmers with a deep knowledge of their land and a lifetime's experience of tending stock or growing crops found it impossible to make a profit during the early 1920s. Others succumbed to the odium of the Bankruptcy Court.

Tendring farmer Samuel Oscar Gray of Bretts Hall had made his money as a property developer in London and as a solicitor. In the euphoria of wartime prosperity he bought Bretts Hall for £4,100 with borrowed money and soon annexed Hill Farm. In July 1917 two more adjoining farms Brick House Farm and the Reddings. The following year he rented 21 acres of meadow land at Little Bentley. His principal interest lay in establishing fruit plantings, and altering existing buildings and constructing new piggeries for three herds of pedigree pigs.

In 1920 Gray appeared at the London Bankruptcy Court. He had disposed liabilities of £58,984 18s. 7d. After preferential claims and assets were assessed he had a net deficiency of £7,311.

The full impact of failures were clouded by the numbers who got out before they went bankrupt. They ignominiously retired to a modest cottage, or simply disappeared. It was all reminiscent of the 1870s when "tenants threw up their holdings and it was impossible to find others to replace them. Some did not even give in their notice – they just disappeared in the night".[5] At Terling the bold, and unique decision was made to

15 *1930 Tollesbury Hall Farm. Cart horses after a days work*

take in-hand these vacant farms. This was a major policy departure for traditional landlords and it required an injection of capital to stock and crop the farms.

In the 1920s the farms that became vacant were, in general, owned by lesser landlords who perhaps only owned one or two farms, were absentee themselves and engaged in other businesses or professions. They did not have the expertise or the available capital to take over the farms themselves. Piously they were advertised, but few were brave enough to take them on. Many farms stood empty for years. The fields became choked with weeds, hedges overgrown, ditches clogged, buildings lost their thatch and tiles, and bushes and nettles grew in the farmyard.

Alec Steel, Sutton Hall Rochford, was scathing in his assessment of the situation. "The average farmer today is not so well off as the comfortable town's grave-digger, which might be explained by the fact that the politician has an interest in the welfare of the grave-digger, as well, or perhaps more, than in the farmer".[6] He continued "how different it would have been if the government had taken a drive through the southern or northern portion of Essex and viewed what was once the granary of England, turned into the shambles of desolation".

The farm workers were also in ferment. As farm prices plummeted workers wages were reduced. They reached a peak of £2.34p in 1920 but the following year they were reduced to £2.00 and in October 1922 to only £1.41p per week. The cost of living had dropped by 50% but the prices of agricultural products had gone down three fold.

The 1923 strike by the National Union of Agricultural Workers was an explosion of anger that had been simmering since 1920, when workers had threatened to strike unless they received a minimum wage of £2.50p. There were 8,000 agricultural workers in Essex who were members of the Union. G.K. Mitchell, Great Bentley farmer and chairman of the Colchester branch of the National Farmers Union said;

> "this strike is not a strike against the farmers. The settlement of the wages has been taken out of the farmers' hands by an Act of Parliament...the Wages Board had proposed a wage of £2.34p and only one man had voted against it – George Dallas. Mr.George Dallas is now leading the strike in Essex. They have picked out Essex, out of the southern half of England because they think that here they have the best chance".[7]

The strike did not materialise because individual farmers made their own private arrangements with their men. Most of them agreed to cash bonuses. The harvest additions which were traditional. The individualism of farmers was their greatest strength in cutting corners and cutting costs when the situation was desperate, but it could act against their own interests when individualism became active non-cooperation.

George Mitchell of Pond Hall Wix wrote "it is very difficult to get unanimity in what we would like to cure our ills, and sometimes the conferences may not have been unanimous. I would like, here and now, to implore greater unity amongst all farmers, to sink their differences, and if not members of the Farmers Union already, to join at once".[8]

16 1920s Southminster Station. Mr.Proctor Snr. delivering milk for London Market.

17 1925 Southminster farmers delegation opposed to Tithes, in London

Albert Blomfield of Maplestead, who was an advisor to Lloyd George on the de-rating of farmland, put forward his own formula to combat the crisis. He pointed out the worse a man farmed and the less labour he employed the better of he would be. "Agriculture is in a bad way simply because the cost of production is more than is realised by the sale of the produce".[9] Blomfield laid out a formula for workers' wages. It should he wrote; "be equivalent to 18 stones of wheat for a 52 hour week which at prices current comes to 21s.0d (£1.5p). This is an economic wage, not a living one which has been assessed at £1.50p. The difference should be paid by the government and would be a better investment than the dole".

Essex farmers faced a particular problem. Nationally two thirds of the income of the industry came from the livestock sector but in Essex it was only 34.7%, one third of the county was pasture which would produce livestock products plus a small percentage of the two thirds of the county that was devoted to arable crops, but with 52.5% of the arable land devoted to cereals there was a pronounced detrimental effect upon the chances of survival for Essex farmers – unless there was a drastic re-structuring of the agriculture of the county.

This was unlikely to happen over night. The number of cows crept inexorably up until it reached a peak in 1934 having risen by 1,496 cows per annum steadily for the previous 14 years. Sheep peaked in 1932 having more than doubled since 1921 and increased by 9.827 p.a. Pigs increased rapidly after 1931 but chickens remained hovering just above the 2.25m mark. Lower cereal prices stimulated poultry keeping.

Wheat reached its lowest level ever in 1934 when it was only worth £4.80p ton. Barley had reached its nadir in 1932 with a low of £7.60p and oats went down to a rock bottom £5.60 in 1933. This was bad news for cereal farmers – but good news for livestock producers. More barley was ground for pig feeding than wheat, but more wheat was used for chickens. Oats were crushed and fed to cows and horses. The integrated livestock farm had a laborious task to cash its harvest through the mouths of its animals.

The disunity amongst farmers was always irreconcilable since their interests were often opposed. It was during this time that the apparently contradictory epithet was coined; "the arable dairy farm".

Edward Ruggles-Brise MP Spain's Hall Finchingfield put the matter succinctly

"In any proposals, for instance, to assist the growing of wheat the milk producer should be ready to lend every aid to the arable farmer, so as to keep him from entering his own line of business and becoming a formidable competitor. Similarly, the arable farmer, with only a limited demand for his wheat and an ever-diminishing demand for his barley, should stand solid behind the milk producer in his efforts to secure a reasonable margin of profit on his milk. The balance in the industry must be kept, and farmers in different branches of the industry must realise their interdependence".[10]

The depression did not hit all types of farms equally. J.A. Venn told Essex farmers in 1929 that half the county was tied by heavy clays to certain normal rotations; "there are successful examples of other types of agriculture – that carried on in the Southend district, for instance, or the production of seeds in certain parts – but the principle form of agriculture practised in Essex is a normal rotation on the heavy clays".[11] As the result of a survey he suggested that there had been an average loss of 21p per acre on heavy land farms over the previous four years (1924–8) but that light land farms had returned a profit of 45p per acre. "This shows the handicap which heavy land farmers suffer under in times of depression".

A 1930 survey concluded that nine out of every ten farms failed to make a fair return for the labour and capital investment of their occupiers. For every farm size group from 20 acres to over 300 acres there were losses – and they were higher per acre on the larger farms. "It is a desperate situation".[12]

At Bulmer Lawrence Hyde Parker put a third of Smeetham Hall into grass. "We didn't fence it in...or put cattle on. On Smeetham it just wasn't profitable...we would have lost even more money. All we could do was concentrate on the best land and farm it cheaply...there just wasn't any confidence at all...we were all basically farming on hope".[13]

When Ralph Sadler was appointed Colchester District Officer with the task of giving farmers advice, having come from the South Essex area along Thameside, which itself was a deprived area, he found the situation in North East Essex was, if anything, worse.

"Part of Tendring and much of the land south of Colchester was heavy, wet, London clay. The whole of this area was ranched, some of it very successfully. The land was cheap to buy, much of it changing hands for as little as £5 per acre, and it could be hired for 10s.0d. (50p). No land had been ploughed since the early 1920s, no ditches had been dug and no hedges cut."[14]

This depressed picture was not confined to those areas. It was reputed that 20,000 acres of land "lay derelict and abandoned between Colchester and Haverhill"[14] which remark was reminiscent of Thomas Whitmore gazing out from Rettenden Church in 1905 and estimating that there was over 22,000 acres of vacant land "fast returning to its wild state".

Some indication to the extent of the dereliction in Essex can be calculated by the 42,374 acres which the Essex War Agricultural Executive Committee took over and farmed. This included 6,002 acres reclaimed from planned, but unbuilt housing projects and the total reclaimed from bushes was 8,426 acres. There had been a drop of 50,914 acres in the farmland of the county from the start of the depression to the outbreak of war. Most of it at the metropolitan end and around the larger towns. Southend in particular grew rapidly during this time.

Strangely, despite the efforts of the E.W.A.E.C. there was no commensurate increase in the total farmed area after 1939. It is probable that the reclaimed acres, were included in the annual M.A.F.F. returns and entered as "permanent pasture", irrespective of whether they were grazed or not and part of Ralph Sadler's description; "the whole of this area was ranched". Although referring to the Winstree group of villages on the heavy clay south of Colchester, it could well have been the reason why the total farmed area did not rise. There was a reduction of 170,005 acres in the land listed as permanent pasture between 1939/45. This was patently "ploughable" land and must have been the major source of increasing wartime food production.

Many farms had no occupants. Agents were instructed to find sales for the rough meadow hay, preferring to sell it as a standing crop and let the purchaser take the risks of wet weather. Some were lightly stocked with agisted cattle, animals taken on a per head/ per month or per week basis and mixed on extensive grazings with cattle from other farmers.

Abbotts Hall at Great Wigborough was bought by a fertiliser agent R.M.Mortimer. He was also involved in the forage market and used the 700 acres to cut hay for the London trade. There were still plenty of horses in London in the thirties. In that village there was no ploughed land. On nearby Mersea Island blackberry bushes were prolific, growing over most of the fields. Rabbits were the chief graziers and the impoverished soil between the bushes had little grass cover.

Langenhoe Hall was sold in 1901 after 300 years in the Waldegrave family and purchased by Rt.Hon.James Round MP as an off-hand portion of his Birch Hall Estate. There was 1,420 acres of which only 360 was arable land. Round died in 1917 and the new purchaser was Capt. Alfred Lowenstein, a Belgian financier who had escaped from his native country. Amassing 4,615 acres with Guisnes Court, 1,826 acres at Tolleshunt D'Arcy and Tollesbury, farms in Layer Breton and Abbott's Hall Great Wigborough, later purchased by Mortimer. Lowenstein immediately set up a company to conduct the farming. It was 1917 and there was considerable evidence of prosperity. County Farms and Lands Co.,Ltd. was launched and farm managers were installed. Lowenstein was in financial trouble within 4 years and the farms were offered for sale, without success.

The Langenhoe Estate had seen a succession of short term tenants in the last quarter

18 1920 Thorpe Farms. Hay making. Traditional Essex farm

of the 19th century including one from Westmorland. Finally it was offered to a neighbouring yeoman farmer, Thomas Pertwee, of Langenhoe Lodge.

He paid a modest rent but was also employed as a farm bailiff with the result that he acquired a considerable amount of additional land at no expense. By 1907 he was paying a rent of £400 pa but Pertwee's eldest son, Frank, seeing little future in farming, moved to Frating and the Hall land was given up. A new tenant was found, Alfred Jasper, a west country immigrant who took over and farmed from 1907 to 1917, by which time he was paying £700 pa.

The death of Round created a need to sell the property with vacant possession and when Lowenstein bought it in 1917, Jasper's tenancy was due to expire at Michaelmas 1918. He had been an annual tenant. Lowenstein had paid £10,000 in 1917 but with the euphoria of peace and the promise of the aftermath, Jasper's farm sale set many records. His live and dead stock realised the princely sum of £16,000 with the 12 horses grossing £2,583. The sale was just six weeks before the armistice.

Paul Ohlmann was appointed as farm manager for the "county farmers", as they became known. He finally left in 1924 and it remained moribund until 1930. John Fenn, senior partner of Fenn Wright, Colchester auctioneers was responsible for finding someone to take the annual hay crop. But there were no offers for the tenancy.

In 1930 a catholic commune "The English Land Association", bought the estate for a reputed £4,000, plus an agreement to pay the tithe arrears which amounted to £1,000. When the estate had first been offered for sale in 1921 Mr.Eve of estate agents Savills had valued it at £12,000 or £8.50 an acre. The bidding had stopped £1,000 short and it was not sold. Sale particulars were prepared and it was advertised every year.

The English Land Association was launched with the primary purpose of restoring rural values to urban people. It's advertised objectives set out it's principals.

> "The buildings include two large houses – one with 10, the other with seven bedrooms – and 9 cottages. There are three splendid barns and many outbuildings which could be turned into human habitations. The estate has appeared to us suitable for the settling of a group of people on the land in such a way as to be independent of the abominable and insecure system of Industrialism, under which we all labour against our wills.
>
> When the existing structure tumbles, the soil will be our only hope. The vast, enfeebled mass of our Countrymen know nothing of the great tradition of agriculture which gave them being. They cannot tell a pig's snout from it's tail, or the difference between an ear of wheat and an ear of barley...what must be done"?[16]

A few Londoners paid their money and bought a bare field. Shacks were erected but the bulk of the people, including week-enders lived in the existing houses. Only a small part of the land was farmed at all. Mr.Hawkeswell's comment about a pig's snout and it's tail was certainly applicable to himself. It was all a disastrous failure, and in 1935 they sold up and left.

The new purchaser was Henry Tuke, a Galleywood banker, who bought the estate for the sporting facilities which it offered. At that time it was overrun by thousands of rabbits. This situation continued until 1939 when the War Ag Committee told Mr.Tuke that the need for food was a vital part of the war effort – and he must plough up the farm and sow some crops. In 1938 he had persuaded a farmer to take the Hall and a few surrounding acres where he kept cows. This was heavy London clay and totally unsuitable for dairy-ing, particularly in the winter months.

The tenant was ousted and the war committee took over the farm. The first year cost Tuke £500. Gangs were drafted in to cut back the wildly overgrown hedges, to re-dig the ditches, help prepare the land by ploughing with tractors. The total value of the harvest came to less than the expenditure. The following year the War Committee gave up the farm, Land agents Strutt & Parker managed it on behalf of Mr.Tuke. Thus a marshland manor that had once been a highly productive holding deteriorated during the black spot in the century – and was rescued. It was not an untypical story.

In the '20s successive governments did little to alleviate agricultural distress, but in the early '30s there was a spate of activity. In 1928 J.A.Venn posed a timely question to Essex farmers; "Have we see the worst of the depression, or is there worse to come?" [17] He could not answer it, but pointed out that it had not (at that time) been as bad or as long as the period of depression which followed the Napoleonic Wars, or as prolonged and severe as the depression in the '80s and '90s. There was, however, for Essex farmers a very big difference and the inter war depression hit deeper and harder. Always having had the advantage of its proximity to the London market, and in the 19th century when farmers languished, the nation enjoyed an industrial boom, but in the '20s not only were farm workers' wages reduced, but urban workers too. The malaise was self evident in the unrest which emanated from the manufacturing centres, and even London, without heavy

AGRICULTURAL WAGES

Minimum and Overtime Rates of Wages for Workers employed in Agriculture for time work in

ESSEX

I. MALE WORKERS

Years of Age.	Rates per Week.	Hours per Week.	Overtime Rates per Hour. On Weekdays (including Easter Monday, Whit Monday and Boxing Day).	Overtime Rates per Hour. On Sundays and on Christmas Day.	Employment to which Overtime Rates Apply.
	s. d.		d.	d.	
21 and over ...	31 6	41½ in the weeks in which Easter Monday and Whit Monday fall; 50 in any other week in summer; 31 in the week in which Christmas Day and Boxing Day fall; 48 in any other week in winter.	9¼	10¼	(a) All employment in excess of 6 hours on one weekday in each week as agreed between the employer and the worker. (b) All employment on Sundays, Easter Monday, Whit Monday, Christmas Day and Boxing Day. (c) All employment in excess of 41½ hours in the weeks in which Easter Monday and Whit Monday fall; 50 hours in any other week in summer; 31 hours in the week in which Christmas Day and Boxing Day fall, and 48 hours in any other week in winter (excluding in each case all hours which are to be treated as hours of overtime employment).
20 and under 21	29 6		8¾	9¼	
19 ,, 20	27 11		8¼	8¾	
18 ,, 19	24 2		7¼	7¾	
17 ,, 18	21 1		6¼	6¾	
16 ,, 17	16 9		5¼	5¾	
15 ,, 16	13 9		4¼	4¾	
14 ,, 15	10 5		3	3½	

II. FEMALE WORKERS

Years of Age.	Rates per Hour for all time worked throughout the year.
	d.
21 and over	6¼
18 and under 21	5½
16 ,, 18	4½
14 ,, 16	3½

NOTES.

1. The above rates will operate as from 12th April, 1936, and will continue in force until 27th March, 1937.
2. For the purpose of the above rates winter shall be the period commencing on the last Sunday in October and ending on the last Saturday in February, and summer shall be the rest of the year.
3. For the purpose of the above rates, the hours of work shall not include meal times, but shall include any time during which, by reason of weather conditions, an employer has prevented from working a whole-time worker who was present at the place of employment and ready to work.
4. Deductions from the above rates may be made only in cases where a Cottage, Milk, Potatoes, and/or in the case of male workers only, Board and Lodging are supplied. Particulars of the amounts at which these allowances are to be reckoned in part payment of wages may be obtained from the Secretary, Essex Agricultural Wages Committee, 7, Whitehall Place, London, S.W.1.
5. Forms of application for a Permit exempting a worker from payment at the minimum rates (in cases of workers who by reason of physical injury or mental deficiency or any infirmity due to age or to any other cause, are incapable of earning the minimum wage) may be obtained from the Secretary of the Committee.
6. Complaints as to non-payment of the prescribed rates of wages, should be addressed to the Secretary, Ministry of Agriculture and Fisheries, Kings Buildings, Smith Square, London, S.W.1.
7. Complaints as to inadequate piece rates of wages should be addressed to the Secretary of the Committee.

N.B.—**The above particulars are merely a summary of the Orders, and for full details of the legally binding provisions reference should be made to the actual Orders, copies of which may be obtained from the Secretary of the Committee.**

April, 1936.

(35319—23) Wt. 8074—8 1125 4/36 P. St. G. 372

19 *1936 April. Essex wage levels*

industries. The farmer was robbed of customers. The degree of anger was greater.

A century earlier farmers had bewailed the repeal of the corn laws, and fully expected a downturn in farming. Due to extraneous circumstances this was delayed by 30 years and when it arrived starting in the 1870s the rate of decline was slower. Farmers had more time to assimilate, if not to take counter measures. They had ample warning of the awesome future. In 1921 farmers had no warning at all and many farm products dropped by 25% between March and September. It caught farmers unawares.

Farming was a less cash orientated business in the 19th century, subsisting very much on the barter system, but in the 20th century it had become a cash society. Andrew Young, Manor Farm, West Tilbury, took the ferry weekly to Gravesend and came back with gold sovereigns and half sovereigns to pay his men. The National Provincial Bank Ltd. advertised that "a banking account today is a necessity"[18] and boasted of five branches in Essex with three more in Southend.

Barclays boasted of; "numerous branches of the bank established in the agricultural districts throughout the county"[19] and displayed its agricultural links with three prominent Essex landowners as local directors. J.Oxley Parker of Faulkbourne, J.J.Tufnell, Langleys Great Waltham and Henry Tuke Despite the fact that the depression only lasted, in its most intense form, from 1921–34, and thereafter farmers had come to grips with their new found situation, yet the state of Essex farms was far worse in 1939 than it had been in 1914. By this criteria it must be adjudged to have been a more serious problem.

A mass meeting was held at Colchester in December 1938 organised by the Colchester NFU branch and supported by the auctioneers, agricultural engineers, chairman of the Suffolk County Branch and the farm workers, it was another protest at the dire straits which still faced farmers. James Blyth with farms at Walton-on-Naze and Ardleigh said; "for the past 10 years the average arable farmer has had only a hand to mouth existence, and in the last two years of this period there has been nothing in the hand when it comes to the mouth."[20]

Farmers described their plight as working in "a starved and enfeebled agriculture". The workers union man, Mr.B.Frost, supported the mass protest as "he was doing something to assist the worker as well as the employer. Farm workers had been slighted more by the present government than any party going". With less than a year before the outbreak of war Essex farming was still in a parlous state yet there had been some changes. In 1926 the Felsted sugar beet factory opened and nearly 6,000 acres were grown in the county. In 1928 the first Essex Commercial Fruit Show was held and it continued to be an annual event. A new fruit packing station was opened at Witham in 1937. A poultry station was opened at Galleywood in 1931. The Young Farmers Club movement started in the county in 1931 and expanded rapidly. The Essex Seed Trade Association was formed in 1933.

There was another injection of new blood, and energy into Essex farming circles with the arrival of more Scottish families from 1925 and in the early '30s Lancashire farmers arrived. Orchards and small fruit continued to expand in the county and this sector was encouraged by newcomers, often military men. There was a phenomenal rise in the number of poultry farms, often only 5/10 acres, although Messrs. Girling at Holland-on-Sea, with 250 acres had a farming system that relied heavily on hatching and breeding chickens – the wheat was grown to feed them – and cash eventually received. They were organised and run in an exemplary manner.

Poultry farming became an important sector whereas egg production had previously been pocket money for the farmers' wife. A new agricultural college was built at Writtle when the attendance at the foundation stone laying ceremony in October 1938 was reduced "by the disturbing international affairs which exist".[21] It was anticipated that the building would be completed and occupied as a college within 18 months. It was to be six years before courses got tentatively under way.

Farmers became more conscious of attention to details. Milk recording and egg and pig recording schemes were instituted. TT testing of milk became obligatory.

Folkards of Copford boasted that their seed corn was "cleaned and graded by the very latest machinery which has just been installed" (1934) and they promoted "white horse-tooth maize" (1932). Matthews of Harold Wood that their; "high grade general manure contains Peruvian Guano", Richardson & Preece at Witham, Goulds at Loughton, Ongar and Saffron Walden, and Cole and Lequire at Grays (1934) said that farmers "cannot afford to ignore sulfurophosphate for every crop. Truth will out". Christopherson at Ipswich had three grades of fertiliser for sugar beet and potato crops and said, "all soils are improved and assisted to withstand drought conditions. They can be lifted earlier and produce better quality. The extra cost is negligible when compared with ultimate results". (1936).

East Essex Farmers Ltd. at Southminster advocated; "a balanced ration dairy cube for cows. A.F.P. of Upper Mall, London said; "pig and poultry farmers who fed Vitamelo are invariably men of sound judgement". May & Butcher of Heybridge advertised their "Cluck, brooder and rearer for chickens". It was followed by the "Cluck carry-on", and the "Cluck folding unit" (1933). In 1938 they said that their pig houses imbodied, "all the latest discoveries in this country and Denmark". Alfa-Laval kept improving their milking machines and recorded that Charles Draper, Hill Farm Woodford had just purchased his third milking plant for his off-farm at Epping.

Dozens of other firms pushed their products to reluctant farmers who, with bitter memories, would not incur expenditure on unproven products. But mechanisation was insidiously creeping up. The first combines appeared in Essex and tractors were less unusual. The Maldon Iron Works Co.Ltd. was advertising sugar beet hoes, hayrakes, a new hay-sweep that pushed a complete cock at a time to the foot of the elevator – they were all horse drawn! (1931).

Gartons at Witham invited farmers to inspect the 10 varieties of winter oats which they had planted on trial grounds on the main Chelmsford-Witham road.

Most seed corn was saved from the threshing and was dredge or "seconds", preferring to sell the better grain – and not waste it on seed. They remembered the recent years and relied on old fashioned muck to grow beet and other root crops. Whilst cows could show some profit most fat cattle did not, but farmers were content to winter-in bullocks in yards, sell them for negligible profit, but regard the resulting muck as the profit. It would bring a return in the succeeding crop. Essex farmers considered that this was a reasonable policy.

There had been some government injection of money but the aid was puny compared to the problem. The most useful, and important development for Essex farmers was the creation of the Milk Marketing Board in 1933. It stopped the wasteful process of tipping milk down the drains. The price was not high, but there was a guaranteed market for everything that was produced. The increase in cows between the wars amounted to

20 *1920s Thorpe-le-Soken. Cyril Bray often took children to school in the milk float sidecar.*

15,810 (40%) and there was an average increase before the MMB was created of 1,640 cows pa. The new stability in the milk market did not, strangely, show an immediate increase in dairying.

In the seven years up to the war the Essex herd went down four times with the net result that there were only 146 more cows on farms in 1939. But dairy farming was still the mainstay of the county. In 1939 there were 2,732 bulls and on the assumption that only one or two of the very large herds would have required two bulls it is reasonable to suggest that there were 2,700 herds, which would be approximately 50% of the farmers with over 10 acres, and an average herd size of 22 cows. In every village most farmers kept cows. They were a common sight and were often driven along the lanes to summer grazings.

As the wheat acreage tumbled by 30,000 acres and oats by a similar amount there was an increase of 71,000 acres in the area of permanent pasture. The extra cows required some of this, but 54,000 more sheep also grazed the fields. There was an additional 6,000 beef cattle 45,000 extra pigs and 1.27 million more chickens, a 300% increase. Turkeys had also increased by the same percentage.

It was a classic story of salvation, with a switch from arable to animals. The pasture area occupied 47.5% of the land in 1933. At over a third of a million acres it was the highest figure since records had been produced. Arable crops reached their lowest ebb in 1933 with only 52.5% of the farmland and only 47% of this was growing cereals. Clover and grass leys went down by 30,000 acres, lucerne by 11,000 acres but the swing was more marked in the coastal clay belt particularly in the Winstree and Dengie Hundreds and parts of South Essex. Most of the heavy clay farms were ill-drained and unsuitable for arable crops. They went over entirely to grass. In a large area south of Colchester and stretching along the northern coast of the Blackwater there was not a single ploughed field.

A picture of the reliance which small farmers gave to cows is encapsulated by the story of West Bergholt farmer Edward Barrow with 50 acres including grazing meadows in the Colne Valley. He kept a small herd of cows, 10/12, a bull and disposed of bull calves at birth but reared some of the heifers. The whole farm was devoted to feeding the cows. Winter exercise land, summer grazing, land for hay, a long term lucerne field (usually left down for seven years), a field of oats, and about five acres of mangolds. A meadow for the two horses.

He had a retail milk round in the village with both morning and late afternoon deliveries. He kept some chickens in the orchard and sold eggs on his milk round. He grew enough potatoes for his family and a few over for sale. His oats were taken to nearby Newbridge Mill, Lexden for crushing and brought back the same day. He fed brewers' grains occasionally which he collected from Daniell's brewery in the same village. It was a closed economy; producing the milk with virtually all home grown food and selling it to the villagers. He killed a pig once a year and had haunches of hams and sides of bacon hanging in muslin bags over the fireplace. The water came from a spring. Lighting was by oil lamps and there was no telephone.

Edward Barrow had moved to this small farm in 1901 and had farmed through the better days of the first war. In the early 1920s he bought a motor car for a reputed £600 but he died in 1929. His son carried on with the milk round and the cows until his retirement some 40 years later.

At the other end of the scale a large farmer, Gardner Church, with 600a, a tenant on both the Birch and Messing estates evolved a side-line of contract pea growing. His farms had a dairy herd of 30, he grew mangold, turnip and Essex red clover for seed and also cereal crops.

His elder brother had founded the seed firm, W.A. Church Ltd. at Bures but had died. Gardner Church found an outlet for flagging seed sales by offering farmers the opportunity to grow peas without risk. He supplied the seed, adjudged the right time to pick the peas, drafted in hordes of women pickers and gypsies, transported the peas to Covent Garden – and took a risk on the market. In return the farmer did all the work. He drilled the peas, hoed them twice and kept the resulting pea haulm which was useful cattle fodder.

By the mid '30s he was contracting more than 1,000 acres. By 1938 his wife had a car as well as himself. Unfortunately there were many who were unable to exhibit this spirit and succumbed to the financial pressures of the times. There were others who, by inventiveness, hard work, ability and flexibility to change survived this black spot in the century. When war was declared on 3 September 1939 the dark clouds gathered over Europe – but blue skies started to shine on Essex farms.

ESSEX VALUERS PRICES (DECIMALISED)				
	1st Cut Clover	Low Meadow Hay	3 Horse Work	Motor Ploughing
1918	£ 7.00	£5.00	£1.35	£1.00
1919	£11.00	£7.00	£1.55	£1.25
1920	£ 8.00	£6.00	£2.00	£1.50
1932	£ 2.00	£1.25	£1.20	.85
1937	£ 3.75	£1.80	.80	.75

CHAPTER 6

A Land of Milk and Money

In New Zealand; Dunedin can be literally translated as 'New Edinburgh'. The low rolling hills and the verdant pastures are reminiscent of Scotland. The same can hardly be said about the Essex landscape, yet it was to Essex that large numbers of Scottish farmers came, and they injected life into moribund Essex farming and provided impetus, energy, and optimism. Between 1924/34, a second wave of immigrants transformed the Essex farming scene. There had been an influx between 1883 and 1900 but thereafter there were only occasional times when Essex farms were let or bought by Scotsmen.

Why the Scots chose Essex is a phenomenon that deserves examination. Cornish farmers migrated to Hertfordshire, Welsh farmers moved into Warwickshire and Northamptonshire but Ayrshire farmers migrated to Essex although Hew Watt wrote, "50% of my relations at that time went to New Zealand where they still are, in the third and fourth generations".[1] New blood into Essex farming circles had been injected at periodic times. The movement of both farmers and labourers, was much greater than historians had supposed. In 1806 Alexander Thomson, Tweedside, Near Coldstream, offered to rent a farm at St. Lawrence owned by St Bartholomew's Hospital. It was 460 acres in total, 400 arable, 20 meadow and 40 of saltings which were tidal. Thomson offered £720pa on a lease of 21 years.[2]. The rent amounted, with adjustments for the saltings of £1.71p – when average rentals for the district were only 75p. Thomson's offer was declined and a lower one, with different proposals for the farming policy, was accepted. This highlights the willingness of farmers from Scotland to consider moving to Essex.

Another Scotsman, John Claudius Loudon, who toured Essex in 1825 admitted that the arable land in the county was cultivated- better than 9 in 10 of other counties. "He could not conceal his admiration for some features of Essex farming but he disliked what he learned about it with some intensity ...to a Scotsman the atmosphere of Essex was not very agreeable".[3] The Scots were not the only ones who were attracted to the prospects of farming in Essex. Stephen Padfield arrived in Chigwell from Somerset in 1885. He was followed by his five brothers.

Dr. Collins[4] identified other west country immigrants, W. Vellacott, Tunnel Farm, West Thurrock (1879), C.W. Hawkins, Mucking Hall (1896), Wm. Bucknell, East Horndon Hall (1885), R. Tuckett, Whitfields, Orsett (1900). Ashley Cooper[5] identified 16 families who came to Essex between 1890 and 1930. Most of these settled in the Great Yeldham/Steeple Bumpstead area of the county. One notable member of a Cornish family was J.R. Tinney who became the first farmer-president of the Essex Agricultural Society. He was a leading potato grower and a member of the PMB. Tinney and Hitchcock were settled at Rickling.

In the late '20s/30s a minor invasion of Lancashire farmers settled in North Essex. The Baines family came from Fylde to Chappel in the 1920s, Fred Calverley from

Outlane to Great Wigborough, Fred Bradshaw and John Chamley from Stalmine to Fordham. The Lofthouses to West Bergholt and Tiptree, Taylor to New Hall, Little Wigborough and the Fishers to Southminster. There were others.

The Lancashire farmers generally took less extensive farms than did the Scots. The Lancastrians were excellent sheep and pig farmers. Some were poultry men. The Cornish farmers gravitated to the arable parts of Essex and the Somerset Padfields settled around the Epping area with an eye towards the profitable London milk market. Selling liquid milk was less laborious than working the product into butter and cheese, particularly when most of this work had to be done by hand. London was also an insatiable market. At Waltham Cross in 1901 one of the largest glasshouse growers was a Scotsman.

By 1900 66 Scottish families had arrived at what they called "the land of milk and money". 433 'foreigners' took Essex farms by 1930. 119 came from south west England and 170 from south west Scotland, mainly but not exclusively from the Kilmarnock area.

The invasion by 1900 amounted to an occupancy of 1.9% of Essex farms over 50 acres. By 1930 the Scottish contingent amounted to 4.6% of the 3,679 Essex farmers listed at the time. This does not take into account daughters who married local farmers' sons. These were comparatively small percentages, yet the influence into Essex farming life was profound.

In 1939 four out of 13 chairmen of the War Ag local committees were Scotsmen (30%) but of the total of 90 committee places they had 12%. They had acquired a greater influence than the numerical proportion would have warranted.In the 1924/34 period 104 Scots settlers took farms in Essex. The migration was nearly double that which occurred in the 19th century, but by the time the second 'wave' arrived the first settlers were usurping the natives in the leadership of the farming community.

G.K. Mitchell, Pond Hall, Wix, was chairman of Colchester Farmers Union for 20 years from 1917 to 1937. Many achieved long service as chairmen of their parish councils. A selection became county councillors. William Orr of Stock was chairman of Chelmsford Rural District Council from 1968 until 1974. There were many others who contributed to the affairs of the county beyond the farming leadership.

Out of 32 chairmen of the Colchester F.U. from 1912 to 1998, 50% were Scots. It was amongst the younger element in the Young Farmers Clubs that the second, and third generation took leading roles. Wix YFC had 12 Scots out of the first 43 chairmen, Colchester had 14 in the same number of years. The Young Farmers rally's were enlivened by displays of Scottish dancing resplendent with kilts, sporrans, and tartan sashes for the girls.

In the 1960s three out of the four Essex delegates to the NFU in London were Scots. In 1957 Andrew Davidson, Dengewell Hall, Wix, brought the world winter wheat championship from Toronto to Essex. The first time it had come to the UK. A local shop displayed the massive trophy in its window. His brother, Robert Davidson arrived in 1925 went firstly to Stock Street, Coggeshall, on the Marks Hall Estate, moved to Old Moze Hall, Beaumont where he had one of the first combine harvesters in Essex in 1937. When the family moved to Brick House, Peldon in 1947 his son, Andrew and grandson, Robert, hosted the NIAB wheat variety trials for over 30 years.

Andrew McBain, Little Clacton, invented a pea harvester and a water-furrower. Hew Watt of Orsett became famous as a broadcaster, writer, chairman of the London Farmers Club and played a leading part in national agricultural affairs for many years. Alec Steel

21 Orsett. Scottish settlers. Matthew Watt, centre, brought his family and his cows to Heath Place in 1889. The two girls in front, Lily and Jessie were born in Essex.

won gold medals for his Friesian cows and was a pioneer breeder. He was the second working farmer and the first of the Scottish settlers to become president of the Essex Show in 1960. John Steel of Rochford had one of the largest herds of Essex pigs and founded the breed herd book. Henry Ritchie, Margaret Roding, was President in 1979, Alec Craig, Lexden, was mayor of Colchester in 1955.

Another Scot who played an important role in farming affairs was David Macaulay, whose father had come from East Kilbride in 1900. David was born at Channels, Little Waltham and in 1933 acquired the tenancy of Beckingham Hall on the Birch Hall Estate. He was chairman of the Essex Agricultural Executive from 1952 to 1960. It was during his tenure as chairman of the EAE that the Great Tide of 1953 swept through the coastal defences innudating thousands of acres. The Macaulays were one of four Scottish families on the Birch Hall Estate. Faulds, Strathern, Campbell; all acquired tenancies.

By the end of the century the comparatively small numbers who emigrated from Scotland had become the largest single farming group in the county. By this time some were in the fourth generation and many with three generations born in Essex. The links with the homeland were getting tenuous. Hew Watt estimated in 1996 that "over 30% of Essex farmers are of Scottish descent".[1] Although there was an almost 100% intermarriage between the Scottish families in the first generation, this was extended in later years. His 30% estimate relates to those of 'pure' Scottish descent. At the end of the century those with a Scottish connection would probably compute to 60% or more in some areas where they achieved almost blanket coverage. In the Tendring area, for instance. Around Chelmsford and in the south of the county at Orsett, Stifford, Chadwell, Horndon, South and North Ockendon and West Thurrock. There were other enclaves around Halstead and Maldon.

By natural selection they were the intrepid adventurers who were prepared to leave their ancestral homeland and make the bold move to another country. Although enclaves of Scots congregated in other parts of the world, such as the southern half of South Island, New Zealand, where the names of the townships have a Scottish ring to them, the only place in England where they arrived in considerable numbers was Essex. A small number settled in Hertfordshire and there was a large contingent in Suffolk.

The Enigma

Despite this apparent domination the actual numbers of Scottish newcomers was numerically below the influence they wielded. The 19th century flood produced a second generation who had become prosperous and settled and it was their children who left the fields for public duties, their children provided a dominant influence in the young farmers clubs in the 1950/60s. Yet this influence was far in excess of the proportion of Scottish families. The figures suggest that the 66 families who had arrived by 1900 represented less than 2% of Essex farmers. Under 5% in 1928 and 12% by 1997. Estimates that it was over 30% are, in fact, more realistic.

These families were often prolific. By 1937 there were 12 members of the Watt family in Kelly's directory (Not all related). There were 11 Hodges, eight Mitchells, Craigs, and Gemmills, six Crawfords, Andersons, Kerrs. This is a small indication of the way in which the Scottish blood was extended. It did not take into account the daughters who married Essex farmers and their children were descendants of the original settlers. Not all the sons remained in farming. John Kedar came from Strathaven, Lanarkshire to Fordham Place and had four sons. One farmed in Suffolk then Australia – and one continued the farming tradition until he retired when a Lancastrian descendant took over the farm.

Why, then did such a comparatively small proportion of Essex farmers become so powerful? Firstly there were vacancies caused by local farmers, and abdication of the traditional role of the squirarchy, which left a vacuum. It was the Scots who filled it. The percentages also disguised the land area of the county which Scotsmen occupied. Inevitably they did not take smallholdings.

When the Brown family went to Beacon Hill Farm, Kelvedon Hatch, they exchanged 60 acres near Kilmarnock for a 200 acre farm. Four years later they moved to a better farm of 240 acres at Orsett. The Browns expanded to 500 tenanted acres, and purchased Maldon Hall, of 300 acres. The general tendency was for the immigrants to acquire more acres in Essex than had been traditional in Scotland.

If the average Scottish farmer had 300 acres then their share of the county farmland would represent 2.5%, the 66 families having approximately 20,000 acres. In 1930 the 170 families would have farmed 51,000 acres or 5.1%. By 1998 many were swallowed up in family partnerships, and multiple holdings. It would be reasonable to suggest an average of 600 acres for the Scottish farmers. Thus, whilst the numerical strength of farmers steadily increased, they farmed a higher percentage of land than their position warranted.

22 1973 Orsett Show. Hew Watt,
OBE. Hon. organiser son of
Matthew Watt. He was a leading
farming figure with an
international reputation.

There were four major reasons why the Scots came to Essex. The first, and most obvious was the availability of farms. During the 19th century depression there were empty farms and landlords could not attract local tenants. The alternative to farming themselves was to offer them rent free in the hope that times would improve, the tenants would prosper, the farms would be cleaned up, and negotiations for rent income could commence at a later date, When visiting Scots discovered the wide choice of farms that were going begging, they could not resist a bargain. The slowing down of the immigration between 1900 and 1924 occurred because there were few vacant farms. It was only in times of depression that they became available.

The next important reason why they chose Essex, as they did New Zealand, was because they found plenty of former neighbours, friends and particularly relations who were already ensconced. The settlers did not feel "outsiders" because the buzz of Scottish tongues in the markets was reminiscent of home. They could mix on a social level and feel amongst friends. There were many cases where one member of the family moved, and his relations followed

"On a certain night in June 1885, 16 Scots slept at Ongar Park, and 15 of them
eventually took farms in Essex. One of them was Mr.Hugh Craig, who took
Paslow Hall on the very next day. Before leaving he had settled the tenant right
valuation with the previous occupier, Surgeon-Gen. Bean, even to taking over the
household effects".[6]

There were also pressing reasons to leave Scotland, not least being the tragedy of spoilt crops by inclement weather, and the contrast of blue skies, sunshine and low rainfall in Essex. Farming was less harsh than it had been on the west of Scotland.

They were attracted by the lack of religious discrimination. In Scotland both the catholics and the presbyterians were highly active. There was a pervading influence from Scottish landowners that their tenants should follow the same line of religion. The Scots were hide-bound by a long tradition of religious fervour and more than one tenant farmer had been ousted because he did not observe the rigidity of religious attendance that his landlord expected. The Essex settlers found it refreshing, and almost unbelievable, that the new landlords were not interested in their tenants' religious beliefs.

Basically the English landlords were Protestants, there had always been a few recusants but there had been a considerable increase in non-conformity through the 19th century.Most Essex villages had both a 'chapel' and a church. The premier Catholic landlord in Essex was Lord Petre, Thorndon Hall, and Ingatestone with over 19,000 acres was not a factor of any consequence to them. The Scots newcomers normally supported the Congregationalists centres of worship but many joined the passive, and non-compulsory Anglican communities.

The other compelling reason why they left Scotland was the insensitivity of the landlords. Primrose McConnell was born among the hills of Kyle in Ayrshire. When he was still a young lad his father moved the family to Ongarpark Hall, and was one of the first to settle in Essex. This was 1882/3. The son, Primrose, moved to North Wycke, Southminster in 1905. In 1891 he asked "why so many Scottish farmers come to this (Essex) and other parts of England? The question may be answered in a very few words – excessive rents at home".[7] Primrose McConnell's "The Agricultural Notebook" first appeared in 1883. An agricultural student himself he was more inclined towards scientific solutions to farming problems that some of his advice would suggest. "The Agricultural Notebook" was in its 17th edition in 1980.

In Scotland, and particularly in Ayrshire there was competition for every farm and landlords were able to obtain high rents. Families were large and there were many energetic young men who wanted to farm independently. In Scotland the custom was long leases, which gave security to the tenant, but encumbered him with a high rent if prosperity declined.

> "Coming from a country where long leases were the rule, it was a novel
> experience to have farms as yearly tenants; but I, for one, prefer to have it so. On
> this farm where I write there was at first a short lease – now expired – and we now
> sit on at a Twelve-months notice...the majority of in-comers, however, have had
> their choice in this matter, but I have not heard of any who have taken a long
> lease".[8]

Another attraction was the milk market in London which offered an outlet for all they could produce. Market garden produce and poultry. Not specialised Ayrshire enterprises, although early potatoes were, also found a market that was accessible. The congregation of Scottish settlers in the western half of Essex was prompted by the greater concentration of landed estates in that part of the county, and the availability of tenancies, rather than the advantages of London customers. The close proximity was a bonus.

It was also suggested that Essex men were short of capital. The Scottish contingent moved at very little expense. They nearly all brought their own herds of Ayrshire cows on special trains, sometimes two/three farmers together and stopping to milk them half way down the line. In earlier days it has been suggested that some were driven down the 300 mile road. This would appear to be unlikely and some who attempted this, put their cattle on a train after they had accomplished only part of the journey. Mr. Col MacDonald Bain brought his herd of 45 tuberculosis-tested Friesian cows and 40 young stock by train to Bulmer via Sudbury railway station in 1936.

The Scots farmers farmed with considerably lower expenses. They regarded the Essex labourers as slothful and when Mr. Maule went to a Suffolk farm at Assington, later moving to Essex, he is reputed to have lined up the 16 farm labourers and said to them "I have six sons who are worth two of you. That's 12. I am worth three of any man amongst you – that makes 15. I shall require one man"! This may be apocryphal but symbolises the attitude which they brought from Scotland. They were hard working men, accustomed to the rigours of a harsher climate and saw no social stigma in working themselves – in contrast to the attitude of many Essex farmers at that time. Salesmen would see a group of men hoeing and approach the best dressed one. They had usually passed the more unkempt hoer who was, in fact, the farmer. They worked beside their men, and acquired reputations which were commensurate with the world wide reputation of the Scottish nation. Some was incorrect.

Whilst there were few English farmers who were prepared to take these vacant farms, it appears uncharitable to have denigrated the intrepid "Scotchmen", as they were called rather than 'Scotsmen'. The native emblem of Scotland was to Essex farmers a pernicious weed and a scourge of both arable and meadow land. Giant sized thistles, inedible to cattle, could severely detract from the grazing potential of meadows. In some minds the unsavoury reputation of the thistle reflected onto the new neighbours. They spoke a different language and were not easy to understand.

When Percy Mee, Wick House, Bulphan, met his new neighbour, William Brown, who took over Wyfields, Orsett, he commented "when you get broke you'll have plenty of water to drown yourself in".[9] The Essex farmers regarded the Scots as "cow-keepers". This was a form of denigration. Keeping cows – was not farming.

Milkable animals were housed in the main street in Romford and Ilford, for instance, and in London itself the "cow-houses" were three stories high. The animals were driven up to the top floor and did not come down again until they died. Thus the reputation of "cow-keepers" was not a good one.

The Scottish newcomers not only worked hard, they played hard which was the antithesis of the farmers' staid philosophy. He enjoyed his hunting and shooting but considered that wearing a kilt and embarking upon energetic pipe-swirling dances were the first signs of a creeping madness. Socially the Scots circulated amongst themselves. The other two products which had made Scotland famous – its whisky and its porridge also came in for ridicule.

The reputation of hard drinking preceded them. In reality, although they were not teetotal, many were abstemious and respectably sober. G.K. Mitchell, when he was at Easthorpe, had the reputation for using two spoons for his porridge. Whilst one was going up – the other was going down. No doubt another exaggeration but it symbolised the curiosity which the locals exhibited towards these newcomers with strange tongues, and strange habits.

23 *1957 Toronto. Andrew Davidson (Wix) (Right) with the world winter wheat championship trophy. The first time it came to Britain. He came to Essex from Scotland in 1925.*

Caledonian societies blossomed, Colchester and District was founded in 1928. They spread over the county to Southend, Chelmsford, Halstead. It provided another link in the network of a community, within a community.

The Scots found some of the new customs difficult to understand. In Scotland milking the cows was traditionally the job of the farmer's wife. In Essex it was a man's job. The Scots were unaccustomed to Boxing Day as a holiday so they continued to work, fully expecting that New Year's Day would be a day off. They were aghast to discover that Hogmanay, one of the most celebratory events in the Scottish calendar was not observed in England.

It was not aimed at fleecing the newcomers but was customary practice for auctioneers to bid themselves. The owners of stock bid up their own goods. When David Wyllie leased Great Warley Hall. He complained that he had been gazumped by the auctioneer. He found that some of the items which he purchased did not conform to the description given, and when he learnt that the auctioneer had been the only other bidder he sought a legal ruling. "High legal opinion assured him that such action on the part of the auctioneer constituted a fraudulent sale...when confronted with this opinion the auctioneer got the fright of his life. It led to the recasting of the conditions of sale by auctioneers".[10]

Apart from economizing in wages, and living a more frugal lifestyle, there were other changes which they instituted in that fundamental of all farming operations – ploughing. "I may mention that no Scotsman can possibly approve of the native Essex wooden implement...it has two faults; the mould-board has not got twist enough...while the share commonly used has too wide a feather. These defects do not appear in stubble or fallow ploughing, but become at once apparent in Lea land".[11] They found it wasteful that Essex farmers gave their fields five, even six ploughings to prepare for a crop.

The Scots generally ploughed deeper and criticised the Essex farmers who reckoned two/three inches was enough for wheat! They vowed by the tradition that it needed a solid bottom and consequently many of the Essex fields had a plough-pan. The Scots used a grubber for fallowing which could cover five acres a day against a plough team doing one/two. There was a crescendo of acerbic criticism between the two approaches. The Scots neglected the hedges and ditches and did not regard a fallow as vital for cleaning a field. All charges they vehemently denied. They replied that they thought the Essex men were wasteful with labour, used more horses than were necessary to haul implements or for carting. They denied the necessity for hand weeding. They made their farms pay – and the locals did not.

Inevitably the Scottish farmers, without local experience, took the worst farms. They were the ones at which the indigenous farmers had failed. In very few cases did the settlers remain in the first farm that they rented. It was a proving ground and within a few years they found farms where they could make a better living. Some did not like Essex and went back to their homeland. The Montgomeries went to Ongar in 1882 but later moved to the Isle of Thanet. John Mason, Butler's Farm, Belchamp St.Paul went bankrupt in 1938 although he had a lease which granted him a free farm until such time as he made a profit.[12]

The First Settlers
Possibly the first was George Torrance who took Ashlyns, Ongar in 1878. By 1924 the majority of the 66 families who were ensconced by 1900 had moved farms, and had produced sons who had taken other farms. The Scottish community had expanded and when James Dunlop of Prestwick went on an investigative tour in 1924 he visited 21 of the farms occupied by Scotsmen. Many were in the second generation. Dunlop confined his travels to the south west corner of Essex with the exception of a farm at Finchingfield. His primary purpose was to trace those that had moved from the Kilmarnock area and his reports provide a valuable contribution [13].

Matthew Brown Watt, the original immigrant from Fenwick to Heath Place, Orsett, had died but his three sons carried on the farming tradition. William Orr Watt, the eldest son, occupied the paternal home as a tenant on the Orsett Estate. "Mr.Watt is a born professor. Without prejudice for any class of stock or any particular kind or crop, he is ready to try any new thing calculated to reduce costs and increase returns", wrote Dunlop who described some of the other innovations upon which W.O. Watt had embarked.

He used a pronged plough to lift his early potatoes. He invented a Scarifier to reduce the labour needs in singling root crops and a shallow broad-bottomed drill which spread the seed. He had an automatic water-stall trough for dairy cows. W.O. Watt thought that more water and lucerne hay could give his cows a palatable diet which would reduce the need to grow "expensive green crops like mangold or turnips". He thought that lucerne was cheaper than silage. He was exploiting the drier conditions of Essex against the problems of rain which had always spoilt the Ayrshire farmers' hay crops.

He tried experiments with a new method of turning straw into dung. "Large quantities of straw accumulated on some farms during the late war years and since, for which there was no market". Watt treated some of this straw with chemicals to fix the ammonia although he admitted that the end results did not indicate "anything sensational in its favour". Red clover was always sown by a 'barrow' which was trundled up and down the fields.

Watt decided to sow his grasses after harvest by discing them into the top tilth. It was a successful approach. His brother, Andrew, farmed near Brentwood. "He is a fine musician, and freely gives his services for all worthy objects over a wide district". The third brother, James, had a farm near Woodford and a herd of Friesians. Dunlop and his friends were impressed; "this was probably because they approximated more to the Ayrshire type, looked milky, and were a uniform lot".

W.O. Watt as the patrition head of the family and a leader of the Scottish community in South Essex, found a farm near Hornchurch for George Torrance. No relation of the original first Scot to settle in Essex. Torrance took over this farm at valuation, which was a walk-out and walk-in, it was a dairy and market garden farm which had been partly used as a camp for New Zealand soldiers during the war. He knew nothing about market gardening. "He is mastering this new business but will always depend on his dairy cows as his sheet anchor...he is not dismayed at his 53s.0d (£2.65p)pa rent, but full of hope for the future". At North Ockendon David Murchland had 300 acres and diversified his dairy farming to a mixed livestock policy with sheep, pigs and poultry. He was not an arable farmer by choice but recognised that wheat, beans, oats, mangolds and lucerne were all food for his animals. He was dismayed at the 20ins. annual rainfall – when he had been accustomed 40ins.

In a speech[14] Murchland gave pungent reasons why he had reluctantly left the farm in Scotland that had been tenanted by his forbears for more than a century. They had laid out the fields, dug the ditches, planted hedges, erected most of the buildings – without help from the landlord. "Their reward was periodical increases of rent until it reached £96. When protests were made, the factor said the proprietor was requiring money and he could only get it where it was – the bad farmers had none, and the improving tenants had to pay up". From £96pa the rent went up to £130 "it was more than flesh and blood could stand". A new tenant came in paying £125, "but both the tenant and the farm were ruined".

Robert Lindsay at Chadwell Place, Grays, had a large dairy herd grazing the marshes abutting Tilbury Dock. He supplied milk for the expanding housing developments and was able to sell early potatoes at £14 per ton in Grays. He found that, even on light soil, lucerne was profitable.

Chadwell Place had been tenanted by James Young who had come down from Scotland in 1896. His wife was Elizabeth Gemmill. The Young family gave up Chadwell and moved to Giffords Cross Farm, Corringham.

The family later moved to Manor Farm, West Tilbury and to Corringham Hall in 1940. It was Andrew Young's son, James, who, with his own son founded A.G. Young and Son the Dairy Company. His painted wagons were seen, with the name 'J.Young' and a

24 William Brown of Lt. Horkesley "Man of the Century" 1898-1999. Picture taken 1986. He drove his first tractor in 1916. He came to Ongar from Scotland in 1901.

green livery, at agricultural shows throughout the remainder of the 20th century. A keen judge he was presented to H.M. The Queen in 1973 following his demonstration of an old wooden Essex plough at Windsor. "This type of plough had been in use for hundreds of years, until comparatively recently"[15]

Robert Lindsay told Dunlop that "40 years ago the Scots found derelict farms because the native farmers would not change their hide bound, obsolete farm practices. With the application of methods which have gained Danish farmers the admiration of the world, what a bright prospect opens up for the future of our country".

William Wilson bought 500 acres near Tilbury and rented another 300. He came to Essex in 1887 and by 1924 three of his sons were the owners of, 'well-selected large farms as proprietors with clear title deeds'. Half of William Wilson's farm was old pasture reclaimed from the Thameside marshes. On the 400a of 'upland' he was growing 100a of potatoes with imported Scottish seed. He was receiving £16 per ton, as against the £14 which Robert Lindsay was getting in Grays. He had 30 acres of green peas and employed 300 women to pick them. Prices had been up to £1 per 40lb bag. Between the rows of peas he grew cabbages, cauliflowers and sprouts to take up the nitrogen left in the soil by the peas. He grew scarlet runner beans, spinach, broccoli but also kept a herd of dairy cows and needed lucerne, oats and mangolds.

William Wilson cultivated a trade in provisions for the large liners destined for Australia and New Zealand, which embarked from Tilbury. A large part of his potato crop was sold to the shipping companies. He also had his own motor trucks and delivered to Spittalfields or Covent Garden. Dunlop commented that Wilson was "a young man of great business acumen and tireless energy and may become a second Carnegie!"

Robert Currie who lived at Moulsham Lodge and also farmed at Little Baddow and Roxwell, was one of a family of 20 and in addition to his farming activities he had a second enterprise – importing thousands of tons of Scotch seed potatoes annually. Alec Steel of Prittlewell was accorded the honour of being the leader of the Scottish contingent in Essex. Dunlop considered that Wilson ran him a close second.

The patriarch of the community was John Gemmill who went to Bilsdens, Ongar in 1882. "It was a derelict farm afflicted with poverty and weeds. It is now one of the most productive farms in the county".[10] Gemmill had 10 sons and four daughters. By 1924 five of the sons had bought farms of their own and in 1937 there were eight Gemmills farming in the county. The daughters too married into farming families. Gemmill, contrary to many of his compatriots was an enthusiast for Shorthorn cows, Alec Steel was a Friesian breeder, but the majority stuck to the Ayrshire cows they had brought from Scotland with them.

William Brown many years later, "We had Ayrshire cattle but Shorthorns were predominant. Father made a mistake having a Shorthorn bull on Ayrshire cows. He should have had a Friesian. Many Friesian herds were bred out of Ayrshires. The butter fat in the Ayrshire was good, but low in the Friesian".[9] John Gemmill won prizes at the Essex Show for his Shire horses. One of his sons built up a pedigree herd of Essex pigs.

Another son specialised in poultry and had 1,000 hens on free range. A gold medalist of the Institute of Agriculture, he was an innovator in modern poultry keeping, incubating his own eggs and designing his own sheds. The incubating house was a converted farm building. He sold 80% of his chicks as day-olds. One of John Gemmill's daughters married Hugh Craig's son whose father had come to Paslow Hall in 1883.

The fourth son, Bill Gemmill, born at Bilsdens, joined his brother James farming in Canada. He enlisted in the Canadian Cavalry in 1914 and won the Military Medal at Vimy Ridge. He acquired the tenancy of Little Forest Hall, Ongar in 1921 and married Margaret Shanks of Moor Hall, Writtle. Bill Gemmill took over the farm in 1948. Chairman of the Ongar branch of the NFU, a judge of Clydesdale horses, his grandsons farmed at Writtle.

The eighth son was, perhaps, the most famous. David Gemmill represented the Essex Farmers Union in London, was county FU chairman 1946/9, was a JP and was given the OBE for his services to agriculture. He was a judge of Ayrshire cows, president of the Royal British Dairy Association, a frequent broadcaster and a persuasive orator. He managed 5,000 acres for the London Co-operative Society at Paslow Hall. It was said of John Gemmill Snr. that "Essex proved to him an Eldorado"[13]

Most of the earlier migrants had settled in the southern part of the county, but in 1913 John Pollock obtained the tenancy of Park Farm on the Spains Hall Estate, Finchingfield. He was an inventor, having invented a rick lifter, a hay fork which was used in hay sheds for many years. He did not patent his ideas "but allowed the public to get full benefit of his inventions".

Mrs. Wyllie and her son, Robert, had 200a near Grays where they sold all the milk they could produce. Another son, David, leased Great Warley Hall and married a sister of William Brown. The ramifications of the inter-marrying between the Scottish families

25 The Scots were innovators. First combine in the county in 1936 at Gosbecks Farm, Shrub End. A Case imported for evaluation by Oxford University was collected in pieces from Wembley. Driving is Andrew Barbour. On the platform; Jimmy Barbour (cap) and Ernest Doe (trilby).

were complex. In the 1950s probably 75% of the weddings recorded in the 'Essex Young Farmer' were between Scots. This is not to deny that probably 25% were to Essex natives but resulted in an extension of Scottish blood into families with a lineage in the Essex soil.

As one tenant moved on it was not unusual for another Scot to take his place. James Craig took Barnards at Horndon, the elder brother of Hugh who had settled at Paslow Hall. Adjoining Barnards was a flat heavy clay farm named Fieldhouse which Thomas Picken took. Picken had seven sons and several daughters. The sons opted out of farming and were all successful in other careers. Fieldhouse adjoined Barnards and Little Tillingham Hall (not to be confused with Tillingham in the Dengie Hundred). James Craig farmed Little Tillingham Hall, Childerditch, but it then passed to Robert Orr who bought the farm from Lord Petre for £20 per acre in 1922 "yet many fine farms have been bought in Essex for around this figure, which seems cheap compared with the price of land in our countries, also dependent on the London market, and situated thousands of miles from it".

Germains was taken by William Barr in 1886. He had been one of the most enterprising farmers in the Kilmarnock district stimulating an improved method of cheese making, the first to grow Timothy hay, built a large dairy byre with only 4 inch bricks – which everyone said would fall down, he moved to Essex, driven out by proposed rent increases – at the age of 60 years. The family later moved to Sandon and one of the sons founded a farm machinery company operating in the county.

The composite picture painted by Dunlop gave a microcosm of farming Essex life in 1924. The Scottish farmers presented a picture of highly enterprising men who exchanged their Scottish farming habits for those of their new homeland. They embraced that which they perceived to be sound, but disregarded that which they felt was bad practice, such as ploughing five/six times for wheat! By a natural process of selection they were inevitably the most courageous and enterprising farmers.

Eventually the exodus from Ayrshire, mainly around Kilmarnock, induced the Scottish landowners to reduce the rents. Landlords were pleased to find tenants. The removal of the better farmers robbed Ayrshire of some of its best brains. It, however, enhanced the farming reputation of Essex and, slow to respond at first, and scathingly disregarded by their new Essex neighbours it was the Essex farmers who eventually and reluctantly followed the standards and the pattern set by the 'invaders'.

Ratio of Scottish Farmers			
Yellow Pages 1998 Telephone Area	Total Essex Farmers	Scottish Descent	%
Colchester	308	65	21
Harlow	115	5	4.4
London East	59	8	13.5
Southend	414	31	7.5
	896	109	12.1
1907	3,910 (Over 50a)	66	1.7
1928	3,679	170	4.6
1997	896	109	12.1

CHAPTER 7

Saved – By the War

Without the Second World War, the Essex countryside would have been an unkempt scrub area akin to an African landscape. It would have been dotted with derelict and tumbledown buildings, devoid of crops, covered with rough weed infested fields filled with red poppies, yellow charlock, buttercups, speedwell and cleavers, wild oats and prolific black grass. Thistle down would have been carried on the prevailing winds and would have blown from Tilbury to Harwich. Farmers would have settled into a subservient peasant-status.

That none of this happened was due to the wartime boost in production which transformed the moribund countryside into a food producing machine. Farmers became the heroes of the hour.

1939 launched farming into sixty years of prosperity (more or less). It heralded the start of the second agricultural revolution. A shake-up that would fundamentally change a system of farming that had existed since medieval times. Such was the scale of improvement that it put all other agricultural revolutions into proportion. Before 1939 little had altered in agricultural practice. The impetus had been created but it was not until the second half of the century that it took place.

Until 1950 labourers hoed the fields in gangs, horses pulled many of the binders. Most milking was done by hand in draughty cow sheds. Animals were turned out at night in all weathers, sheep lambed in the fields, pigs had their litters under a hedge or in a ditch, chickens scratched the farmyard, ducks swam on the pond and the farmer was either a hands-on slave to his animals and crops, or a gang-master with an army of workers. An arable/stock mixed farm in Essex employed an average of one man for every 20 acres. The modest 300 acre farm had a staff of 15 men. Cottages were still unsanitised, most farms were too remote for main water, electricity or sewage. Telephones were not uncommon, neither were they universal. Farmers with cars, vans or small lorries were more prevalent.

The position of the farmer in village life had not changed before the war. It still survived in its traditional fashion. The villagers went out to the harvest fields to chase the rabbits, and glean the lost ears. It revolved around the farmers who were the major employers and the major customers of local tradesmen and the now familiar petrol garage. Until well after the war, and food was still rationed until 1955, the village remained a largely self sufficient unit, as it had always done. There were village bakers, milkmen, millers etc. and a post office in almost every community.

Lorries, carrying loads of 3/5 tons each took the surplus corn to the town and carried heavier loads than the wagons of yesteryear. Cattle floats transported animals and every farmer's car had a small trailer into which a few squealing pigs or clucking chickens could be carried. Yet on the horizon there were indications of fundamental changes.

The war years were a watershed. This was said about the First World War when perhaps the most tangible social upheaval had been the unwillingness of parishioners to do domestic work at the "big house". It had not disappeared but had been severely curtailed.

Despite the wartime ploughing-up programme there were 2,000 less working horses on Essex farms at the end of the war than there were at the beginning. Tractors had replaced them and from 240 in the county in 1918 there were 4,282 wheeled and track-laying tractors in 1942, and 5,668 by 1944. An average of one tractor for every 93 acres. There were 500 less horses in 1945 than in 1944. But in the last year of the war 11,000 working horses still helped to carry out the work of Essex farms. Orsett farmer Hew Watt wrote;

"This time the ploughing campaign was greatly assisted by modern tractors and machinery of all kinds. Output in Essex of temperate food products increased by 50% and although the diet of cereals and potatoes may have been plain and lacking in protein, at least no one went hungry".[1]

But first the war had to be won. It was not be an easy transformation for Essex farmers. It started innocuously enough.

The Day War Broke Out

Essex agriculture was already on a war footing in 1939, Six years later the need for higher output had transformed the scene. In the First World War the frenzied activity had been confined to the last two years. The Second World War lasted six years and at the end there were more shortages than when German submarines were sinking thousands of allied ships bringing food to beleaguered Britain. There was a greater awareness of the potential problem before the war started.

No-one was under any illusions that the new war would be totally different from the last one. In 1939 the omens had been apparent for at least two years. Any war with Germany would place in jeopardy British food supplies. The U-boats of the Nazis were notorious. Britain would be threatened with starvation. The First World War, with its county executive committees armed with legislative powers to force farmers to produce more was but a rehearsal for the big show which, even after 1918 was foreseen. This time Britain would be ready.

In April 1938 the Great Sampford Air Raids Protection Committee was set up and farmers took the leading role. Air Raid Wardens were nominated for each village and equipped with their own whistles and cycles. Farm workers co-operated with their employers against the threat of invasion. There was a sense of unity which had not been evident when wages were reduced. The L.D.V., later called the Home Guard, was formed in 1940 when farmers and their men, united with pitch forks and little else, trained and prepared to rebuff invading German troops.

In July 1939 Essex farmers were given detailed information regarding the effects of mustard gas; cattle should be housed if possible and kept off contaminated pastures until weathering had destroyed the gas – it was held that most crops would recover from the effects of non-persistent gases and grassland would be safe for stock when it was sufficiently palatable to eat – although there might be some exceptions it would generally be best to slaughter affected stock quickly – skin contamination with mustard gas would have a less serious effect on edibility than Lewisite and other arsenicals, the risk of serious contamination to water supplies was considered light, only the outer layers of haystacks and sacks of grain were likely to be affected.

26 1943. Prices had already started to rise.

As soon as war was declared the black-out was rigorously enforced. This affected cow sheds where hurricane lanterns were used for the early morning milking during winter. In 1940 the clocks were not put back and summer time hours persisted through the winter. It meant that the black-out was enforced until 8.00am and gave farmers more difficulties in the dark mornings with the milking. "...but recent dark mornings have shown that others have not yet taken effective measures. Such neglect is not fair to the neighbourhood. It is hoped that nothing more severe than this reminder will make them more careful". [2] Detailed instructions were issued to remove the possibility of enemy troops being landed in the fields. They would need, the Regional Commissioner for Civil Defence said;

> "300 yards free of obstructions in order to land without crashing, and in dry weather crops up to one foot in height will not form any obstruction. Fields greater than 300 yards should have at least one, or if possible, two lines of obstructions placed across them, so as to prevent there being used as landing grounds. The best obstruction would be a line of posts six or eight inches in diameter fixed firmly in the ground at intervals of five yards. Failing these, waggons, carts, ploughs, rollers, horse rakes etc. should be readily accessible and suitable. The wire ropes of steam ploughing tackle loosely supported three feet above the ground would form an excellent obstacle...It is realised that on any farm there will not be sufficient implements to make a continuous line of obstructions, but if scattered at irregular intervals they should be quite an effective deterrent, and if an attempt is made to land, should overturn at least some of the aeroplanes and kill the occupants".[3]

Abberton Reservoir was 'sown' with mines to prevent seaplanes landing on the water. Another question mark was raised about the behaviour which farmers and workers should observe when meeting a German airman. "Should he be invited to tea pending the belated arrival of the village policeman or shot out-of-hand as a representative of a nation of savages?"[3]

When this situation occurred with increasing frequency during the Battle of Britain there was often confusion amongst his captors about the nationality of the pilot. One RAF pilot had his teeth damaged which slurred his speech. He was mistaken for a German. A German airman who came down on the Essex marshes, losing his flying boots as the jerk of the parachute opened, was given a plate of bacon and eggs and the policeman was told that he could not have him until he had finished his breakfast. Later the policeman cycled off and his prisoner resignedly walked beside him.

Almost every farm in Essex had either an aircraft crashing in its fields, or bombs jettisoned by German pilots. The cows were killed at Cooks Hall, West Bergholt in 1940 when a string of random bombs were released from a German plane.

In the late summer of 1940 German aircraft began their attack upon the R.A.F. base at Debden. On 26 August Dornier bombers attacked in daylight. At Thaxted Captain J.O. Barbrook was conducting his weekly auction, but when battle was engaged in the skies above, he shut his book and hurried off to send parties out to hunt for shot-down German airmen.

> "We were carting wheat at the time when a Dornier crossed my farm, very low, belching hot oil which started small stubble fires wherever it fell. Then we looked up and saw parachutists. Excitement was intense. I rushed in, grabbed a rifle, took the car and tore off to where I was sure they would come down. Actually I was about half-mile out but I found that the three parachutists I had seen had come down at Finchingfield, two severely wounded, and had been picked up by the Home Guard there. I rushed back to my platoon area and found the other two had been picked up by my own men",[4] recounted Walter Schweir.

Philip Chapman of Byballs Farm Great Sampford was carting wheat. With him was

Harry Gowlett, a farm-hand. Both had pitchforks. They suddenly became aware that two parachutists were coming down in the next field. He seized a gun, and rushed towards the parachutists, who showed no disposition to continue the war. Both Germans spoke English, having been educated at Cambridge.

Putting them into the family car, Philip, with Harry, drove towards the village. On the way they met P.C. Carlton. They stopped and the constable, despite the protests of the Germans, handcuffed them together. The prisoners were driven to the police constable's house and confined in the lock-up. Mrs.Carlton catching sight of them – they were only boys, and since they had left a French airfield at dawn, had been through a lot – exclaimed; "Poor dears, I will make them a cup of tea". This she did and "the village never quite forgave her".[5]

In 1944 a Flying Bomb (doodle bug) fell on Trylos Farm, Black Notley. It killed two cows, fired three stacks, destroyed the farm buildings and blew the old beam constructed farmhouse over. "This farm has been in my family a hundred years; my father and grandfather lived here before me, and I hoped to live here, but now it has been blown away. The damage I sustained by the Flying Bomb amounts to £3,000", said farmer, Walter Hammond.[5] Three major problems faced the task of putting Essex farming onto a war-time footing; a shortage of labour, a shortage of cash, and bringing back the derelict farms. All of these problems were outside farmers' control, but solutions were found by a desperate government. The labour shortage was partly remedied by the formation of the Womens Land Army, and later prisoners of war. The cash deficit was remedied by increasing prices, yet there was an inherent belief that no-one should profit from the war. A delicate balance of encouragement was required.

The last problem – derelict land – was solved by the formation of the War Agricultural Executive Committees and the draconian powers with which they were invested. This trio of solutions resulted, six years later, in a revival of agricultural confidence, an almost unrecognisable improvement in the overgrown countryside.

War was declared on 3 September 1939, it was a Sunday, and the following Monday morning the Essex War Agricultural Executive Committee was formed. The principal of The Institute, J.C. Leslie, was appointed as the Executive Officer. With three District Agricultural Organisers to superintend the 13 districts into which the county was divided. Within a month 91 farmers had been recruited to serve on the local bodies.

Financing the expansion of food production was not an easy problem to solve. The 10 month delay between planting and harvesting required a continuing level of expenditure. "Cash is short and credit sparingly obtainable" said the 1939 Annual Report of the E.F.U.[6]

Farmers, as with factory manufacturers could not dictate their own prices. There was a rigid system of price controls. And yet to stimulate production, there must be financial incentives. In 1939 the Essex Farmers Union had fought for an increase for cereals from the 1939 harvest. "It came as one of the biggest shocks we had experienced since working for the Union when we found the Standard Price Committee recommending that there should be no increase".[6]

Labour Shortage. Between 1921 and 1939 7,790 workers (23%) left their jobs on Essex farms. The call for increased production was replied with pleas that there was insufficient labour. Farm workers were not reserved from call-up. 5,000 were forced to leave their farm work and join the services during the course of the war. Initially those

27 1944 Magdalen Laver. A Service of Thanksgiving being held in a harvest field at Bushes Farm.

under 25 years were reserved from military service, this was reduced to 18 years but for the bulk of farm workers, shepherds, pig men, cattle men and green house workers the call up age was 21 years.

There was a graduated scale; for instance specialised experts could be exempt. The matter was always subject to appeal but by a sustained effort the army of farm workers in the county rose by 6,218 during the war years. They fell into many categories, full-time regulars, both male and female. Part-timers, casuals, under-age workers. The deficit in 1939 and the increase by 1945 was made up by the Womens Land Army, which at its peak boasted of 4,000 girls working on Essex farms.

There were school boys who helped in their holidays. There were Italian prisoners of war and by 1942 it was decided to permit "good conduct" prisoners to "live in" on farms and work for the farmer. They were usually experienced farm workers who had been drafted into the Italian army. There were hostels where girls were housed and farmers had to collect and return them before blackout. By dint of recruiting every available person the acute labour shortage in 1939 did not detract from war time productivity.

The "phoney-war", meant that call-up was slower than was expected, recruiting for the W.L.A. continued and three months after war was declared there were 100 employed in the county; "the majority as milkers, but a fair proportion as tractor drivers and poultry girls".[7] Another 47 were on private farms, 72 in farm training institutes and 30 girls were trained at the Institute of Agriculture which had been taken over by the E.W.A.E.C. It was a two month course and gave the girls a grounding in what was expected. Recruitment to the W.L.A. was on a voluntary basis. It later became a compulsory alternative within the framework of the general call-up of women for the armed services.

In June 1940 the E.W.A.E.C. decided to form a Womens Emergency Land Corps because of the inability of the W.L.A. to recruit temporary local assistance.

"This Emergency Corps will accordingly be composed of local women and girls who are willing to work in their own district for whole days, half days, or in the evenings at any kind of farm work of which they are capable, such as weeding in the corn, potato planting, harvesting, potato and root lifting, fruit picking, etc. They will work out of their own homes, forming parties if they wish among themselves being transported, as necessary, to fields by the farmer concerned".[8]

The impetus for this scheme, which was unusual in Britain, came from the Womens Institutes who acted as local organisers. Armlets and service stripes were awarded and by September 1940 over 1,000 women had registered. Many of them continued to work on Essex farms until the 1950s. Those who were directed onto farms by the W.L.A. came from places like Walthamstow and Leyton where they were unaccustomed to fields. It was a hard baptism yet the number of defaulters was remarkably low. A year later the W.L.A. contribution was a work force of over 1,000, but farmers were still worried about the call-up of their experienced workers.

Hollis Clayton who farmed at Stisted and was chairman of the EFU reported at the AGM "the news of the calling-up of agricultural labourers is a serious matter" and addressing the farmers the Minister R.S. Hudson outlined the dilemma. "It is, of course,

28 1941-2 Ingrave. Housewives harvesting flax at Salmonds Farm.

impossible for this country to put millions of men under arms and at the same time increase enormously the output of war materials not to mention maintaining, and indeed increasing our home grown food supplies".[9]

The major difference between the W.L.A. with their corduroy breeches, green jumpers, shoulder insignia and bush hats, and the local women from the village was that the latter volunteered, and became attached as a regular part of the work force on nearby farms, whereas the W.L.A. were drafted to villages where they were billetted in pubs and private houses until hostels were built, such as at Peldon and Coggeshall House which was requisitioned as a hostel. Thirty-six girls lived there. The W.L.A. were involved in the clearing of Nazeing Common before it could be cropped.

By 1943 Training Farms had been established. In the Dunmow area Mr. Trenbath, Ravens Farm organised 12 local farmers to train these girls. Mrs.Tom Howard, Kingstons, Matching, had trained 190 volunteers by this time and girls were employed on 1,287 Essex farms.[10] Exhibits were staged at Corn Exchanges at Saffron Walden, Braintree, Chelmsford and Colchester. It was an effort to break down the resistance of farmers. They much preferred local women from the village who understood farming and did not flinch at inclement weather.

The Institute of Agriculture became a hostel and Betty Marsh later recalled;

> "three days after my 18th birthday I was called up. We worked in gangs of four, being taken out to farms on the back of a lorry. We had to use an outside soil toilet which we had to dig holes for and empty. At Writtle we had to thread worms by passing a strychnine thread through them to be used for poisoning moles. We had no protection and our hands soon developed sores. We trapped and poisoned rats and mice on local farms and airfields.
>
> Life in the hostel was what you made it. We were paid £2.8s.(£2.40p) per week of which £1.5s. (£1.25p) was rent. That gave us £1.3s (£1.15p) to spend on ourselves. We had to be in at 9.30pm but were allowed to go to a show or dance once a week with a late pass until midnight. One show I will always remember was when Bob Hope came to entertain the troops at the American Air Base at Wethersfield. On another occasion, Bing Crosby gave a concert at Great Dunmow".[11]

The W.L.A. was more 'army' than the Home Guard which has gone down in history as the caricature of "Dad's Army". On 24 June 1942 the Essex girls marched, bearing banners with precision, but without martial music into the grounds of the Institute of Agriculture and past Lady Denman, the Hon. Director of the W.L.A. On the platform were the leading luminaries behind the Essex success; Olive Tritton, Brent Hall, Finchingfield, Hollis Clayton, Chairman of the EFU and Stanley Ratcliff who was National President of the NFU in 1933 and farmed at Beeleigh, Woodham Walter, Latchingdon, Woodham Mortimer, Maldon and Hazeleigh. The W.L.A. continued in existence after the war and in 1948 formed part of the Guard of Honour for King George VI and Queen Elizabeth at the Essex Show at Orsett.

Their contribution to the success of Essex farming during the war was unquestionable. There were 2,099 W.L.A. members on Essex farms in 1945, and there were 2,687 other women workers as part of the regular work force at that time. The W.L.A. membership dwindled rapidly to 917 in 1946, 667 (1947) 636 (1948) 353 (1949) and in 1950, the last year in which the W.L.A. operated had dropped to 203 although there were

29 1944. Birch & Layer Breton Air Raid Wardens. The farmer J.G. Church (Centre). Seven of the wardens were his workers. Four of them the Andrews Family.

still 2,122 women workers. At its peak Essex came second only to Kent in the strength of its "army".

There were continual worries about the shortage of labour to increase output. Soldiers were occasionally employed and Essex County Council roadmen were used for sugar beet work. Boys from Felsted and from grammar schools at Colchester, Chelmsford, Maldon and Earls Colne were encouraged to help out on farms during their holidays. Some of which were tailored to the requirements of the harvest in the same manner that holidays in village schools had always been arranged with the needs of pea picking and harvesting. An approach was made to the Chief of Colchester Borough Police by Alec Craig, Lexden Lodge, to release a number of Constables for farm work at harvest time.

Fruit picking was a job done by women and school children. Black currants, which were grown extensively in the Stour valley at Langham Hall and encouraged as a supplement of vitamin C, to sustain the health of children. Strawberries, raspberries and other small fruit covered 1,410a by 1945. It dropped by 1,059a during the war years but orchards rose by 1,264a. There was additional stock work, and women were adept at rearing calves.

Land Clubs were formed in 1943 with the intention of putting town dwellers in touch with farmers who needed additional labour for urgent work. "Land Clubs create an essential reserve labour force which can be of the greatest help with unskilled work, particularly pea-picking, some types of hoeing, weeding and singling, potato planting, lifting and riddling, hay-making, harvesting and other such jobs".[12] Able bodied men over 21 years were paid the equivalent of 5p per hour. No unemployment Insurance was required for such work.

The EWAEC offered to liaise between farmers and their nearest Land Club Organiser "every encouragement should be given to these workers since their help may easily be the deciding factor for food production in 1943".[12] This was before the tide turned in the Allies favour. 1943 was also the year when the UK wheat acreage touched 3.28m acres and it remained just over 3m the following year.

The image, status and popularity of farmers rose significantly during the war years. They had the largest houses and took in the largest number of evacuees from East London. They supplied the leadership of the Air Raid Wardens, but less often the Home Guard which was a more natural ambience for retired military officers.

Farm buildings provided look-out posts for parachutists and, along the coast, for invaders. Many an old barn was hastily rigged-up with a look-out loft where a rota from the L.D.V. observed the surrounding countryside. Searchlight positions were situated in fields and in every direction the public was aware of the contribution which farmers were making.

Although food was severely rationed throughout the war farmers and farm workers were never short. Items such as sugar, bananas and sweets for children were strictly curtailed or disappeared completely. Farm workers could always supplement the meat ration from rabbits, which they did, thus performing two services, reducing the damage from an excessive rabbit population, and providing meat. Poultry meat was not rationed although eggs were, and farmers , apart from feeding themselves were able to supply local butchers, who looked forward to his visit on market day. If there was a surreptitious parcel wrapped in newspaper – this was an added bonus to farmers' popularity.

There was an allocation of one pig per annum which could be killed without restriction. Farmers lived well enough during the war years. The Essex W.I.s channelled home-made jam through their shops which they opened in such places as Colchester. It was staffed and supplied by farmers' wives.

Farmers had a new spending power. It enhanced their status with the town trades-men. Not only were they befriended for the chance of some under-the-counter extra food, but they became better customers. All in all the period between 1939 and 1945 saw farmers as the "hero of the hour".

How well did Essex respond to the Nation's call? The total area under crops increased by 140,000a which was an outstanding triumph for the ploughing-up campaign. The cropped area of the county rose from 53.1% to 72.7% in 1945, but cereal crops hardly rose at all, a modest 68,000a (less than 1%) of the farmland. It had risen by 3 % in the First World War and in the peak year of 1943 had jumped by 37,000a although in 1945 the wheat acreage was 10,000a less than it had been in 1939.

Barley rose, plateaued, and rose again sharply in the last two years of the war but closed with an additional 53,000a. Oats rose steadily and were 22,000a higher at the end of the war. The pasture area, which should be a direct substitution for the arable land almost halved, coming down from 47% to just over 27%, and in acreage terms a drop of 143,000a which equates to the 140,000a increase in the arable sector. Since only about

45,000a of the pasture reduction was reclaimed derelict land then the ploughing-up campaign seems to have inspired the ploughing of 100,000a. There were some other crop increases.

Beans went up by 3,500a, sugar beet by 7,000a or a 50% increase, potatoes more than doubled adding over 14,000a, clover and grass leys up by nearly 36,000a, linseed up 500%, but only just over 2,000a. Flax was used to make parachute ropes and tent fabric. Small fruit down by 1,000a, orchards up by just over 1,200a. Turnips, swedes (sheep feed) went down but mangolds (cow feed) went up. Mangold seed was used to make khaki dye for uniforms. On the livestock side the number of cows in milk went up by 2,841. Bulls reached a peak of 3,556 in 1942, remained fairly constant followed by a slight dip and finished up at the end of the war with an increase of 287. Total cattle population went up by 10,000 but sheep declined by 106,000 and pigs by nearly 76,000 (a 50% drop).

Chickens had declined to only half their pre-war numbers by 1943, by 1945 they had risen slightly although there were 750,000 fewer than in 1939. The strict rationing of feeding stuffs was responsible for the decline of both pigs and poultry and the average feed conversion ratio of 4-1 was not conducive to economic sense when it took four tons of grain to produce one ton of meat, and some of this was bones! The turkey population more than halved and at one time, 1943, had dropped to less than one third of the number in 1939.

The chicken population, and to a lesser extent pigs in the Ministry of Agriculture returns do not tell the whole story. The numbers of chickens kept as "back-yard hens" is unknown, but they spread into many town gardens and were fed on kitchen scraps, or tail corn donated by a farmer when the Authorities were not looking.

The contribution from home grown vegetables was not inconsiderable, but is not reflected in the statistics. School children dug and grew vegetables on parts of their playing fields. Vacant building plots were often dug as allotments by a neighbour. The "Dig For Victory" campaign made an uncounted contribution.

Farming and farm life had seen a radical shake up. There were fears amongst farmers that they would be jettisoned when the war was over. Most of them could still remember the let-down of 1921. But there were irrevocable changes. There were now more tractors on the farms and by the end of the war there was hardly an acre ploughed in Essex by horses. They still had a role on the average farm but the tractor had well and truly arrived. Farmers could not have foreseen that bread and potatoes, neither of which had been rationed during the war, would be rationed in 1947. A socialist government was in power and it did not want a repetition of the labour disruptions which had been the hallmark of the '20s and '30s. This did not make them natural friends of farmers but expediency dictated that adequate food supplies were given a priority.

A wartime survey which involved visiting every farm in the county was carried out by Ministry officials between 1941 and 1943. Its objective was to assess the food potential of each farm and direct efforts to where it could be most effectively utilised. The result was not published until 1946.[13] What was not disclosed was the A-B-C gradings which were given to every farmer. This was a confidential assessment of his abilities and the 'C' category group were watched very carefully. The Survey, as published gave a revealing pen-picture of Essex agriculture. The analysts faced the perennial problem that bedevils all agricultural statisticians; when is a farm not a farm? For MAFF purposes a

30 1942 Epping. Mrs.Churchill, gavel in hand, auctioning a lamb for the farmers Red Cross Appeal. Land Army girls in uniform in the front row.

'holding' was a piece of land used for quasi agricultural purposes that rendered an annual return.[14]

The survey confirmed that there were 5,700 holdings, but that only 88% of them were proper farms. The remainder, which occupied 7% of the land was used in a part-time capacity. It fell into five categories.

(1) Hobby farmers not dependent on a farm income although these could still be viable farms.

(2) Land used for ancillary purposes such as butchers and cattle dealers as temporary accommodation for stock.

(3) The Home Farm of an estate.

(4) Land taken over by the EWAEC.

(5) Land attached to educational institutes such as the 240 acre Lordship farm attached to the Institute of Agriculture at Writtle.

(6) Playing fields such as the extensive area at Felsted school and other land used for sports.

With these caveates 88% of 5,700 holdings gives a reasonably accurate total of 5,016 full and part-time farmers. 95% of 676,000a equates to 642,200a or an average farm size of 120 acres. This 'average size' disguises the range, but 61% were under 100a and only

10% above 300a The 61% was an identical comparison with East Suffolk, but there were a greater number within the 25-100a.

When they assessed the balance between tenants and owner-occupiers. Essex was decisively the county with the largest number of owner-occupiers in England. 55% of Essex farmers owned their own farms. This figure compares with East Suffolk at 53% , Surrey at 51%, West Suffolk down to 46%, whilst the two neighbours of Essex to the west and east were Hertfordshire only 38% and Kent 53%. The Essex figure was the highest. Not unexpectedly it was the lowest in terms of tenantry.

In area terms the owner-occupiers possessed 51% of the land, equal with Berkshire. The absence of landed estates had always been a feature of Essex land tenure, and the 1920s sales had further reduced them. Farmers, despite the lack of confidence, were forced to buy their farms if they wanted to continue. There was no security of tenure until the 1948 Act. The new owners found to their chagrin that their mortgages were inflexible, unlike an indulgent landlord. The national average of owner-occupiers for all English counties was only 34%.

Rents on the other hand showed that Essex farming had suffered a more serious

10, Downing Street,
Whitehall.

2nd June 1942

My dear Mr. Abbey

I must write and tell you how much I enjoyed my visit to Epping yesterday. I do hope that you made the amount you hoped for from the Gift Sale. I should be so much interested if you would tell me the total result. I was much struck by the kindness, enthusiasm and generosity of the bidders. I thought it was wonderful of them to run that lamb up to such a high figure.

May I congratulate you warmly upon the splendid way in which the Sale was organised.

Yours truly
Clementine S Churchill

31 1942. Thank you letter from Mrs.Churchill to Epping NFU Secretary, Percy Abbey.

77

downturn in the depressed pre-war days. At £1.20pa it was the third lowest in the country and was one of the reasons why there had been such an influx of farmers from the west and the north. The farms were cheap! The only other areas which were cheaper to rent were Rutland and the North Riding of Yorkshire. The highest in the country was arable Norfolk, very largely tentanted where rents were almost double Essex levels. The highest group in the Essex rent survey were the small farms under 25 acres. When the survey divided the rent of cultivated land they found that the 10/20a group paid the most followed closely by the 20/30a group.

The longevity of farmers in the same farm showed that only 13% had been settled for more than 25 years, 9% for 20/25 years, 24% for 10/20 years, a very considerable 54% had moved to their present farms during or after the 1930s. A reflection upon the rapid movement out of farms at that time and of these 13% had moved since the war started. In England 50% of land changed hands in the 1930s, but it was 54% in Essex, Kent 60%, Hertfordshire 62%, East Suffolk 66%. Although the Essex turnover was high it was not the highest. The average length of tenure (13 years) was on a par with the national average.

Looking at the condition of farms, one in four had no farmhouse, and nearly one in seven had no farm buildings. Essex had the third highest number of farm cottages, with 9,950 spread around the county. Few of these were in the village street, some were clustered around subsidiary 'greens', or hamlets but the largest number had been built to house labourers on the farm. Most of them were of ancient origin although there were some brick cottages built in the mid-19th century. Only Lancashire and Norfolk had more farm cottages than Essex, but they were both larger counties. 44% of Essex farms had at least one cottage. Of those farms with cottages 51% had only one or two and only 2% had more than 15.

6% of farm houses had no water supply, 40% had a well or spring nearby and 54% had a piped supply. When the assessment of field availability was examined it seemed that 40% of the fields had no water supply. They probably had little need for it but 26% of the farms in the county had a stream, tributary or river running through them. This reinforces the contention that almost every Essex village had natural running water from a stream or river. The coastal villages with saline water can be excluded from this observation. Only 11% of farmers complained about a shortage of water.

Since irrigation only applied to a very small number of businesses with glass houses or highly prized market garden crops, and the water table had not been lowered by the demands of housing, the few farmers who complained about a shortage was representative of the times. In the 1970s, and particularly after the drought period of 1975/6 when farm reservoir building escalated, and potatoes were the main target for irrigated water, did the water requirements transform the situation.

Electricity was still far from universal. 35% of farms had a supply by 1943 and 22% of these had a proportion of their needs supplied by a private generator. This had always been a drawback against the installation of automatic milking machines. It spawned a small army of farm generators which could supply the electricity for the machines, but was switched off outside milking times and was not generally extended to the farmhouse. Throughout the war years 65% of Essex farmhouses still relied on oil lamps and candles for their lighting requirements. The availability of electricity to Essex farmers was higher than the national average which in 1943 only recorded a supply to 30% of holdings.

THE PLOUHING-UP CAMPAIGN

	Extra Agreed by 10/39	Extra Ploughed by 12/40	Taken-Over by EWAEC	Reclaimed by private Farmers	Reclaimed by EWAEC
Billericay & Brentwood	828	3,957	4,603	90	1,314
Braintree	1,740	4,180	1,625	225	250
Chelmsford	2,029	6,199	3,171	145	1,211
Dunmow	1,471	3,778	4,418 (Incl Saffron Waldon)	66	312
Epping	865	3,251	1,174	60	156
Halstead	1,160	4,469	745	6	146
Lexden & Winstree	1,400	6,368	6,653	33	300
Maldon	2,800	7,692	4,473	317	1,035
Ongar	1,400	4,062	3,179	40	384
Rochford	526	3,738	6,789	20	1,009
Saffron Walden	3,000	3,728	See Dunmow	See Dunmow	See Dunmow
Tendring	1,900	6,676	3,189	82	672
Thurrock	1,552	3,876	1,637	85	1,637
Totals	20,671	61,302	44,292	1,169	8,426

The Red Cross Sales

The Red Cross sales for the Essex Agricultural Fund were a major contribution by Essex farmers to the war effort. The scheme was nationwide and it aimed to raise a million pounds. By the end of the war £7,000,000 had been raised. It started in a successful, but tentative manner. The Essex scheme, organised through the EFU branches organised auctions in the cattle markets. By September 1940, Essex had collected just over £6,000. They were level pegging with Cumberland and Westmoreland.

Farmers gave livestock, produce, bottles of whisky and a wide variety of other items. Merchants and local tradesmen made contributions. The farmers' wives ran sales of produce, teas, flags and raffle tickets and the auctioneers gave their services free.

In the autumn of 1940 the first sale at Colchester raised £2,200. It was quickly followed by others, Dunmow £600, Halstead £300, Southminster £500, a joint effort of the Epping, Harlow, Ongar and Waltham Abbey branches with a sale at Epping raised £700 and Churchill, in whose constituency Epping lay, sent a letter of thanks. Finally, in the first wave of sales Braintree and Great Yeldham, with a sale at Braintree raised £1,500. In 1942 Colchester's gift sale broke all records. It raised £4,250 and by this time the county total was up to £30,000. There were activities in many villages.

"It was notable that there were few outstandingly large amounts in the proceeds (of Colchester 1942 sale) the great bulk of the final sum was made up of moderate amounts from a wide area, and the organisation of many parish activities provided many useful additions to the sale proceeds".[1]

In the same year the Romford branch held a sale at Stanford-le-Hope which raised £1,300. A sale at Chelmsford with a target of £1,000 raised £2,500; £1,000 from the sale of livestock, £360 from fruit sales, £515 donations from the Ladies Committee which was hailed as a record by any Ladies Committee in the whole country. The following year the Essex total had gone up to £61,000 and Hollis Clayton, the EFU chairman, appealed for Essex farmers to make it up to £100,000 by the end of 1943. Sales that year brought in more than double the amounts that had been raised in 1940/1. The Wickford appeal collected £3,000 in a joint effort with Chelmsford. By this time there was rivalry between counties to top the table. Essex was fourth in line in 1943 and Lancashire just ahead. With a charitable gesture the Essex Farmers Journal said;

> "Essex stands fifth in the list of total contributions. That is not quite the same as saying that Essex is fifth in merit Probably the finest record in any county is held by one of our neighbours, Hertfordshire, which has reached £54,000 as against our £61,000, with a smaller acreage and smaller rural population. Congratulations to our neighbour".[2]

There were fewer contributions to the workers, 'Weekly Contributions Scheme'. A few old stalwarts, with memories of the First World War made regular contributions – but many others did not.

Epping had raised £10,500 by 1943 and Clementine Churchill wrote to the NFU secretary, Percy Abbey saying; "I thought it was wonderful of them to run that lamb up to such a high figure".[3] In 1943 the Duke of Norfolk opened a sale at Bishops Stortford a joint affair with the Stansted branch. Horse shows and gymkhanas were part of the Epping sale on August Bank Holiday Monday 1943. The government had hit upon the slogan; "holidays-at-home week". In August 1943 it was announced that Hollis Clayton's target had already been reached. Southminster whose first sale in 1940 had raised £500 quadrupled that figure three years later. Colchester whose first sale had reached the magnificent sum of £2,200 raised £14,500, "easily a record for any sale in the whole of the country".[4] The following year on Whit Monday five branches combined for a joint sale. The first lot was a pet lamb bred by Mr.P. Gray and by the time it had been bought, given back, bought and given back several times, the lamb was finally sold to a buyer who wanted it for an army mascot. It had raised over £1,200! "If everyone who bought a bit of that lamb took his cut they would be very small cutlets"[5]

It had taken four years to raise £100,000 but by October 1944 there was hope of doubling that figure within the next year. Every branch throughout Essex continued to hold gift sales and the amounts made the results of 1940 look puny by comparison. There was a Rural Pennies Section of the Red Cross Agriculture Fund started in 1942. With 16 area secretaries and some 300 village organisers. In the year up to March 1945 nearly £25,000 had been collected and in January alone £2696 3s.4d. The war was drawing to a close and the race was on to find out which county had achieved the highest results. It seemed that Essex was second only to Lancashire. The Essex contribution came to £277,807. A second check of the figures revealed that Essex was the most generous county. It had pipped Lancashire by just £336. As a final comment J.Edgar Walker EFU secretary wrote; "when the returned prisoner of war says "without those Red Cross parcels... many people in Essex will take satisfaction from the bit they did to sustain the Red Cross work".[6]

CHAPTER 8

The War Ag – Vital or Vicious?

The Highland Clearances and the Second World War Agricultural Committees both achieved an odium in retrospect. Both were agricultural necessities. The Scottish Clearances were conducted with cruelty. The War Ag's were sometimes insensitive They were scathingly criticised as being run by farmers who had themselves failed in business. "A lot of broken-down old farmers who couldn't make a go of it themselves, and now they are telling other people how to do it", was an oft made accusation. The men who worked on the War Ag were also accused of being malingerers. Many, if not most, were conscientious objectors, 'conchies', who were trying to escape the army. They were not steady farm workers who were attached to a farm for their lifetime. War Ag staff tended to be the itinerant worker who was accused of being "the useless sort of chap that no-one would employ". These attributions have no specific origin but were well repeated at the time.

The antagonism derived from the close relationship between their dictatorial powers and a bureaucratic implementation of them, which came when the dictatorial barbarism of Hitler was being paraded for the fight against the Nazi 'oppressors'. The War Ag's attracted some similarity which was exploited by its critics. In the same manner the activities of the Happy Valley playboys in Kenya assumed a greater significance because they presented a vivid contrast with beleaguered Britain, its's black-outs, rationing and conscription. The War Ag's missed the mood of the public although they were vital to the food production campaign.

The clearance and rehabilitation of thousands of Essex acres would not have been accomplished without the injection of considerable sums of money, and the legislative powers to carry out the agreed, and necessary, policies. This is not to excuse the more extreme cases of dispossession but it explains the driving force which propelled their actions.

Created, in embryonic form before war was declared, there was a movement to ensure farmer co-operation by appointing a system of local committees comprised of leading, large farmers. It was attacked because the larger farmers were dictating to the smaller ones. In retrospect it was inevitable that the larger farmers had more experience, were more articulate, and could spare the time away from their own farms. Yet the label persisted. It was to be several years before the War Ag's achieved a smooth plateau of activity. Initially there was a considerable back-log to be tackled. As Churchill was exalting the nation in its hour of need so the War Ag's played an important part in sustaining and supporting the war effort. Supplies of food from America in particular were drastically affected by the U-boat campaign.

The priority for shipping was munitions and the accoutrements of war, tractors came into this category but food imports did not. It was adjudged that by reason of the sheer bulk requirements for food, and Britain's natural fertility and climate, that farmers could produce sufficient to sustain the population – albeit with strict rationing. In the first year of the war there was a drop of 44% in the importation of human and animal foods. The task of the War Ag's was to impose a strict regime on farming output, and use extensive powers to see that it was done. There was no intention of simply asking farmers to produce more and hoping they would do it. The stick was used instead of the carrot!

The objectives were to plough up grassland, increase yields and increase livestock products and to set targets for each county. The Committees were given unprecedented powers to put their programmes into operation. There were Land Commissioners to whom final arbitration could be referred. It was a poor attempt at an appeals procedure in contradiction with the normal code of British justice. There were many who thought the War Ag's went too far.

The government gave them the right to direct a farmer to plough up grassland, to grow any specific crop they ordered, to buy and spread fertiliser, to reduce, or increase, the number of cattle being kept. Farmers could receive 'orders' to cut down overgrown hedges, destroy weeds, spray crops and many other jobs associated with good husbandry. The sting was in the tail. If a farmer failed to carry out the 'directions' he was given the War Ag could forcibly enter his farm and take possession of the land. They could terminate a tenancy and carry out, in a ruthless fashion, any jobs they wished they also had the right to charge the owner for the work which they did. Every farm in the country was assessed and graded into A;B;C categories. To ensure harmony and co-operation from the farming community a system of appointing local farmers onto the committees was designed to ensure that both local knowledge and neighbourliness would result in persuasion rather than coercion. The Essex Executive Committee was constituted before war had been declared. The chairman was Hugh Kemsley, High Laver. Gerald Strutt, Terling, Dennis Brown, Barling, Hollis Clayton, Stisted, Gilbert Kemsley, Great Totham, Olive Tritton, Great Leighs and F.W. Paul representing the farm workers. Illness forced Hugh Kemsley to resign in 1942 and the Minister appointed his cousin, Gilbert Kemsley to take his place. At that time the Executive was expanded, Olive Tritton also having retired the new members were J.A. Matthews, Good Easter, Joseph Smith, Saling, Lawrence Taylor, Galleywood and Stanley Webb, Mistley. Under the county executive was a tier of 12 local committees. Seven of the chairmen were Justices of the Peace. There were 91 local farmers recruited to support them but throughout the war years the personnel changed in respect of death or retirement.

In the 1920s, as a token towards agricultural support the county councils set up District Organisers who were under the auspices of the Institute of Agriculture obstensively charged with education on the ground. They had a roving commission to organise events which could further that aim. Employees of the county council they were attached, and under the wing of the Institute of Agriculture, whose principal, J.C. Leslie became the county executive officer for the War Ag. He appointed three of his colleagues into senior positions. J.C. Fletcher covered the north west.

H.E. Nichols was appointed D.O. for Wickford which covered the south of the county. It was totally unconnected with the unpopularity of the War Ag's but only months after he had been appointed, Mr. Nicholls was mistaken for a German airman by a member of the Home Guard. He was shot in the stomach and died, being buried at Danbury. The third appointed, Ralph Sadler, had been district organiser for the South Essex Deprived Area ranging from Rochford to Grays. In 1934 he arrived in Colchester to take over the North Essex division which included the Tendring, Lexden and Winstree

32 1940 Rettendon. The Minister, R.S. Hudson said; "Do it now - you may never get another chance".

and Maldon Hundreds. He had been instrumental, and was an enthusiastic supporter of Young Farmers Clubs. the day after war broke out his role suddenly changed. The district committees of farmers had no executive powers, despite the wide ranging powers which the War Ag's possessed. The district officers were all powerful in making recommendations and J.C. Leslie was the supremo for Essex. It made the district organisers into very powerful men.

When Leslie was transferred to the staff of the Ministry of Agriculture David Ewing was appointed acting principal of the Institute. In 1943 Leslie became Deputy Secretary to the National Farmers Union and Sadler was appointed as the Executive Officer for Essex.

Thus the county was ruled by academics who had little experience of personal farming themselves. It was not entirely harmonious. Sadler recorded,[1]

"I must say that this committee (Lexden and Winstree District advisory committee) has given me a certain amount of trouble. You are well aware of it's attitude towards the heavy land in the district, and it needs no further comment from me except to say that Mr.Hutley is definitely a representative of the farmers of this heavy land, and his whole attitude is to safeguard the interests of the farmers, and not to do the work for which the committee was originally appointed. The chairman of this committee (Charles Round of Birch Hall) works very hard, but quite definitely in his own way and I find it quite difficult to keep him on the straight and narrow path. One member of the committee, Mr.Cooper Bland (West Bergholt) now lives at Sheering Hall, Shalford, some 15 miles from his district, to which he only pays very infrequent visits.

   Three members of the committee, Messrs.Frank Warren (Great Tey) Alec Craig (Lexden) and Alec Page (Great Horkesley) are cattle dealers and have, during the past two months been very busy buying cattle while Col.Furneaux (Fingringhoe Hall) has a very meagre knowledge of agriculture".

This local committee of farmers were practical men and they were fighting the beaurocrats. Sadler was concerned that their attitude favoured the interests of farmers – and not the progression of the War Ag committee. It was a confliction that echoed down the chain and many smaller farmers, whilst disturbed by the overlordship of their larger neighbours, found that they were a buffer between something that might have been worse. Even Sadler admits that; "a few were somewhat puffed up with their own importance and threw their weight about".

The bungles which were perpetrated were a cause of laughter in the pubs, but with anger for those who were at the receiving end. Farmers were ordered to plough up grassland and then refused a permit to buy a tractor and plough to do the job. In order to meet (on paper) prescribed targets, grassland was often ploughed and drilled with wheat when a practical farmer knew it was too late in the season and the resulting crops often produced less grain than the seed that was sown. The second class nature of the War Ag workmen meant that the workmanship was shoddy, the amount of waste was criminal

> "On two Essex farms which I visited the Committee had ploughed in three cartloads of cut clover on a six-acre field after refusing to allow the farmer to cart it to feed his stock. They also ploughed in six acres of tares, five and a half acres of beans, and six acres of wheat, five weeks before they were due to be harvested. The farmer, who took over the farms four years ago when they were derelict, tells me that whereas they had only produced two sacks of corn to the acre, he raised the yield to four quarters of barley and five acres of wheat and was willing to do all that the Committee ordered and pay all the expenses. His offer was refused.
>
>   I myself saw eight acres of good hay and ten acres of fairish wheat ploughed in a few days before both were ready to cut".[2]

Although not in Essex one farmer was ordered to plough up the main line of the Great Western Railway! The Committee were working with out-of-date maps. The farmer replied in writing and promised to do his best but felt he must point out that the embankment at this point was rather steep. "Some mistakes, of course, were inevitably made from time to time", commented Sir John Winnifrith[3].

Mistakes were more common on the ground than ears of wheat. The EWAEC had two sets of O.S. maps – one six inch, one 15 inch. The smaller series did not have the fields numbered, and the larger maps were kept at Writtle. It was not unknown for Committee workmen to go into the wrong field. One field was sown with wheat, but when it came up it turned out to be white turnips. Inexperienced labour caused many problems. In one instance the Committee mistakenly ploughed in a farmers' growing crops then had the effrontery to charge him for the work. The case was dropped just before they went into a police court.

33 1943. Writtle Agricultural College. Minister of Agriculture R.S. Hudson and EWAEC chairman and executive committee. Four ladies included.

Fifteen men were given the task of cutting off the grass in half an acre at Salcot. They came from miles away in a lorry and were taken back at night. There were tales that three land girls took 20 minutes to pull three thistles. They were transported every day in a motor van which one girl spent most of the day cleaning – and making tea. Another land girl did not feed the chickens because she "thought the old hen did that". On an Essex farm some Committee workmen laid out the bottom of a hay stack too large so that there was not enough hay to finish the stack. Their inexperience, and self interest lay in the assumption that if it was wider at the bottom they would not have to pitch the hay so high at the top. To remedy this matter 10 land girls were sent 13 miles on a lorry to dismantle the stack and start again.

Apart from muddle and mismanagement the Committee had its own unfeeling beaurocratic control. They told Ralph Sadler to plough up large areas of the derelict land in the Lexden and Winstree Hundred. Only 10 Fordsons were allocated to the county by the Ministry. They were puny and inadequate for ploughing heavy clay. "It was some months before I could convince the Executive and the Ministry that heavier and more powerful tractors and equipment were needed. Eventually I was given two Allis Chalmers Model K crawlers".[4]

Daniel McKerracher, of Ewell Hall, Kelvedon, a Scottish settler in middle age was evicted from his farm and committed suicide. A 67 year old widow, Mrs. Ellie Brown, Hill Farm Lamarsh, with two sons in the army was evicted from her cottage, her few acres were possessed, the doors and windows nailed up and her furniture thrown out of the house;

> "They had taken all the land – 26 acres of cultivated land-in February 1941 and the remainder, 50 acres that I had let to Mr.Pengrun of Wickford for cattle grazing. He had about 20 heifers which had to be sold, and I was compelled to return to him £18 which he had paid me two weeks previously".[5]

Mrs. Brown was evicted and only saved from the workhouse by Mr.H.W.Cook Chairman of the Parish Council who said "I did not believe such things were possible in England. The behaviour of the officials was positively German". Neither were these incidents isolated. There were many more which rumbled in quiet discontent but did not reach the Courts. There was little doubt that the Committee were acting in a manner beyond their remit. The economic case on agricultural and food production grounds for evicting Mrs.Brown was nonsensical. It was, unfortunately, all too common and the impression was given that those in charge of the EWAEC were failed farmers themselves, or academics who had never had mud on their boots. It was a charge that stuck.

There were other inefficiencies which were not necessarily laid at the door of the War Ag's but emanated from ministerial edicts. It was, for instance, unlawful to keep more than 50 chickens. And pig keeping was also discouraged. The largest decline in pig numbers in Essex was between 1940 and 1941 when they went down by 46,000. Another 18,000 drop the following year and 12,000 fewer the year after that. Some critics saw this as a foolish policy, "on any arable farm he (the farmer) could keep far more and feed them from the farm itself...a hundred chickens could have been turned out on a 10 acre stubble field, penned up at night and fattened for the autumn markets. Chickens are natural gleaners of any farmyard."[6]

The fallacy of this argument rested upon the fear that once the chickens had cleared the spilt grain from the stubble fields they would make inroads into Britain's perilous grain stocks to feed them. The 50 chicken limit had some semblance of rational thought behind it, where a small number could be regarded as "natural scavengers".[6]

The ploughing up campaign was well under way in the month of September 1939 as soon as war was declared. It was, fortunately, a very fine month and as the blackberries ripened on the bushes throughout large areas of South Essex, the locals turned out to pick them quickly before the Committee tractors arrived to pull them out. Busting up terrain that was still littered with the roots of these and other bushes was not a first class job. The old matted turf did not invert as neatly as a traditional arable field.

The campaign was directed at ploughing-up these fields. It was not anticipated that they would produce instant crops. Food shortages were a genuine concern of the government which had hived off the organisation of food supplies three years before the war when a food department was established within the Board of Trade. Thus one Ministry was responsible during the war for setting the targets, and another "agriculture" responsible for implementing the policy. There was inevitably some overlapping.[7]

Initially the ploughing-up campaign had twin targets; to reclaim the derelict farmland in the county, and to persuade farmers to plough up their cherished pastures.

The ploughing up done by the EWAEC fell into two categories; those complete farms that had gone derelict, mainly along the coastal belt on the northern coast of the Blackwater, and in the Dengie and Foulness areas, and secondly the overgrown scrub land which had no visible owner and was not part of a farm. The first category proved easier and in practice the owners were not averse, such as Henry Tuke the banker who owned Langenhoe Hall and Roderick Mortimer, forage merchant who owned Abbott's Hall, Great Wigborough. These were substantially sized farms and could be targeted. There were the village commons which county-wide amounted to 1,234 acres in 1939. At Tiptree 45 of the 60 acres of common land was ploughed and wherever it was considered possible to grow crops the ploughs moved in.

From the turn of the century, as the railway had moved east, there had been a movement to popularise the southern area of Essex to Londoners. Grandiose estate plans were produced showing pleasant tree-lined avenues and rural homes. Osea Island had been launched as an Temperance centre although it was called a "Sea-side and Health Resort". It had not been a success but was symbolic of the movement by Plotlanders. The catholic commune at Langenhoe in 1930 was another movement with it's backs-to-the-land philosophy. The direct line to Shoeburyness was constructed in 1888. Pitsea, Laindon and Basildon were centres where these plots were sold. Usually fetching between £5–£25, at £20 per acre it was an enhancement on agricultural values. Flimsy bungalows which became permanent homes during the period between the two wars when housing was short. The sales had been in a chequer board fashion and the land between them grew giant blackberry bushes. The tracks were rutted and overgrown. No-one knew exactly what was underneath.

> "It was here that when we were surveying the bushes we came across a bungalow; that was not unusual, but by this bungalow was a garage and in it a perfectly good car. In course of time the bushes were removed, and eventually the land was ploughed, stetched and drilled with wheat. The garage and the car remained, an island in a sea of wheat".[8]

This shanty town stretched for many miles and it's exact acreage was difficult to determine. The area designated for Basildon New Town after the war amounted to 7,818 acres although it had not all been occupied as plots. Typical of the overgrown condition of this land is the account that "on one occasion bending down to peep through the undergrowth we saw a large pole erected and eventually discovered it to be a lamp standard, complete with gas lamp glass holder! In another area, coming upon a hut completely surrounded by thorns, a peep through a crack in the boards revealed a very ancient car"[9]. There were many week-end caravans, some on wheels, railway carriages – off wheels, wood and tin huts with a brick chimney and plenty of amateur attempts at brick bungalows. Where materials were short the sides of chicken sheds were nailed up with brightly coloured iron advertising plates. Cocoa, tea, Tobacco and petrol etc. It was a "shackery".

Of the bush land reclaimed from building estates the largest area 1,407a was in the Thurrock and Hornchurch districts with Rochford (1,139a), Chelmsford District (1,020a) and Billericay and Brentwood (960a). By contrast there was only 75a in the Braintree district and the much maligned Maldon and Lexden and Winstree districts only produced a combined total of 415a. Dunmow and Saffron Walden at the northern end of the county had 78a. This was patently a potential source for increasing the ploughed land in the county – but it could only be done at a cost. When the Minister of Agriculture, R.S. Hudson, came to Laindon in 1941 he went to One Tree Hill where he could see nearly 1,000a of impenetrable thorn covering the derelict land. He ordered; "get it cleared and

***34** Rochford Pests Officer, C. Byford and his Land Army assistants with their morning bag of rats.*

cropped now; you may never get another chance". The need for food superceded any calculation of the likely costs involved. It is doubtful if any of the EWAEC farming activities ever made a profit.

The task of bringing this scrub land into a state where it could produce a useful crop must be measured by the swings of the harvest. 1943 was the highest wheat crop ever grown in the UK, at 3m acres. The same was true in Essex which recorded 144,000 acres. It was to be expected that as the unkempt land was cleared, and fallowed the following summer to prepare it for drilling, that there would be a jump in the fallow acreage of the county. The figures do not prove this. There was a very slight increase in 1940, a sharp decrease in the next two years followed by similar declines until 1945 when it rose again. The accompanying table reveals this pattern.

WARTIME HARVEST (ALL CEREALS)		
	Cereal Change	Fallow
1940	+16,288	+ 310
1941	+41,861	– 6,549
1942	– 6,937	+ 196
1943	+26,991	– 5,283
1944	+ 2,156	– 3,355
1945	–11,869	+ 8,122
40/45	+68,490	– 6,559

Farmers did plough up a considerable extra area and the ploughing-up campaign was adjudged a success. The comment by 'Observer' revealed a new picture of the Essex landscape. It describes the scene that R.S. Hudson had looked upon and declared "get it cleared".

"In many places large areas of derelict land covered with bushes had been replaced by cultivated land. Surveying the isolated shacks and small pieces of poor land around them in the Laindon area, my guide exclaimed "There you see the result of complete freedom to do what you like with your own". I was interested to hear that when these small units are taken over there is always a valuation by an independent valuer in private practice, and if the owners are dissatisfied with his opinion of the value, the matter can go to arbitration.

As a small boy, I had gazed at the great length of the wall surrounding Braxted Park, but I never anticipated I should ever enter the Park and find 200 acres ploughed up. I am told the Park alone contains about 500 acres and the Minister of Agriculture himself "looked round" the Park before the final decision was taken. It was clear to me that a great deal of useful work had been accomplished under difficult conditions".[10]

There was a £2 per acre ploughing-up grant which although an indication of government support was too small to encourage a massive swing into cereals. Farmers were; "a little indignant"[11] but also pointed out the lack of justice when they were forced to plough

35 1939 September. At the outset of the war there was an urgent need to plant wheat.

up pastures whilst unfarmed land bred vermin. "Areas which were harbouring vermin were, therefore, menacing the surrounding arable...The importance of the distruction of rabbits and of areas harbouring starlings and magpies could not be overlooked in face of the increasing corn acreage".[12] The Committee had the enthusiasm to reclaim derelict land, and at least some of the requisite machinery.

Having once cleared it the problems of growing crops up to the stage of harvesting, threshing and disposing of the grain, particularly when, as in many cases there were no adjacent farm buildings to provide cover from rain, gave them an incentive to hand back land as soon as they could. This was the avowed policy. In June 1942 they invited farmers to apply for tenancies. "Here is work of urgent National importance for Essex farmers to undertake".[13 They offered tenancies with a promise for two years and thereafter annually with the promise of at least three years after the war was over.

This was a sensible policy since much of the land was in fields of only 10 acres, or 50 acre blocks without houses or buildings. They offered special facilities for machinery (did this mean jumping the queue for a tractor?), but concluded "when it comes to cropping no-one is so well fitted to grow the maximum crop as the good Essex farmer whose land is just over the hedge".[14] At the end of the war the Committee were farming in-hand 18,000 acres but of the total amount they had taken over 24,000 had been handed back. It represented a significant step of the 43% they had 'annexed'. The case of Barnston Hall, Dunmow was one example where land was not retained by the Committee.

In 1941 they visited Henry Turner, an elderly long established farmer who had been an advisor to the Minister of Agriculture in the First World War. It was recommended that he should be dispossessed. Archie Matthews of Good Easter went to have a look with Ralph Sadler. "He invited me to accompany him and we were appalled. The Dunmow Committee's recommendation was supported and on Easter Monday 1941 the area Committee took control".[15]

The farm men, eight elderly survivors from call-up went to the Spotted Dog at Barnston that day. There was also a small encampment of gypsies and two of them had been occasionally employed. They had five horses grazing. There was a herd of 40 pedigree dairy shorthorns and followers. When these were sold only one animal made more than £100, and to everyone's surprise it made 1,150 guineas. She was a descendant from a champion of 1906. Mr. Turner's farm was put under the management of Archie Matthews

During the war years the War Agricultural Committees nationwide took possession of 355,942 acres. Essex, with 2½% of the farmed area of the country should have 8,898 acres. In actuality it was nearly five times above the national average. This can be interpreted as illustrative of the run-down state of Essex farms, where patently there was an immense back-log, or it could be seen as assiduous application by the EWAEC. It was estimated that Essex was "probably the most expensive in the country and cost the tax payer approximately £1m a year against £300,000 in Norfolk, a larger county with far fewer complaints".[16] At a meeting in the Red Lion Hotel, Colchester, between 200 and 300 farmers unanimously passed a resolution calling for a government enquiry into the "high-handed and dictatorial methods, injustices, and waste of public money by the Essex War Agricultural Committee" [17]

The Essex Farmers and Countrymen's Association was formed as a result of a crescendo of criticism from the Peldon area, which had been one of the most depressed clay areas in the pre-war period. Rev.John Wilson, the rector wrote to James Wentworth-Day in May 1943, "We are in great distress in this parish because the Essex War Agricultural Committee have taken a most high-handed attitude towards several farmers here, and are threatening evictions which apparently they have the power to carry out".[18] A meeting in Peldon Rectory was attended by Peggy Greer, Blind Knights, Layer-de-la-Haye, "tweed-clad, her dog-cart in the drive", Ted Hutley, Brick House, Peldon, William Butt, Barn Hall, Tolleshunt Knights, Tom Mann, Virley Hall "bluff and keen-eyed, looking as though he had a gun in his pocket for any official who troubled him". There was Roderick Mortimer of Abbott's Hall, Great Wigborough, Captain Sergeant, a retired military officer and Edwin Prior, the village postmaster. Another dozen small farmers also came to the meeting. "They told their story. How farmer after farmer had been given notice to quit without any good reason at all and without any possibility of appeal to an independent tribunal".[19]

The impetus for the Essex Farmers and Countrymens' Association soon began to spread and Thomas Tod, Blackmore End, took the chair at another meeting in the Braintree Corn Exchange. "Mr.Tod is the best type of Scots farmer, thoroughly efficient and conscientious. He never had any trouble personally with the committee, nor had his farming methods been critisised by them, "[20] but Mr Tod was threatened by Ministry Officials. It was suggested to him that he might be reported for growing a bad crop of beans, and that when he wanted a new tractor it would be very difficult for him to get one. What Wentworth-Day called "blackmailing abuse of power".

Mr.Prior, the Peldon Postmaster, who was secretary to the Association received a letter from the wife of a 70-year old dairy farmer. She wrote "I dread him going to milk at 5.00 in the morning unless I go with him in case I should find him hanging in the barn like that poor farmer we read of in the paper. He has had suicide in his face for days. A wife knows". This was only representative of many similar situations.

Wentworth-Day claimed that the Minister, R.S. Hudson was shocked by the reports and rushed down to Essex to put a stop to what appeared to be an impending farmer revolt against the excesses of the Committees. Soon after the Colchester meeting came a response; "the answer was a swift, unheralded, and certainly unsung, visit by Mr.Hudson to Peldon".[21] Mr.Hudson did lunch at the Peldon Rose in 1943 when he met the members of the local Committee. Ostensibly his visit was to congratulate the local Committee and the District Officer for the magnificent job they had done. Therein lies a conflicting remembrance of this "unheralded and certainly unsung", visit.

No government inquiry was set-up. The whole episode was flavoured with unpatriotic tones. When the war situation was not running in Britain's favour it was hardly the time to make complaints.

How justified were these worries?

In retrospect the achievements of the EWAEC were considerable. Not only did they bring back into cultivation many derelict acres but by persuasion, the farmer members increased the arable land in their neighbourhood. The Committee itself had set about the enormous task of drainage. In the first five years 4,000 miles of ditches were dug out in Essex. 70,000 acres were mole drained and 2,000 acres were tile drained. This was an achievement in itself. If the success of the Committees' policies can be judged on performance alone then they achieved all, if not more, than their targets. Like the

36 1943. War Ag members inspect crops now growing where dereliction had been widespread before the war. Dollymans Farm.

Highland Clearances it was not that the policy was wrong – it was the methods employed to implement it. There was little doubt that the operations of the War Ag were muddle-some, they were often inefficient, they did not always produce the best results, they used powers of eviction that bordered on cruelty. At least three farmers committed suicide after being dispossessed. Their houses and cottages were not razed to the ground as were the Scottish Crofters, but they acted impecuniously.

Could it have been done without them? The government ploughing-up grant was insufficient to encourage the breaking of pastures. If it had been multiplied by 10 times it might perhaps have produced a result not dissimilar to that which was achieved by one farmer suggesting (politely) ideas to his neighbours. Perhaps, if the carrot had been larger the pastures would have been ploughed. This would have presented an unsuperable problem with the shortage of tackle to do the job.

The War Ag's system of allocation with new tractors may have at times been incestuous, with a farmer getting a tractor because his brother was on the War Ag. Family relationships got favouritism, as indeed did compliant farmers as opposed to intransigent ones. Without some sort of allocation system the distribution of new machinery would probably have been even less fair than it was. There would have been opportunities for those in-the-know to hide a few new machines away and sell them on the black-market. At least this sort of behaviour did not occur.

It would not be unreasonable to suggest that, eventually the target wheat crops would have been sown – but it might have been a couple of years after the actual dates. Rigid organisation, discipline of a nature unknown to farmers before, was instituted as the nation was mobilised for war-time production.

There is no doubt that the commons would not have been ploughed by private farmers. Some of the derelict acres might have been revitalised but the plotlands of Basildon would certainly not have made any contribution to the national larder. In this area the work of the Committee could not have been done by private farmers. Even if tantalising grants had been offered the clearances. Were they vital or vicous? Probably both. Essex agriculture would not have undergone such a dramatic and radical revitalisation without the impetus, and the dictatorial powers of the EWAEC.

They were vital in ensuring the food supplies of the nation. On the charge of being vicious. They were certainly unfeeling and when people were driven to suicide by the actions of petty beaurocrats then there was something radically wrong with the morality of the nation. They were very vicious but perhaps it was necessary in the circumstances. Unfortunately in a war that was designed to topple a dictator they used some of his methods. It is on this charge i.e. "that they were not whiter than white", that the case must rest. They have been reviled by historians since they were abolished. They will probably be misunderstood and criticised for many years to come. This chapter is a contribution to the debate.

With the ending of hostilities it was not the ending of the War Ag's. They then had the task of handing the land back to its rightful owners. Some had been let on leases which extended for three years after the end of the war. There was an armoury of farm machinery that could not be dismantled immediately. There were staff and offices. The War Ag's proved reluctant. This reached its climax in the case of naval war hero Commander Marten of Crichel Down. This was unproductive land in Dorset which had been compulsorily taken over, had been cleared and farmed, but had then been transferred to another Ministry and offered as a tenancy to a local farmer. As the owner Cmd.Marten wanted it himself. The case resulted in the Minister of Agriculture, Sir Thomas Dugdale, resigning his office on the floor of the House of Commons. He accepted the blame for the maladministration of his Civil Servants but this case gave a clear indication that it was only right to hand back land that had been taken from private owners. This was 1954, nine years after the end of the war and after a Labour government committed to land nationalisation had discovered that it was impractical.

The objectives of the Ministry of Agriculture towards food production did not have the same urgency, or the force of law which had existed during hostilities. The powers of Land Tribunals had been strengthened in the 1947 Agriculture Act. In 1954 there were supervision orders in force covering over 1,000 farms. Two hundred and twenty farmers were dispossessed on grounds of bad husbandry between 1951/4, soon after what became known as the 'Battle of Crichel Down'.

The case of Mr. & Mrs.Woollett concerned four acres at South Woodham. It was part of 217 acres requisitioned during the war. In 1947 Mr. & Mrs.Woollett bought a four acre plot with a bungalow. He had been advised to seek outdoor work for his health. They gained possession of the bungalow but the Ministry of Agriculture decided that they would not release the land. They threatened a compulsory purchase order.

The Chelmsford Agricultural Land Tribunal turned down her Appeal although Mrs. Woollett was supported by 18 others who were being dispossessed of land they owned. The case was lost! She then took it to the Queens Bench Division on a point of law submitting that the Land Tribunal had not been properly constituted. They had been selected from the NFU and CLA panels by the secretary of the tribunal in conjunction with the chairman.

Mr.Justice Stable agreed and ruled that the requisition and compulsory purchase orders were invalid. Mrs.Woollett and her friends had won their case, on a fine point of law, but the Appeal Court again reversed Mr.Justice Stable's decision. With embarrassment the Ministry of Agriculture announced in November 1954 that it would abandon its proposal to purchase compulsorily the Woollett land.[22] This Essex case cemented the principle of Crichel Down and made legal history. It prevented the officials from acting arbitrarily thereafter.

The EWAEC finally left the Institute in September 1948 but it had been a struggle between the college authorities and the Ministry. They ensconced themselves at Beeches Road, Chelmsford, which became the MAFF administrative centre for the county. The 'war', part of the title, was dropped but limpet-like the agricultural executive committees continued a desultory existence until they were finally abolished by the new labour government in 1997. They had long out-lived their usefulness.

Despite the Herculean efforts to reclaim lost farmland the 9,595a eventually reinstated was less than the land perfunctorily and compulsorily taken out of farming to build air fields alone. Considerable but unspecified areas of land were also perloined by the military authorities, notably around Colchester, Shoeburyness and Foulness for military training. Land was taken for gun emplacements, pill boxes, a radar station at Great Bromley, 'Q' sites which were decoys disguised to look like army encampments, marshalling yards, docks etc., such as East Mersea, an explosives factory on Bramble Island. There were multifarious uses which were of greater importance than the usage of land for food.

There were 23 airfields in Essex, 20 of them constructed, by US construction teams, and three by British firms, and two pre-war grass fields were expanded. It was a criteria for bomber airfields that they should be as close to sea level as possible, under 650ft. to avoid the possibilities of hill fog and as near as possible to the continent to reduce the flying time. Essex provided all of the attributes that were needed. In addition to those completed, four more sites, Cold Norton, Beaumont, Southminster and High Roding were all given station numbers although never built. Sites at Bulphan, Ingatestone, Little Clacton, Maldon and Weeley were also surveyed and would have been built if the fortunes of the war had ebbed away. Of the completed airfields only Birch was non-operational. But with a mile long runway for bombers, perimeter tracks, hangars, ancillary control buildings, air raid shelters and housing; each airfield required a minimum of 800 acres.

The 20 Essex airfields took approximately 16,000 acres most of which was prime agricultural land. The soil in most of the parishes concerned was excellent. It was not all farmland since at Boreham, 86a Dukes Wood was removed in the construction process. The land was requisitioned and after the war was returned to its owners. There were some difficulties in discovering where the true boundaries lay after bulldozers and concrete runways had obliterated them. At Boxted they attempted to give the same owners their same land. It was done successfully.

The airfields were not handed back immediately the war was over. It was an uncertain peace although the 'Cold War' had not materialised, never-the-less the government were nervous that these airfields might be needed again. Farmers were allowed back to cut hay between the runways but had not been allowed to make hay cocks when the airfields were operational. With the war over tenancies were arranged and farmers could plough up the land between the main runway and the perimeter track.

"In the early summer of 1946 it was decided to plough up the whole 'drome (Birch) and the various plots were allocated to the dispossessed farmers. For our 150a lost we were given about 90a which was proportionate to the acreage of solid concrete.

Eventually the land was in some order to drill and we drilled the whole area with wheat, which despite its open position withstood the arctic weather quite well, and we cut it with the binder in August last year. It was a patchy crop, thin where the top soil was thin, and fair in places. The sheaves being short we carted it in good time and it was all ploughed up with our own tractors in September in preparation for a spring corn crop".[23]

CHAPTER 9

The Great Estates

In 1900 the hieretical pattern of the land remained as it had done for centuries – one man owned the land, one farmed it and another worked it. A triumvirate structure that had many advantages. The transformation during the century resulted in a sharp decline in both landlords and workers leaving the middle man, the farmer, who raised his status to become a landowner, with mortgages which were little different from many of the aristocratic predecessors. At the same time the farmer lowered his status and became a tractor driver.

The decline of the landlord was more dramatic than the decline of the estate which had a mansion, a park and its surrounding acres. In the 18th century landowners were agriculturists. In the 19th century they took less interest in practical farming, with one or two notable exceptions such as Lord Western, Felix Hall, and in the 20th century those landowning families that survived turned again to become active and practical farmers.

The estates diminished, but did not become extinct. The influence of the old families withered. They became quaint survivors in a countryside that teemed with newcomers, their village dominance was lost as they sold off their lands. Servile tenants became landowners. Cottagers were replaced by commuters.

The disparity of incomes was re-aligned and professional men with incomes greater than the squire, moved into redundant farm houses, and week-end cottages. The grand houses were vacated, and the grandeur went with them. The secluded magnificence of the parkland became less authentic when it was planted with wheat, and the Range Rover became a universal vehicle. The coat of arms had disappeared from the carriage door.

A landowning aristocracy with its strata of gentry and squirearchy survived, with a lifestyle that had been exclusive – pheasant shooting and hunting, now opened up to those who could pay. The county families still regarded Eton and Winchester as the excellence of education and a passion for dogs and fishing preserved the tastes of a class that was not extinct.

Political power vanished. Pocket villages became represented by Labour councillors. The landowning community could not stem the overwhelming tide. They retreated into their own circle and some joined the opposition. Evelyn (Daisy) Warwick, Easton, was an ardent socialist. Noel-Buxton, Warlies, was Minister of Agriculture in a Labour government in 1924. Valentine Crittall, Stisted, was Labour MP for Maldon. He created Silver End with 478 houses and a community hall. John Tabor, Bovingdon, and the representative of an ancient Essex family became Labour leader of the Essex County Council. But the landowning interest still preserved its havens of power. The Lord Lieutenancy passed effortlessly from the owner of Easton to Bishops Hall. Monklands. Orsett. Spains Hall. Briefly to a landless admiral and to the owner of Audley End.

In the House of Commons four out of eight MPs were Essex landowners in 1900. In 1937 only two of these Divisions had a landed representative. Twelve new constituencies had been created and from a representation of 50% it had dropped to 10% before 1939.

37 1900 approx. Harvest Supper at Terling.

The two pre-war members were R.A. Butler, Stanstead Hall (Halstead) and Sir Edward Ruggles-Brise, Spains Hall. Post-war; Brian Harrison, Copford Hall, represented Maldon and by the 1990s the only tenuous connection was that of Bernard Jenkin whose wife. Anne, was the sister of Lord Rayleigh, Terling.

In other spheres the estate owners carried the leadership of the county until they were usurped. They were, variously, chairmen of the Quarter Sessions, had a predominance on the Magistracy, served on the largely unknown and unseen Tax Commissioners, carried their political enthusiasm into the Country Landowners Association. Essex provided three national presidents of the CLA, Sir John Ruggles-Brise, Spains, Sir Nigel Strutt from the Terling Estate and John Norris, Mountnessing, both a tenant and an owner-occupier. Only a few landowners took a leading part in the EFU. Olive Tritton, Great Leighs, Charles Gooch, Wivenhoe, Charles Round, Birch, were some who took a small part. Col. Jimmy Round was Chairman of Lexden & Winstree Rural District Council (1966-9)

Before 1900 the old families had effectively handed over the control of county politics and only represented 5.5% of the councillors on the ECC, but 27% of the aldermen giving an overall representation of only 10.6%. By 1937 not one of the estate owners who had been on the 1900 list were still in office. This did not entirely create a vacuum of agricultural interest. The farmers, many now owner-occupiers gave a small representation which diminished in the second half of the century although in 1970 the farmer/farmers' wives lobby amounted to 11%, very similar to the landed interest in

1900, By 1990 the agricultural representation had become further reduced to only 5%. Two farmers were raised to the peerage, Lord Dixon-Smith, Houchins and Lyons Hall, Braintree, and farmer Paul White became Lord Hanningfield in 1998. Both had been chairman of the ECC. Another life peer created in 1997 was Paul Channon, Kelvedon Hall, Brentwood who became Lord Kelvedon.

The Owners
In 1873 there were 93 owners who had 301,722a or 35.5% of the farmed area of the county. Eleven of these had less than 1,000a although they gained entry into the landowners list by virtue of qualification of 2,000a in other counties or £3,000pa. There were 53 resident in the county. They were defacto the landed estates of Essex. Newby defined an estate as; "a functioning centre of political and social influence across the territory which it comprised".[1] Deducting the 11 owners who had less than 1,000a in Essex the remaining estates covered 33.7% of the county with an average size of 3,376a.

Essex was considered one of the least aristocratic counties in the 1873 landowners survey.[2] It was estimated that only 9% of the land was covered by the 'great' estates although there was a wider distribution of gentry and squires. When the 'small proprietors', who had 11% of the land, is deducted it would appear that 89% was in the hands of landlords. There were some owner-occupiers but not many large-scale farmers. 89% of the land was tenanted, or if the aristocratic element of 9% is deducted the figure then becomes 91%. It is a reasonable assumption that in 1873 90% of the farmland was tenanted. In 1900 there were 7,472 registered owners with over 1a in the county. This excludes private houses but many of the smaller areas could not be described as farmable. Later evidence seems to suggest that the number of viable farms was around 5,000.

A quarter of a century of depression created considerable land movement. By 1900 the estates had, in some cases shed outlying acres, whilst others had taken the opportunity to buy adjacent vacant farms. This interchange resulted in a small depletion of the area covered by the estates. In some cases it was a larger reduction. Marks Hall, Coggeshall, embraced 6898a in 1872 but when Thomas Price bought it at auction in 1897 he only purchased 2,200a.

Forest Hall, Ongar, was 3,723a in 1872 but when it was sold in 1920 it had already depleted to 1,560. Berechurch was bought by Brewer Octavius Coope in 1877 comprising 3,400a and although it was divided into 47 lots Coope bought 3,280a. The eight farms covered 1,483a at a cost of £33.98 per acre. The remainder being woodland. He essentially acquired an 'estate'.

The aspirations of successful men in the 19th century embraced the acquisition of a county estate for the social respectability which it would bring. Only nine of the 53 estates changed hands in the 19th century. Most of the buyers were brewers but Stisted went to the Colchester engineer, Joseph Paxman in 1893. He was followed by Cecil Sebag-Montefiore in 1907 and then by Valentine Crittall. Samuel Courtauld bought Gosfield and Richard Arkwright son of the Lancashire inventor bought Mark Hall, Harlow. Hylands, created by brewer Arthur Pryor increased his original 840a to 3,255a between 1840-73, and sold virtually intact to Sir Daniel Gooch in 1908, whose fortune had been founded by his grandfather from railways. It was sold again in 1920 to the brewer, Hanbury.

Six estates were sold between 1900-14 all with mansions and parkland. One of these,

Felix Hall, Kelvedon 2,160a, was divided into 10 major farms and eight smallholdings from 13-46a were bought by the tenants. The Bonner, Cullen and Siggers families buying their farms at this time.

Philanthropic Experiments

Skreens, which had been in the possession of the Branston family since 1635 was sold in 1908. It had been 5,424a in extent in 1873 but was reduced to 4,925a when it was bought by noted game hunter William Otho Nicholson Shaw. His son, Henry, inherited the estate in 1910, enlarged the mansion which more than doubled its size, installed his own electricity generator and laid on central heating. There were considerable mortgage debts and in 1914 William Able Towler, Littleport, bought the estate for £90,500. He purchased the property as an entity three days before an auction had been scheduled. Towler immediately gave the tenants notice to quit. He re-lotted 3,000a into 16 farms and the following year eight more. By the end of 1915 the land had all been sold at an average price of £20 per acre. Most of them became owner-occupied but some were bought by small local landlords. Only three were bought by existing tenants and by December 1916 the Essex War Agricultural Committee Census showed that only five of the 1914 tenants were still in possession of their farms.

W.O.N. Shaw's widow lived in the mansion during the 1914-18 war but it became a military hospital for wounded Belgian soldiers. After the war the house was systematically dismantled. Various embellishments such as the grand staircase, some stained glass windows and the impressive gates and fireplaces were sold off in 1920/1.

In 1925 the land and the lake in front of the old mansion was bought by Rev'd. Samuel Tilney, Alfred Lafontaine and Hugh Charrington, which Rev'd. Tilney developed as a holiday home for his parishioners from St Luke's, Victoria Docks. He built a timber bunk house, a dining hall and other brick buildings including a timber framed chapel, covered in canvas. In 1971 Canon (as he had become) Tilney gave the property to the Essex County Scout Council for use as a camping ground.

The Bramston had moved from the county to the south coast and Skreens was occupied by a succession of tenants one of which was Walter De Zoete who entertained 700 parishioners of Roxwell in 1902 with a dinner for 400 giving each man an ounce of tobacco. De Zoete left Skreens in 1908 and bought the Layer Marney Estate which, when it was sold by his widow in 1949, consisted of 912a. The majority of its surrounding acres were sold to private owners. Wick Farm was purchased by the Parker family from Lincolnshire who built up a farming empire towards the end of the century. The largest farm, Rockinghams, being sold to a builder from Hutton.

De Zoete's daughter married Charles Round from Birch Hall. At the 1949 sale the imposing eight storey tudor tower, the mansion and a small part of the estate was sold to Gerald Charrington of the brewing and coal factoring family. His son, Nicholas, developed a deer park and diversified into venison production, and corporate functions the mansion remained the family home.

Despite the breakup of Skreens and Felix four major estates were sold intact after the war. Amongst these was Braxted, with its 4 mile long brick wall surrounding the 500a park and built by the Du Cane family in 1833. Peter Du Cane, Coggeshall, bought the estate and adjoining Tollesbury Hall in 1751. The family became MPs for the county. Bought in 1923 by Sir Alan Clark, the founder of Plessey, the estate and the mansion

38 1950 Birch Hall. Built 1844. Demolished 1954.

continued to be the home of Sir Alan's son, Michael, and a nine hole golf course was constructed near the Lakes.

In the same year (1923) James Arthur Findlay, a leading Glasgow stockbroker, bought the Stansted Mountfichet Estate, (Stansted now better known as an airport), became chairman of the Essex County Council, and also Ayrshire, but was passionately interested in agriculture although his other penchant was psychical research, philosophy and religion. The mansion owned by the Fuller-Maitland family since the early 19th century was destroyed by fire and a new one, which took seven years to build, completed in 1875. When Findlay died in 1964 Stansted Hall was bequeathed to the Spiritualists National Union and renamed 'The Arthur Findlay College for the Advancement of Psychic Science'. The estate had covered 3,128a in 1873 although William Fuller-Maitland had 3841a in Brecon where he was the Member of Parliament.

The brewer, Charrington, bought Osea Island with the intention of creating a commune for reformed alcoholics. Henry Ford bought the 3,000a Boreham Estate which had been in the hands of the Tufnell-Tyrell family since the New Hall and Boreham House Estates had been split about 1800. Ford saw the large unkempt, derelict land and the magnificent Georgian mansion with its long lake. He thought it would be a good place to employ some of his Dagenham car workers in the off-season. Car manufacturing in those days being subject to considerable monthly fluctuations. He created Co-Partnership farms to manage the land. In 1946 the estate became a public company but Fords retained the mansion and surrounding land as a training school. The Boreham Estate was sold by

Co-Partnership farms in 1973, with 2,500a, to the insurance group Matthews Wrighton. Its subsidiary, Fountain Farming Ltd., changed the vegetable growing policy to dairying. It was not a successful transition and it was sold again in 1980. New Hall was purchased in 1799 by the Canonesses of the Holy Sepulchre and continued as a nunnery, and then a school for the the next two centuries.

The theme of philanthropy was evident in the story of Marks Hall. Tom Price a keen aboriculturist and, having bought the estate in 1897, decided by 1907 that Kew Gardens should be moved from the polluted atmosphere of London to the fresh untainted air of Coggeshall. He did not succeed during his lifetime but when he died in 1932 the estate was left to the Nation. The castleated mansion was to be the residence of the Director of Kew. He left his third wife an interest in the estate during her lifetime. A very much younger woman, she survived him by 33 years during which time American airmen had occupied the mansion house and left it in a condition of considerable disrepair.

When the Treasury finally accepted Tom Price's bequest the house had been demolished and the farms were in a neglected state. Mrs. Price had felled many of the massive oaks which the previous owners, the Honywood family, had preserved by forbidding any of their successors to fell timber, other than for the maintenance of the estate. A fire had destroyed Bouchiers Grange and the average rents being paid by the tenants were £1.50, when rents were about £3. There were 11 farms, but only six were self-sufficient, the remainder being farmed by neighbours.

39 Boreham House, the ancient seat of the Tufnell/Tyrell family bought by Henry Ford. Used as a Farm Institute then a Training Centre and later a private house again.

A Trust was set up, an arboretum was established, trustees such as Lord Braybrooke of Audley End and Robert Brice of Rivenhall were appointed. During the last quarter of the century some of the past glory of Marks Hall was restored.

There had always been an ebb and flow amongst the county families. Estates changed hands for the lack of an heir, a profligate owner, or mismanagement. To some extent, up to 1914, the nouveaux replaced them with industrial money to invest in respectability.

Before 1914 Sir Thomas Barrett-Lennard sold off his 2,124a Norfolk estate, his 570a in Suffolk and his vast, but unproductive, Irish estates of 8,027a although it produced an income of over £11,000 in 1873. He retained his Essex estate, Belhus. The Orsett estate disposed of 2,000a although the Thurrock portion remained mostly intact. Landowners, during the agricultural depression adopted a policy of expending large capital sums on their farms in the vain hope that with new barns, better drainage etc. the tenants could sustain the existing rent levels. Farming was not profitable enough to allow this policy to be successful. They also continued a lifestyle that was unsustainable. Mansions and extensive gardens were a heavy drain on the revenues.

Felice Spurrier, Lord Warwick's granddaughter of Easton Lodge wrote, "my grandparents' financial straits began before the turn of the century, and by 1919, the year I was born, they were at their lowest level. This was the year when a vast slice of the Easton Lodge estate, together with farmland, was put up for auction in a Bishop's Stortford salesroom...there was another sale in 1921 of lesser proportions".[3] Easton Lodge had covered 8,617a in 1973. Lord Verulam's Messing estate saw the rents reduced from £1,964 in 1869, almost at the peak of land values, to only £547 by 1889, a reduction of 65%. On the Terling estate the income in 1893 at £3,091 was 30% of what it had been 11 years earlier – but still the mystique of land ownership remained.

Between 1900-37 the top 12 estates in Essex were reduced to under 60% of their previous area.

The 19,000a Thorndon and Ingatestone estates of Lord Petre was reduced to about 3,000a largely as a result of the death during the First World War of the 16th Baron who died of wounds in 1915. At the end of the 20th century the Petre Estate was only about 5% of its size in the mid-18th century.

The Round family was particularly unfortunate. Rt.Hon. James Round MP died during the First World War and his son, Charles, died just after the Second World War, again when taxation was high. 2,667a were sold in 1917 and a further 600a in 1947/8 which included many properties in the centre of Colchester and the 85a of Beacon End and Cherrytree Farms at Stanway which was developed for housing in the 1970s/80s. Most of the farms were cashed at a time when owning land was unpopular and the value had not risen to the heights which it later achieved. Owners had little choice, but in retrospect they sold out too soon.

Also unfortunate was the Audley End Estate where the 7th Lord Braybrooke died in 1941 and his son was killed in action two years later. There was some alleviation for men killed on active service but in 1948 the Jacobean mansion was sold to the government and the family, who had owned 9,820a at Littleport and 3,691 in Berkshire reduced the estate to 7,000a which remained intact for the remainder of the century.

Pre-1914, aristocratic landowners were still buying more land. Lord Onslow bought 102a of the Tendring Hall Estate to add to his 1,500a which was adjoining. In 1910 he paid an average of £15 per acre. The remainder was sold to farmers. During the inter-war period 25% of the tenanted land on the major estates passed into the hands occupiers. No longer were estates bought in their entirety. The Berechurch been sold three times without breaking it up but in 1920 and again in 1929 and the farms were bought by farmers. Robert Lennox, a Scottish settler had acquired the tenancy of Wick Farm, Layer-de-la-Haye. He moved to a farm at Tollesbury but took the opportunity in 1921 to buy the Wick farm, which his descendants continued to occupy throughout the remainder of the century.

The post-war sales were precipitated by the withdrawal of government support and the lack of confidence in the future. They were also instigated by the enhanced value which land had acquired during the war-time prosperity. Authoritative figures [4] suggest that there was an increase from £24 per acre to £28pa. Essex sales do not correspond to these figures although the increase of £4pa is in line with the trend. The £10pa at Tendring in 1910 was reflected in the £14.71 (asking price) for the Virley Estate being sold by Sir William Abdy in 1921. The Abdy family, ensconced at Albyns, Stapleford Abbots and landowners in the county for 300 years decided to cash-in when it was reputed that one third of England was for sale. Many of the early post-war sales were not forced upon the owners. The Abdys sold Virley in 1921 but retained Albyns until 1925.

Other estates which were reduced or sold completely included Forest Hall Ongar, Warlies, Hallingbury, Stisted, Rainham, Gosfield and St Osyth Priory which although it had extensive manors before the dissolution they were widely distributed. Sir John Henry Johnson had acquired nearly 4,000a, with farmland spread along the coast as far as Walton-on-Naze. The Benyon De Beauvoir Estates in North and South Ockendon and Cranham extending to 3,438a in 1873 were sold to cover death duties in 1937. The Benyon family retained Englefield in Berkshire. The Essex estates were all sold to individual farmers.

Away from the purely agricultural areas of the county there was considerable activity along the Thames, and development on such estates as Belhus. The Burness estate at Tilbury, Mucking Hall, the Benyon estates. The Corringham land of Sir Clifford Cory became Coryton later Shellhaven. Cory was an entrepreneur involved in the petroleum industry. Mucking was owned by Sir Ebernezer Cox. There were buyers as well as sellers and Lord Cowdray, who as Sir Wheetman Pearson, had been the MP for Colchester, purchased 3,000a between Ockendon railway station and the Thames.

There were other buyers. The War Department had established a practice and testing range at South Shoebury in 1855. In 1900 they bought part of Foulness Island but the Lord of the Manor, Alan Finch, whose family had been in possession for more than 200 years, refused to sell the copyhold interests in the Sands. He died in 1914 and his half brother, Wilfred Henry Montgomery Finch, sold the Lordship to the W.D. in 1915. The Department had been purchasing farms, not within the Manor of Foulness, and by 1918 the island was owned by them with the exception of the church, rectory, mission hall and school. The W.D. were also active at Brentwood and South of Colchester where they acquired considerable land in Fingringhoe before 1914 and Langenhoe Lodge, which they bought in 1937.

Between the wars nine major estates were split up. Three more shed large portions of their lands. In total the major estates sold 43,000a but during the period from 1900/43 over 406,000a were transferred from landlords to farmers. Clearly the smaller gentry had also decided that owning farms was a bad investment.

Despite the diminution, life on the estates continued in its time honoured way until the Second World War. There was a reduction in the domestic staff but the tenants were invited to a Christmas sherry party, the parishioners to a summer garden party, the hounds met annually beneath the great porticoes and the squire regularly read the lesson in church. Three of the 42 mansions were demolished during this period; Skreens in 1920, Hallingbury Place 1922 and Gidea Hall 1930. Two were severely damanged by fire. Copped Hall, Epping was gutted in 1916 but the walls remained. Easton Lodge suffered a fire in February 1918 which was more damaging to the contents than the fabric. Lord Warwick moved to Devon. The house remained standing. Albyns was dismantled in the 1920s but not finally demolished until 1954.

Some stood unoccupied and others were occupied by tenants. In the 19th century many owners had been forced to economize by letting their mansions to suitably wealthy men, an oversized house was the greatest burden on the estate income.

There were 46 major mansions in the county, including nine that were later designated 'historic'. During the century 16 were pulled down, 15 were converted to other uses and 15 remained occupied as private houses. Amongst those demolished four succumbed before 1950 when the owners realised that the lifestyle had gone forever. The First World War proved to be a watershed. Staff to run the large houses were not so subservient. Many owners continued to live in mansions overlooking depleted acres until after 1945 when a Labour government under Essex MP Clement Attlee and the nationalisation of land hovered as an ogre in the background. The days of the large country houses as a dominating presence over its satellite villages, was over. There had been a clinging to past traditions until the Second World War.

Amongst those that found a new role, Wivenhoe Park became the University of Essex, Orsett Hall a hotel, Gosfield and Stisted Halls homes for the elderly, Audley End a museum, Thorndon Hall after considerable reconstruction became the centre of a golf course, Ingatestone Hall housed the Essex Records Office, Durward's Hall an antique centre and both Hylands and Danbury Palace were owned by the Essex County Council. Boreham House a Ford training centre, but in 1994 became a private residence again, Moynes Park, the home of Lord Ivor Mountbatten, a centre for corporate entertaining. These erstwhile 'seats', found a new role and in most cases were better maintained. Hylands had been bought by Chelmsford Council, remained empty, and was deteriorating until it was rescued by the ECC.

Among the other historic houses St Osyth Priory remained a private residence as did Hedingham Castle, Layer Marney Towers, Faulkbourne, Terling and Spains Hall Finchingfield. Holfield Grange Belchamp Walter, used for the TV series Lovejoy, Quendon Hall owned by shipping magnate Lord Inchcape but sold in 1980 with 2,502a to a consortium and farmed by a company known as Maces Farms. Blake Hall owned and occupied by the Capel-Cure family from the 19th century continued as the heart of its surrounding estate and Langleys descended in the Tufnell family. Braxted Park remained the centre of an estate. Copford Hall owned by the Harrison family for 200 years was sold to a Middle East purchaser although the hall had been occupied as flats whilst the owner lived partly in Australia and in another house in the village.

Birch Hall was demolished and the owner Col.Jimmy Round moved into a farm-house on the estate. Berechurch Hall remained for another 30 years when it was demolished and a block of flats erected on the site. Belhus was systematically

40 1908 Widford. Sir Daniel Fulthorpe Gooch at Hylands Park with his family. He bought the Estate from the Pryor family of Brewers and sold it to the Hanbury family of Brewers. His money came from railways. An explorer, he accompanied Sir Ernest Shackleton to the South Atlantic.

demolished, the park converted into a golf course and country park. The foundations of the house still provided a hazard for golfers. Belmont Castle, Stifford, and home of the Button family was pulled down in 1944.

After 120 years 98 of the 110 landowning families who held substantial estates in Essex had gone. Amongst the 12 survivors one family had their origins in the 16th Century, two in the 17th, six in the 18th and three in the 19th. F.M.L. Thompson said; "in Essex a quarter of the 102 identifiable families were of 19th century origins, but nearly half had made their appearance in the 18th century".[5] Thompson also concluded that one third of Essex landowners survived until 1952 "in possession of their country seats".

The turnover in property during the 20th century exceeded any previous period, with the exception of the Dissolution of the Monasteries. In previous activity ownership of the land had remained within a class barrier. The farmers, or husbandmen, were little more than peasants. The 20th century changed that image and the opportunity to buy their farms came, not so much from the disposal by traditional families, who had always ebbed and flowed, but from the lack of a significant entry by the middle ranking, later to become, gentry families. When land was a poor investment, yet offered a lifestyle which embraced political and social power, it was a powerful aphrodisiac. When these factors disappeared farmers faced little competition in the negotiation of the freehold rights to their farms.

The oldest continuous landowner was the Dean and Chapter of St Pauls who been granted Tillingham Hall by Ethelbert king of Kent pre-Norman conquest. They held this land for 1,000 years. Other owners included the New England Co. who, in 1711, were given Beckingham Manor, Tolleshunt Major to support the college of Cambridge in New England and two itinerant preachers. They held this historic manor continuously. The Glebe lands, small parcels in nearly every parish amounting to around 8,000a were progressively sold during and after the First World War. The Church Commissioners purchased the 2,600a Navestock estate which had been in the Waldegrave family, for three centuries until it was sold on the death of Lord Carlingford, the fourth husband of Francis, Countess of Waldegrave; when it reverted back to the family and after successive short term owners the C of E added this to their extensive farmlands throughout the country. Dudbrook, Lord Carlingford's home, became a hotel. Navestock Hall and 1,000a were let to the Parish family and Loft Hall to the Pryor family.

Institutional owners followed the fashion. Charterhouse which owned the Lordship of the Manor of Little Wigborough sold the property around the 1918 land sales boom. A later owner and chairman of EFU Victor Gray established, in the 1970s, his entitlement to the moorings at West Mersea used by yachtsmen. The evidence came from a deed in the archives of Charterhouse.

St John's Cambridge had estates at Rawreth, Ridgewell and Thorrington from the 16th century with Caius College Cambridge also a major land owner at Thorrington. Wadham, Oxford, had estates in Fryerning, Hockley, Walthamstow and Writtle. New College Oxford 2,128a in seven parishes mainly in the western side of the county. St Bartholemew's Hospital had 4,426a with 1,400a at Steeple and 1,225a at St Lawrence and Asheldham. Most of these farms were sold in the 1950/60s.

Tenants were able to buy their farms at heavily discounted rates, sometimes as little as £10 per acre. There was no security of tenure until the 1948 Act, but in 1919 Daisy Lady Warwick refused to evict her tenants. At the auction a farmer proposed a vote of thanks for giving them the opportunity to purchase. On the Benyon de Beaviour estate in 1937 the tenants were evicted and the land sold with vacant possession.

Tenants were generally reluctant buyers yet the swing was greater before 1940. Farmers owned 5% of the land in 1900 but by 1943 it had risen to 53%, a transference of 406,570a, the bulk being bought in the 1920s when farmland prices averaged £23pa. In the 30 years after 1940 the area owned by farmers increased by a further 9% and in the succeeding 27 years by another 6%. In the initial years the buyers were mainly the existing tenants, and in the latter period, such as the break up of the Orsett estate it was neighbouring farmers who were the purchasers.

The escalation of land prices vindicated them. A rent of £2pa became a mortgage payment of £4pa, which illustrated the low return which land owners were achieving. Farmers, although they complained, enjoyed being tenants. They had no capital requirements draining away their profits, or necessitating borrowings. Storm damage was repaired by the landlord, new barns were erected, farmhouse improvements effected. Tenants were cushioned from the responsibilities of ownership. During bad times rents

41 1912 The ancient Maynard estates were inherited by Daisy, Lady Warwick. Sales were being forced upon owners from 1900 onwards. What had been an 8,000a estate was progressively reduced to under 2000a.

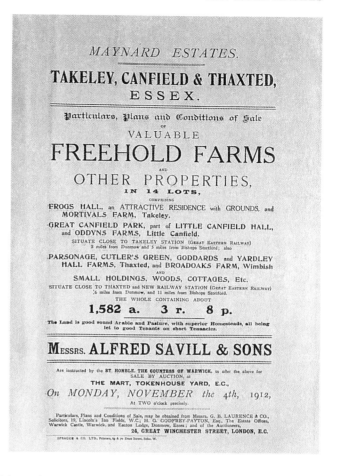

MAYNARD ESTATES.

TAKELEY, CANFIELD & THAXTED,
ESSEX.

Particulars, Plans and Conditions of Sale
OF
VALUABLE
FREEHOLD FARMS
AND
OTHER PROPERTIES,
IN 14 LOTS,
COMPRISING

FROGS HALL, an ATTRACTIVE RESIDENCE with GROUNDS, and MORTIVALS FARM, Takeley.

GREAT CANFIELD PARK, part of LITTLE CANFIELD HALL, and ODDYNS FARMS, Little Canfield.

SITUATE CLOSE TO TAKELEY STATION (GREAT EASTERN RAILWAY)
2 miles from Dunmow and 5 miles from Bishops Stortford; also

PARSONAGE, CUTLER'S GREEN, GODDARDS and YARDLEY HALL FARMS, Thaxted, and BROADOAKS FARM, Wimbish
AND
SMALL HOLDINGS, WOODS, COTTAGES, Etc.

SITUATE CLOSE TO THAXTED and NEW RAILWAY STATION (GREAT EASTERN RAILWAY)
6 miles from Dunmow, and 11 miles from Bishops Stortford.
THE WHOLE CONTAINING ABOUT
1,582 a.   3 r.   8 p.

The Land is good sound Arable and Pasture, with superior Homesteads, all being let to good Tenants on short Tenancies.

Messrs. ALFRED SAVILL & SONS

Are instructed by the RT. HONBLE. THE COUNTESS OF WARWICK, to offer the above for
SALE BY AUCTION, at
THE MART, TOKENHOUSE YARD, E.C.,
On MONDAY, NOVEMBER the 4th, 1912,
At TWO o'clock precisely.

Particulars, Plans and Conditions of Sale, may be obtained from Messrs. G. B. LAURENCE & CO.,
Solicitors, 19, Lincoln's Inn Fields, W.C.; H. G. GODFREY-PAYTON, Esq., The Estate Offices,
Warwick Castle, Warwick; and Easton Lodge, Dunmow, Essex; and of the Auctioneers,
24, GREAT WINCHESTER STREET, LONDON, E.C.

SPRAGUE & CO., LTD., Printers, &c &c Dean Street, Soho, W.

were reduced, and late, or mitigated payments were granted in a poor season. The mortgagees were not so accommodating.

The 'estate' looked after its people in a paternalistic manner. The constraints on over cropping, (not more than two white straw crops in a row) were normal husbandry rules. Crop damage by pheasants sometimes required compensation which had to be negotiated. The presence of the Hunt across the crops was suffered but it was a mark of the diplomacy of the Hunt officials that the sport continued after farmland had become fragmented. These small pin-pricks were traditional. The squire and his mansion was a focal point that was friendly if intrusive. Tenants did not like paying rent – but they knew they were well served by the system. The tenant sector did not disappear, it dropped from 95% to 32%, and these figures are conservative.

Many ostensibly tenanted farms were rented from other members of the family and scions of old families formed farming companies to rent farms from the 'estate', an amorphous body without personality. A genuine arms-length calculation of the tenanted sector revealed that it was as little as 5-10%. The main exceptions from this development were to be found on the larger and historic estates.

On Lord Petre's land in 1998 50% of the 3,000a was rented to three tenants. 50% was in-hand, direct farmed by contract. There had previously been 11 tenants and only 5-10% in-hand. On the Spains Hall estate of Sir John Ruggles-Brise 55% was tenanted, or 61% if the woodland is deducted. There were six tenant farmers, a direct farming operation of 735a and a forest nursery business taking 35a. At Audley End in 1980 55% of the land was tenanted. On the Prested Hall estate, 3,000a where in 1955 Nat Sherwood was farming 400a, 11 tenants disappeared and the in-hand farming operation grew to 2,500a.

It was the Terling estate of Lord Rayleigh which was preserved intact through two depressions when the Strutt family took over vacant farms themselves. It was an unusual departure – but it was salvation from break up. The 7,000a owned by the Rayleigh estates was rented to Lord Rayleigh's Farms Inc., which ostensibly transferred this land to the tenanted sector. Mitigation of heavy estate duty could be achieved by transferring assets into limited companies. The 1948 Act had created a two tier price structure for land, with inviolate tenanted property discounted by around 30% against vacant possession values.

As land ownership lost its popularity, there was a void in the number of potential purchasers. A new form of entrepreneurial farming empires arose. The Strutt family saw plummeting land prices as an opportunity to buy. Edward Strutt and Charles Parker a partner in Sparrow Tufnell & Co., Chelmsford bankers which also had another landowner, John Joliffe Tufnell of Langleys and Edward Strutt's father-in-law, decided to take advantage of these give-away bargains. Parker also had antecedents in the estate agency profession and with Strutt's farm management ideas they formed a unique, if unlikely, partnership. It was the founding of Strutt and Parker. Soon after 1900 Parker, who provided most of the money remarked; "I daren't go back to the office because I know Edward will have bought another farm"[6] and they had soon acquired nearly 7,000a which cost £10 66p per acre. "The farms varied in every way...some were suited to intensive arable cultivation, others adjoined or were on the Essex marshes and provided useful summer grazing. Potten and Wallasea were islands accessible only by water".[7] Strutt & Parker (Farms) Ltd. were eventually to build up a farming operation covering 18,000a, although not all in Essex. The property agency became a separate business.

Another Parker, no relation and from the Midlands, bought 5,285a in the county from 1952 onwards. They suffered a blow when they bought Wallasea 2,028a cultivatable acres in September 1952, and the East Coast flood inundated the whole island on 31st January 1953. The land was sterilised by salt. They went on to buy Heron Hall, Brentwood, (582a), Middlewick Southminister (1,312a) and Wick Farm, Layer Marney (347a) only a few yards from the historic Layer Marney Towers and Sherwins Great Wigborough (211a).

In 1876 Samuel Jonas, Chrishall Grange was farming 4,200a, had enlarged the fields so that the smallest was 60a, and some 400a. He had 100 labourers and 76 horses. This scale of Victorian farming in the county was unusual. In the 20th century it became a practical possibility with the advent of large machinery. At one time the Currie family had seven combines and farmed in several villages around Chelmsford.

CHAPTER 10

New Owners – Sky High Prices

A typical example was the transition of the Orsett estate into a farming empire. When Sir Francis Whitmore died in 1961 it was inherited by his son, Sir John, who was a racing driver. Despite a degree of diversification such as a fruit farm, the Orsett basket works, a clay extraction and gravel working enterprise, and a golf course. Land had been sold for housing, roads, dock and industrial uses. The estate was still run on traditional lines.

Building maintenance was carried out by an estate staff with a yard in the village. The cost was a heavy burden and at Orsett Hall itself the gardens were extensive. Sir John reduced them by two acres He pulled down the west wing, the stable, and the garage block. Taking enterprising tenant farmer Hew Watt into partnership in September 1964 they set about the task of bring the estate into the 20th century.

One thousand two hundred acres were drained, the average field size rose from 10a to 80/100a. Fifteen sets of farm buildings became redundant and seven of them were demolished. A new Estate Office was built and modernised equipment installed. The farm staff of 40 men was reduced to 11 and £93,650 was spent on the radical upheaval.

His enthusiasm waned, and it was the Cole family who launched into what was to become a 9,000a enterprise. James Cole rented Wickhouse Farm, Bulpham in 1856. His eldest son, Henry, farmed at West Tilbury and later at Stone Hall, Bulpham. Henry was an enterprising man with his own steam-ploughing tackle and around the turn of the century was cultivating 700a a season. He died in 1909 and his grandsons Alan and Robert, brought half the Orsett estate when Whitmore disbanded it in 1968.

During the pre-war period few traditional landowners involved themselves with commercial farming activities. The estate carpenter's yard cut down the mature timber for estate requirements. It was a proud boast that the barns had been built with timber grown on the estate. But it was more expensive than purchasing the ready-made article. The carpenter's yards were gradually closed down.

Amongst those few who involved themselves in commercial activities was Ernest Wythes, Copped Hall, Epping. The ancient home of the Conyers family which had been bought by Wythes' father in 1870. In 1924 he was actively promoting the 'Copped Hall Stud, Herds and Flocks'. They included shire stallions, Guernsey cows, three breeds of pigs, American bronze turkeys, Embden geese, various poultry breeds and White Runner ducks. Wythes' money came from railways but after 80 years, and a disastrous fire the 4,400a estate was sold in 1950 and purchased as an investment for a family trust whose beneficiary was a spinster. She left it to her nephew J.T.T. Fletcher.

From 1950 the number of tenants was reduced from 22 to 11 and the largest had 1,269a. With Copped Hall uninhabitable the land was gradually sold, with 1,000a on the market in 1992. Close to Epping this estate suffered the same fate of many others when the M25 motorway carved itself through the quiet valley. Harlow New Town was just over the hill and the church towers of Epping visible in the other direction. It also bordered Epping Forest.

In many areas the State took over the paternalistic role which the squires had previously practised. This was a feature of the 8,621a smallholdings estates created by the Essex County Council. As one landlord disappeared, another was created. The smallholdings estate was geographically dispersed over 31 parishes stretching across the county.

In addition 5,500a was purchased for country parks and open spaces as part of the green belt policy. Some of this land was let to farmers. The creation of the smallholdings estate followed the 1907 Act which was designed to provide the first rung on the ladder for budding farmers. It took over 60 years to abandon its founding principals, farmers who acquired a tenancy were settled for life. As a stepping stone it did not succeed but it did provide another potential purchaser for farmland that was difficult to sell, and it gave many families an opportunity for an independent, if not very prosperous, life. Between 1908-14, 3,109a were acquired.

There was an impetus to expand the estate for ex-servicemen after 1918 and by 1926 a further 3,947a had been bought. In 1924 the ECC advertised for applicants stating that the average size holding was 50a. They bought farms and subdivided them. There were also smaller holdings; "suitable for poultry rearing, fruit farms and market gardening. Applicants will have the advantage of a secure tenancy. The period during preference had been given to ex-servicemen has now expired. Applicants must possess practical knowledge, and sufficient capital".[1] (See also pps 198/199)

The following year the Beaumont Hall estate was purchased and carved off four holdings ranging from just under 20a to 73a. The 17th century house with four cottages and 354a was sold. 1,565a were bought. In the 1930s over 1,000a was sold for urban development and the remaining 8,620a was divided into 340 tenancies with the smallest, only five acres, devoted to horticulture. Of these tenancies only 76% were full-time. The initiation of the London green belt policy, originated from the London Society in 1931. The Green Belt Act was passed in 1938 and aimed at recreational facilities, whilst continuing the tradition of farming. Pre-war the E.C.C. bought the Havering estate, Boyles Court, Broadfields, Cranham. Codham Hall Great Warley. Lambourne Hall. part of the Belhus estate, and part of Lord Petre's Thorndon land. 3,530a of which a miniscule 31a were later sold, the remainder of the green belt land, 971a was purchased later, the largest purchase being 498a of the Averley estate.

Metropolitan land was already expensive. The Havering estate realised an average of £156 per acre, Lambourne Hall in 1938 £100pa. The Belhus land £83pa, and Weald Park £65pa. These prices at a time when a good farm could be bought for £25pa. The land for Abberton Reservoir was bought by the South Essex Waterworks Co. in 1935 for £30pa – when the going rate was £15. The E.C.C. later bought 3,112a for the creation of the South Woodham Ferrers comprehensive development area.

Another pre-war buyer was the Marconi Wireless Telegraph Ltd. which bought land at High Ongar. It was in this village that the London Co-operative Society Ltd. started their farming activities. They purchased Paslow Hall and Rookery Farm with others making a total of 5,000a they produced milk to supply their own customers. The involvement was an early example of vertical integration.

The second largest farming empire to be created in the 20th century was H.R.

42 Abbotts Hall, Gt. Wigborough. A sturdy Essex farmhouse with 16th century origins. Centre of a 800a estate. Home of ex-Ford chairman, Sir Leonard Crossland.

Philpot & Sons (Barleylands) Ltd., run by Peter Philpot. The family enterprise started in 1937 when they bought Potton Island from a cattle dealer. The Ministry of Defence compulsorily purchased it in 1954 but the Philpots remained tenants. They built up a land holding of 3,700a and with tenancies farmed 8,531a in the county with additional farms at Raydon in Suffolk. It was mainly purchased in the second half of the century. Barleylands in 1968, Boyton Hall, Roxwell, 967a in 1982 at a price of £2,016 an acre. By 1998 there were 16 forms of diversification including the Barleylands Museum opened in 1984, and two consecutive serial numbered Fowler steam engines from 1919.

These enterprises displayed the versatility which could be garnered to maximise income from multiple uses. The purity of farming, and resistance amongst both farmers and gentry was broken down, not by the decline in farming profitability, but by the necessity to finance the modernisation of farms. It followed the trail of prosperity – not depression.

With its long term benefits tree planting was the prerogative of the estates. Woodlands were normally retained under direct management for their sporting potential, and not included in farm tenancies. There were 33,000a of woods in 1900 and 16,460a in 1997. Despite public critisism of hedgerow removal. This was as illustrated by Samuel Jonas in the 19th century, nothing new. Field sizes always followed fashionable dictates. Most of the thorn hedges were the product of drainage attempts in the 19th century but woodlands were more ancient.

In the second half of the century there was an increasing interest in arboriculture. On Sir Richard Butler's Halstead estate 70,000 trees were planted between 1953-68. At Marks Hall the forestry commission replanted 350a from the mid-1950s. They were

111

coniferous, Corsican, Scots pine and larch. Only about 50a were planted with hardwoods. Towards the end of the century the old wartime bunkers were extant, but surrounded by maturing woodland – an inadvertent camouflage. At Bovingdon Hall and Fennes the Tabor family managed over 500a of mature rich woodland.

The Landowners Trade Union

Eight years after the Essex Farmers Union had been formed the Essex Branch of the Country Landowners Association came into existence. In 1921 it had 55 members. The elitism continued until the post-war prosperity, when the increased value of land convinced farmers, now landowners, that they needed another voice in addition to their own farmers' union. The peak of membership was achieved in 1975 when there were over 1,500 members.

It was originally an aristocratic circle and the first Essex president was Lord Lambourne who, as Col. Lockwood, was MP for Epping until he was raised to the peerage in 1917. Essex landowners for more than 400 years he owned the Bishop's Hall Estate. The first chairman was Sir Francis Whitmore.

The CLA created the Essex Land Use Study Group under the chairmanship of Charles Gooch, Wivenhoe Park. The objective of this study was to ensure that the Essex countryside remained a balanced and pleasant vista.

Democracy and egalitarianism took the place of estates when the CLA created an annual estate visit. The major estates were encompassed in the itinerary, but they also embraced such venues as Basildon New Town, the University of Essex, the grain terminal at Tilbury, Writtle College and Aggregate extraction.

The Land Price Boom

Farms were worth £21 per acre in 1900, and £2,500pa a century later. They had been worth over £50pa in the 1870s It was not until 1947 that level was reached again. In 1877 the Wethersfield estate fetched £55pa and Berechurch Hall £31pa. Great Burwood, Foulness sold for £28.52pa in 1858 and only £4.62pa in 1899. Wenlocks, a 221a Langham farm with a good house, was sold for £12,000 in 1872 but withdrawn at the highest bid of £5,860 in 1902. The harsh realities of economics were a more potent factor than the kudos which land ownership bestowed.

In 1902 Wivenhoe Park, the mansion and estate made £24pa, and a small farm at West Bergholt made £15pa. In 1910 Tendring Hall 703a was divided into 40 lots of which 20 did not reach the reserve price. The successful sales averaged £15pa. In 1914 Goldingham at Gestingthorpe was sold for £8,300 but in 1935 for £5,000. Sampford Hall was bought by Sir William Gilbey in 1910 for £11pa and sold three years later for £13pa.

Prices were moving up towards the First World War but were still below where they had been in 1900. In 1910 an Abberton farm with 97a was bought by a London vegetable merchant for £34pa. There was a considerable variation according to location, soil type, quality of the residence and Abberton Glebe was credited with 'considerable pleasure grounds', There was a short term boom which commenced in 1916 when the average, both vacant possession and tenanted showed an increase of £4pa. In 1921 Rye Farm at Layer-de-la-Haye made £25 and Wick Farm in the same village £26.53pa. Virley Hall, 1,746a in the same year, mainly tenanted and poorer quality land made £14.71. The inter-war period saw prices plummet. Bevingdon at Belchamp Otten was offered at £2.10p pa

By instructions from Miss METSON.

Mainly With Possession at Michaelmas Next.

Sale of IMPORTANT AGRICULTURAL PROPERTY, situate at

BROOMFIELD, ESSEX

About 2¼ miles distant from the Market and County Town of **CHELMSFORD.**

PARTICULARS AND CONDITIONS OF SALE
—— Of the Very Valuable, Highly Productive and Well Placed ——

Freehold Agricultural Property

KNOWN AS

"Broomfield Hall & New Barns Farm"

Possessing the combined qualities required for **DAIRYING AND CORN GROWING,** and in both respects undoubtedly one of the best Farms in the neighbourhood, having for many years past been successfully farmed by the late Samuel Metson, Esq., a leading Essex Agriculturist. It comprises

The historical Old Manor House known as "Broomfield Hall"

(Built in the 15th and 17th Centuries) containing EXCELLENT ACCOMMODATION and enjoying a picturesque position about 100 yards distant from the Church, with

PRETTY PLEASURE GARDEN.   GOOD VEGETABLE AND FRUIT GARDENS, ORCHARD, &c., OUTBUILDINGS, including GARAGE with accommodation for THREE CARS.

Ample and conveniently placed Farm Premises
Including Accommodation for 60 Cows).

FIVE CAPITAL COTTAGES
With Good Gardens, and the various

Enclosures of Rich Pasture and Productive Arable Land
The whole possessing an area of about

430a. 3r. 0p.

The Property has a FRONTAGE TO THE MAIN CHELMSFORD-BRAINTREE ROAD OF **1,500 FEET,** or thereabouts, and is ripe for development as a BUILDING ESTATE, whilst there is also an EXCELLENT BED OF GRAVEL in the Field which abuts upon the Road referred to.

MAIN WATER SUPPLY is laid on to the Farmhouse and Buildings.

WHICH WILL BE SOLD BY AUCTION BY

Messrs. Alfred Darby & Co.
(FRANK BURRELL, F.A.I., AND ALBERT W. CATON)

AT THE CORN EXCHANGE, CHELMSFORD,

ON FRIDAY, JUNE 24th, 1927, at 4 p.m.

Particulars and Conditions of Sale with Plan may be obtained of the Vendor's Solicitors, Messrs. HOLMES & HILLS, Bocking End, Braintree (Tel. No. 22), and of the Auctioneers, Chelmsford (Tel. No. 2).

43 Advertisement. Sale of agricultural property at Broomfield 1927.

but not sold and Hungry Hall, Pebmarsh unsold at £3pa. In 1930 the 1,200a Langenhoe Hall was sold for £4.50pa which included a considerable area of marshland. The same farm fetched £47pa for the upland arable land in 1958.

In 1936 a 43a farm, Kestons at Great Wigborough was sold for under £14pa, had spiralled to£93pa in 1946, £147pa only two years later and dropped back to £139pa in 1951. It was during the Second World War that prices came back to the level they had been 70 years earlier. Excellent farms with good soil such as Poplar Farm, Ramsey, made £50pa in 1943.

By 1950 55% of farmers owned their own farms, which covered 51% of the county. 46% of the farmland had been converted from the tenanted sector. This had been accomplished at prices under £57pa. It was a war-chest of security which was to prove of inestimable value as, during the coming years, farmers had to pay higher prices to annex a neighbour (which was a marked trend due to mechanisation and a squeeze on margins). From 1950 onwards 21% of the erstwhile tenanted land was transferred to owner occupation. By equalising earlier purchases, although this was not always the case, there was an economic argument for paying a continual spiral of increased prices. The first 50 years had seen prices rise nearly three fold.

The 51% of the land owner-occupied in 1941 increased to 68% in 1997. Thus only 17% was bought at escalating prices. Farmers sat on farmland that had been acquired before prices escalated. During the second half there was a considerable stabilization in occupancy. Farmers moved farm more often when they were tenants, but, with pride of ownership and the ability to annex neighbours the land market developed into a situation where, initially only 3% was sold annually, giving an average length of tenure of 33 years, dropping to 2% and by the 1990s only 1%, which ostensibly produced a longevity of 100 years for each family, in the same farm. Frustrated farmers without expansion prospects sold and moved. David Smith, Kentish Farm, Stisted moved to Scotland. The major reason for farms to come on the market was the lack of an heir.

In 1958 Abbotts Hall, Mistley, was sold by Stanley Webb, whose son had died prematurely, for £100pa, 600a of prime grade I land – and a bank base rate (as it was called) of 6%. The buyer was James Fairley, a Scots settler who had tenanted Stock Street Farm, Coggeshall, but had a large family of energetic sons. His ambition was to leave each of them with 300a. When he was killed in a harvest accident he had achieved this ambition. The £100 barrier was regarded with a solemn shaking of heads.

Within five years the price had doubled. The £200 mark was reached in 1963 and Colchester estate agent, Robert Wright, said it was "the biggest jump of all time",[2] and rubber wheeled tractors which could achieve 20mph were advanced as one reason how an enterprising farmer could expand his business. The following year Laurel Farm, Great Horkesley, made £253pa. The purchaser, Peter Rix, "will be farming 460 acres which must be considered a large unit".[3] and a farm at Rivenhall a similar figure. The purchasers, who were expansion-minded quickly sold off the farm houses and reduced the overall purchase price. The old-fashioned, semi-derelict, unmodernised farmhouses suddenly became, in the auctioneers jargon, 'a desirable residence with commanding views over unspoilt countryside'. The spread of commuter land with the electrification of the railway increased the length of its tentacles to the far reaches of the county.

Farmers were also finding that development land could put enhanced cash into their pockets, and the introduction of roll-over tax meant that the money could escape punitive

BRADWELL-ON-SEA & DENGIE
ESSEX.

Near the Market Town of Southminster, with Station on the L. & N.E.Rly., and about twenty miles from the County Town of Chelmsford and within easy reach of Burnham-on-Crouch.

Particulars, Plan and Conditions of Sale

OF THE

Two Valuable Freehold Mixed Farms

KNOWN AS

EAST HALL BRADWELL-ON-SEA

COMPRISING

357 ACRES

of which 94 acres are grass and 236 fertile arable land, including 50 acres laid down to Lucerne.

OLD FARM HOUSE (now Three Cottages) BAILIFF'S HOUSE and FOUR OTHER COTTAGES,

ALSO

EAST WARE, BUNGAYS & GAYNES FARMS, DENGIE

COMPRISING

304 ACRES

with 130 acres arable land, 106 acres Lucerne, and 51 acres Grass, and a very **VALUABLE ORCHARD** of about 16 acres.

FARM HOUSE (now Two Cottages) and THREE other COTTAGES

WITH POSSESSION AT MICHAELMAS NEXT.

MESSRS. KEMSLEY
(W. HUGH KEMSLEY, N. B. KEMSLEY, FRANK GAY).
IN CONJUNCTION WITH

ERNEST J. GALE

are instructed to Sell the above by Auction in Two Lots at

THE CORN EXCHANGE, CHELMSFORD,

ON FRIDAY, 2ND JULY, 1926,

at 4 p.m. precisely.

Solicitors: Messrs. F. H. BRIGHT & SONS, Maldon and Southminster, Essex.
Land Agents: Messrs. STRUTT & PARKER, 49 Russell Square, W.C.1, and Witham, Essex.
Auctioneers: Messrs. KEMSLEY, Broad Street House, E.C.2; and 33 South Street, Romford; and ERNEST J. GALE, Southminster, Essex.

44 Advertisement. Sale of farms at Bradwell-on-Sea 1926.

115

taxation – if it was re-invested in the business. There were many who could afford to out bid each other. House building land was now worth £2,000pa, gravel bearing up to £4,000pa and land near the metropolis £15,000pa. Coupled to the desire to increase the size of farm holdings it provided a powerful thrust to rising land values.

In 1939 there were 148 farms in Essex over 500a. In 1949 there were 174 and in 1962, 243 over this size. It was in the 1980/90s that there was an increase in the 1,000a club. Weathercock Farm, West Mersea, 150a of which some 10a were saltings made £256pa. The following year Long's Farm, Wormingford, made £367pa when two adjoining farmers bid against each other in an attempt to increase their farm size. Independent bidders had dropped out at £200pa.

A new record was set when J.M. Welch & Son of Dunmow in an auction at Chelmsford sold Shorts, Motts and Manns. High Easter. The 297a made £426pa. A 300a farm at Brocksted made £330pa and Horsefrith Park, Blackmore, made £385pa. When Horsefrith was sold again in 1973 it made £1,034pa and was bought by a farmer whose Springfield Farm had been taken for housing development. In 1968 Kingston, Lower House and Elms Farms at High Easter, 201a, realised a record breaking £462pa.

The Lord Lieutenant, Sir John Ruggles-Brise appealed to young farmers not to quit Essex for pastures new, although he quoted that in Australia land was £8pa. The Essex County Standard commented; "if I was a young hopeful I would not hesitate to leave a country where land has reached such out-of-reach prices, for somewhere where the pioneer spirit is needed."[4] The following year there were ominous clouds in the sky and land at over £300pa was labelled 'agricultural suicide'. By1979 the market had slowed down and there was a modest decline. It was short-lived, and as farmers hotly debated the prospects of Britain's entry into the EEC there was gloom amongst fruit farmers, but optimism from cereal growers. The net result was a resurgence of confidence – and it was reflected in land prices.

In 1972 Brooksmead Farm, Mundon, 113a, a Victorian farmhouse and traditional farm buildings went for £664pa. The EFU chairman, Alan Hunter, wrote; "it appears that farmland in Hertfordshire is now worth £1,000pa. Some people must be able to farm much more profitably than I, to justify these figures".[5] Farmers were aghast at the heady level of prices and Michael Wright, Colchester FU chairman pointed out that "in the 1960s it took a farmer about 10 years cropping to pay for the land but now it takes 30 years".[6] The ogre of Maplin becoming the third London airport was illustrative of the rapid pace of development which Essex was receiving. The fact that it was eventually Stansted Mountfitchet which was enlarged was irrelevant. The pressure on farmland from every direction, mainly non-agricultural, was forcing up the price. There was an increase of 18% that year. In 1974 Little Bentley Hall made £726pa. It had been sold for £8pa in 1930

Berwick Hall Estate was sold by the widow of Sir Leslie Plummer who had been responsible for the abortive African ground nuts scheme, for a price of £1,317pa. Holly Lodge, Lawford, in open auction in January 1973, made £1,240pa.

City investors were becoming interested. Matthew Wrighton (Land) Ltd. was an off shoot of a city based international insurance company. They formed a subsidiary, Fountain Farming Ltd., who bought the Boreham Co-Partnership farms, previously owned by Henry Ford, 2,400a for £840pa. The Pension Funds and other institutional buyers flocked to ensure that they had some farmland in their portfolio. Farmers complained that they were forcing up the price of land to levels which were uneconomic.

The £1,000 levels of 1972 plateaued in 1973 and dropped by 40% in 1974, and this was despite the increasing price of cereals which were enhancing farm incomes. The 1,200a Norwood Lodge, Weeley, was put on the market in 1974 but was not sold until the following year. It was bought by the Abbey Property Bond Fund at a price of £650pa. The Fund had bought 8,500a, mainly in the East Anglian region but the Weeley property was thier first, and only, foray into direct farming. They sold it 13 years later at a price of £1,755pa.

Prices were in the doldrums in the mid-70s when Copford Hall, 844a and owned by the Harrison family for nearly 300 years was offered, mainly tenanted farms where the tenant could not be dispossessed, for £420pa. It was not sold but three years later it found a buyer at £1,163pa. The new owners were of Middle Eastern extraction. In 1979 Essex rents were £5pa above the average for England and Wales, and the highest in the Eastern region. There had been a 20% increase in the previous two years but a tenant paying £20.44p would have faced a rent equivalent of £70pa if he had exchanged the tenancy for full ownership. The fact that established farmers had a nest egg purchased many years earlier gave them the opportunity to equalise an expensive addition.

Another newcomer appeared on the Essex scene. City bankers Kleinworth Benson bought Woodhouse, Great Horkesley, 443a for £1,000pa, which included 44a of pre-served woodland. They formed a farming subsidiary Hallsworth (Horkesley) Ltd. and the following year paid £1.12m for the 639a Fordham Hall – £1,752pa. It had previously been bought from the Gunary family by aggregates millionaire Tom Hunnable at a price of £400pa in 1969. In the space of nine years it had quadrupled.

In 1979 Blue Gate Hall, Great Bardfield(302a), made another record at a price of £2,140pa. It had been bought by an Australian Trust, E.J. & M. Davidson in 1938 for £14.50pa. Asked the Essex County Standard; "where, then, is the top in land values?"[7] and continued "does it make sense? Land values, even when they were £100pa 20 years ago did not make sense".

In 1978 Strutt & Parker partner Guy Lyster reported that there had been an increase in a single year, of £400pa. It took 66 years for the price rise from £21pa to £462pa. Now a rise of that magnitude was recorded in a single year. North Farm, East Mersea, 165a of accommodation land without house or buildings made £1,515pa. Mortgage rates were 12% and it represented a rent equivalent of £180pa. The buyer was a local farmer who had a caravan site on another farm. Fen Farm, Great Henny, was advertised at £1,270pa. Hunnable bought Dynes Hall with a mansion built in 1689 by a wealthy Coggeshall clothier, Mark Guyon.

But farmers were still lamenting the high prices.

"It is a sad fact that all owner-occupiers are vulnerable to a massive amount of additional tax which will be heaped upon their heads, calculated from figures which we have not been responsible in producing. It is the same land that it was 12 months ago, yet with the ravages of penal taxation, the burden today is far worse than it was one year ago".[8]

Later in 1979 609a of Ulting Hall was sold for a price of £2,068pa. Oak Farm, Woodham Walter, was withdrawn at £1,840pa and despite hesitation in the spiral Wiseman Bros., Stebbing and Saffron Walden paid £2,020pa for a 693a farm near Bury St Edmunds. Into the early '80s the Maldon estate of Sir Claude De Crepigny, 225a of woodland and 450a

THE SPORTING

Has been well preserved for many years past and the Estate is well known as one of the best shoots in the County.

THE AGRICULTURAL PORTION of the Estate

Comprises several **CHOICE FARMS** of Rich Pasture and sound Corn and Seed-growing Land with superior and picturesque **FARM HOUSES** and Homesteads let to good Tenants, and includes:

Allshot's Farm and Upney Wood ... 300 acres.	Monk's Farm ... 158 acres.
Scrips Farm ... 298 ,,	Porter's Farm ... 153 ,,
Clark's Farm ... 186 ,,	Bridgefoot Farm ... 106 ,,
Leapingwell's Farm 174 ,,	Church Hall Farm 82 ,,
The Park Farm ... 165 ,,	Pound Farm ... 64 ,,

Eight **SMALL HOLDINGS** of from 46 to 13 acres.

NINE ENCLOSURES OF

ACCOMMODATION GARDEN FIELDS,

Six Lots of MEADOW and PASTURE LANDS,

GARDEN ALLOTMENT FIELD of 40 Acres,

Adjoining the Railway Station and suitable for COMMERCIAL PURPOSES.

Houses and Cottages with Gardens, Building Sites,

THE WHOLE EXTENDING TO AN AREA of

2160 ACRES.

WHICH WILL BE SOLD BY PUBLIC AUCTION, BY

MESSRS. SURRIDGE & SON

At the PARISH HALL, KELVEDON;

On THURSDAY, JULY 10th, 1913,

45 *1913 Kelvedon. Felix Hall Estate being sold by the Trustees of Sir Thomas Charles Callis Western, Bart. Many of the purchasers settled for the century.*

46 1921. One of many Essex estates that were sold at this time. It was estimated that half of England was for sale. See page 42.

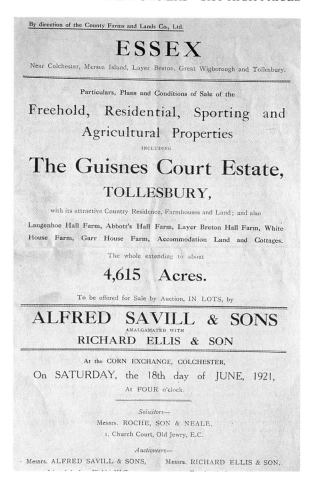

By direction of the County Farms and Lands Co., Ltd.

ESSEX

Near Colchester, Mersea Island, Layer Breton, Great Wigborough and Tollesbury.

Particulars, Plans and Conditions of Sale of the

Freehold, Residential, Sporting and Agricultural Properties

INCLUDING

The Guisnes Court Estate,

TOLLESBURY,

with its attractive Country Residence, Farmhouses and Land; and also

Langenhoe Hall Farm, Abbott's Hall Farm, Layer Breton Hall Farm, White House Farm, Garr House Farm, Accommodation Land and Cottages.

The whole extending to about

4,615 Acres.

To be offered for Sale by Auction, IN LOTS, by

ALFRED SAVILL & SONS
AMALGAMATED WITH
RICHARD ELLIS & SON

At the CORN EXCHANGE, COLCHESTER,

On SATURDAY, the 18th day of JUNE, 1921,

At FOUR o'clock.

Solicitors—
Messrs. ROCHE, SON & NEALE,
1, Church Court, Old Jewry, E.C.

Auctioneers—
Messrs. ALFRED SAVILL & SONS,   Messrs. RICHARD ELLIS & SON,

of grade II and III arable land made 1,851pa. Better grade land fetched higher prices. A small 55a farm Arbour, Fordham, made £3,009pa in 1983, Straits, Felsted, was sold by tender and realised in excess of £2,250 and £2,570 was paid for the 180a Hands Farm, Nr. Ingatestone in September 1982.

Newcomers who bought Essex farmland represented 15% of the purchases. 85% was still going into the hands of existing farmers. Amongst the newcomers was a Chinese mini-cab driver who paid £3,000pa for Bouchiers Hall, Aldham. The stability in land prices reduced the available quantity coming onto the market. In the first three months of 1984 only one third of the amount sold in the corresponding period was available. It was the lowest quantity for 11 years but one large estate was offered.

It was the 1,720 acre Old Hall, Tollesbury, and it was sold at an overall price of £1,020pa with the RSPB buying 750a of marshes to protect the birds. In 1984 average prices of Essex farms were £1,850pa. Lower than they were the previous year. Elbrook, Ingatestone, 141a of grade III land sold by auction and made £1,950. Howegreen Farm, 124a and a dairy farm near Chelmsford was withdrawn but sold privately.

In 1986 farm prices were tumbling. "The headling-hitting days of £3,000pa for top-flight farms is over, but it was only 10 years ago that goodish farms were making £500pa – and we thought they were dear!"[9]

Langford Hall with 569a, some land having been separated for gravel extraction, came on the market with an asking price of £2,548pa including a Georgian mansion, stables and paddocks a farmhouse and some modern farm building. The estate was owned by the Byron family for more than a century and it was 6th Lord Byron who was the poet. The 10th Lord Byron was vicar of Langford and until 1983 it was the home of Col. Geoffrey Byron who succeeded to the title on the death of his kinsman, who was an Australian sheep farmer.

By 1987 there had been a drop of 40% in prices since 1983 but Coggeshall Hall, Kelvedon, 310a made over its asking price of £2,520pa and Mike Shaw of Savills calculated that his firm sold 19 farms at an average price of £2,489pa. There was less confidence in farming prospects in 1988 but Covenbrook Hall, Stisted, 520a made over the £2,400pa asking price and Pleshey Grange, 710a around the same price. Abbey Life sold Norwood Lodge, Weeley, and the Prudential, with 7,000a of farmland in its portfolio, were the vendors of Kelvedon Hall.

In 1990 good farms were on the market at £2,000pa. 150a Holly Lodge, Great Horkesley, was split into five lots Farms such as 402a Dow Street,Finchingfield, and 295a Manor Farm, Great Holland, with Sherwins, Great Wigborough, were all sold at around these figures.

In 1992 prices had fallen. Ulting Hall, 458a, was on the market again having been purchased in 1979 by a private family Trust with other farms in the county, was offered at £1,100pa. "This may be optimistic", commented the Essex County Standard [10] and added "whatever Ulting Hall fetches it will only be half what it would have made five years ago". The Essex Wildlife Trust bought 600a of marshes at Tollesbury for a bargain price of £395pa. There was a revival in 1993 when prices rose by 10%. Set-aside had been introduced under the CAP rules and with 15% of their land taken out of production farmers were anxious to increase their holdings and maintain full employment for their machines and labour. Prices recovered but they only came back to the levels they had been in 1988, and still below the 1990 level.

Wormingford Grove, 773a, mainly Grade I loam over clay was valued at £2,800pa. A 28a Grade III field at White Colne was sold at around £2,850pa. By 1997 good farms had made over £3,000pa although a drop in wheat prices and uncertainty about the future put a brake onto further increases. In 1997/8 Strutt & Parker sold 415a Kentishes, Stisted, 601a Blue House, North Fambridge, 852a Warren Farm, Near Bishop's Stortford, and various smaller farms. Tim Fagan estimated that only 1% of the county farmland changed hands that year.

Before the end of the century the Pension Funds had nearly all withdrawn from farmland investment. They had been severely criticised for pushing up land values. Their withdrawal was an indication of their lack of confidence. The funds flowing from development added to the stability. The Fleming and Bucknell families benefited from development around Chelmsford, investing in farms at Blackmore and Saling, and Purleigh and Elmstead. At Shrub End the Barbour family benefited and David Barbour donated 160a for an archaeological park where a profusion of Roman artifacts were discovered. Others with money from gravel extraction, invested in farms. There was a small intrusion by pop stars and highly paid racing drivers Essex. They were more interested in the residence than the farmland.

The escalation of values brought into question the economic sense of land purchase. It rose from £21pa to £2,500pa. Deflation of the purchasing power of a pound, which dropped to only 2p between 1914/90 and increasing yields paint a different picture. In 1900 with wheat yields at 10cwts pa and £6 per ton it took seven years output to equal the cost of an acre. In 1950 with yields doubled and farmland up by 2.5 times, wheat up three fold, the value of an acre could be recouped, in turnover by three years' crops. In 1997 a market price of £2,500pa and a gross return of £400, which included a six fold yield increase in the century, and an element of subsidy payment, the equation reverted to 6.3 years, or very close to the calculation of 1900.

Relating farmland prices to the purchasing power of the pound, the equivalent price in 1900, taken at 1997 value of the pound, produces a price of £2,433pa. It dipped down to £1,378pa in the '20s, was back close to the earlier level in the '60s but with higher rates of inflation it should have been £5,795pa in 1990. Since such levels were not achieved it would appear that farmland was a better purchase in 1997 than it had been in 1900.

If the money to buy one acre in 1900 had been invested at compound interest it would have increased to a capital value of £10,160 in 1990. From this equation it appears that as a means of holding family money, the ownership of land was not the most advantageous. This was not the whole story as the benefits of a house and the income from the land has not been taken into account. Sources of benefit which would not have accrued if the money had been invested.

Using wheat as a yardstick is not the sole criteria but since it was the major crop in the county it is a barometer that is the most appropriate. Looked at conversely it took three tons to buy an acre in 1900 and 25 tons in 1997, but a six-fold increase in yield reduces this to just over four tons and by this measurement land was 30% dearer than a century earlier. The essential lesson from this multiplicity of calculations is that land at the end of the century, despite its apparent escalation, was only marginally more expensive than earlier.

The diminution, by 25% of the farmland area of the county, produced an effect on a commodity that would command a higher price because of its relative reduction. The other unseen value of 'paper-profit' was that it provided collateral for lenders. Bankers fuelled the rise in values more than pension funds and development sales. They were assured, not only of an increasing capital asset, but that the borrower would be able to service the loan. Farmers, when complaining that outside influences were forcing up values often forgot that their own farm was also increasing at the same time. Most did not want to part with it and thus the enhanced values were of little practical consideration.

CHAPTER 11

The County Show

The Essex Show was the great survivor of the century, when many other county shows lost their identity by amalgamation, the declining agricultural predominance and the extension of the Metropolitan Boroughs. Earlier Essex shows were held at Romford, the last in 1925 and six times in total, Brentwood (five), Harlow (four), Waltham Abbey (two), Ilford, Stratford and Ingatestone. Venues which later had little agricultural significance. The declining livestock removed an important sphere of interest.

In the last quarter of the century there was a lack of support from Essex farmers. They were not alone in this attitude. The vice-chairman of the Warwickshire show lamented[1]"the farmers of the county have let us down disgracefully". In Essex the counter attraction of the Young Farmers Rally, later relabelled "Country Day", the plethora of alternative 'spectacle entertainment'. The final of The European Cup match in 1996 clashed with the Essex Show. There was a boycott by many farm machinery firms due to tax changes. A series of mergers reduced the number of agricultural merchants and problems such as foot and mouth disease, swine vesicular disease and fowl pest which precluded many animals being exhibited.

The survival of the show was achieved by the tenacity of dedicated agriculturalists who were not averse to making sweeping changes. Opening the flood gates to the urban population the Essex Show became a shop window for the multifarious interests, not necessarily agricultural, of the whole county. It lost it's purism and was often denegrated as a second hand car dealers' lot. An unfair attribution. An urban majority on the Essex County Council gave qualified financial support to the Essex Agricultural Society in 1995.

There was a sharper social division amongst the attendance. Bowler hats, dark suits and lapel badges were de rigour for the stewards and officials and considered correct by agriculturalists. It was in contrast with the open neck shirts, jeans, trainers, casual dress and prams of the masses. The Essex retained the dignity and manners of the countryside, and perhaps an age that had passed. It looked out on a showground of multi-coloured mankind. The agricultural element declined.

The polite hand clapping from the grandstand was echoed by the raucous cheers of the farm workers on the terraces. A red rosette on the champion was an award that would be hotly debated afterwards as workers hoed distant fields whilst they argued vehemently, criticizing the judges decision, particularly if an animal from their own farm had not gained a prize. When the flood gates opened it was inevitable that the finer points of stockmanship would be of diminishing interest.

The County shows were led by the aristocracy and the gentry. The itinerant programme of visits by the Royal Family reinforced agricultural shows as part of the royal progress around the kingdom. Essex did not appear to be favoured when compared to Suffolk who received 19 royal visitors in the second half of the century. Essex hosted King George VI and Queen Elizabeth in 1948 at Orsett, later when Queen Elizabeth had

47 1948 Orsett. The Hall (top right) Essex Show.

become the Queen Mother she visited the show twice and HM The Queen spent a day at
Gt.Leighs in 1978. Princess Anne also came.

The presidency of the Essex Show, was more democratic than other county shows.
The first lady president took office in 1912, it took the Suffolk Show until 1959 to elect
a lady. There were 11 in Essex during the century and only three in Suffolk. A socialist
industrialist, Sir Valentine Crittall, later Lord Braintree was president in 1950. There was
a succession of non-agriculturalists; a brewer, the chairman of Fords, land agents and
politicians. The Roman Catholic Bishop of Brentwood. An immigrant farmer, J.R.Tinney,
was president in 1957 followed by leading freisian breeder Alec Steel, a Scottish settler,
in 1960. Prof. Mike Alder, Principal Writtle College. In 1998 The Suffolk Agricultural
Association appointed the county farmworkers leader as it's president in 1974. He
followed a baronet, and preceded a viscount.

The Essex Agricultural Society was formed in 1858 and the first show was held two
years later. The stimulus was provided by a surplus of £540 from the visit of the Royal
Show to Chelmsford in 1856. There had been many localized shows from earlier dates.
An Essex Society for the Encouragement of Agriculture and Industry was formed in
1793. The Orsett Agricultural Association and Labourers Friendly Society was founded
in 1840. A Dunmow Agricultural Society ploughing match with prizes for labourers and
servants. The Tendring Hundred Agricultural Association was holding an annual
ploughing match and sheep shearing competition in the 1840s. There were others that had
emanated from the Protection Societies which sprung up to campaign against the repeal
of the corn laws. Many of these succumbed during the extended depression after 1880.

There was a period of revival around 1900. The South East Essex in 1901, Ongar and

District 1908. Only two; Orsett and Tendring survived the century with an annual show on traditional lines. Others contented themselves with an annual ploughing match; Ongar and Rochford.

The first show at Chelmsford attracted an attendance of between 3/4,000. In the days before motorised transport visitors from far flung parts of the county could not go to the Show. The show had to go to them and by 1900 it had visited 19 Essex towns. Wrote John Walker,

> "By the early 1900s the pattern of the Essex Show was pretty well established. The farm horses on show were mainly Shires and Suffolks with Hunters, Hackneys, Cobs and Ponies and Turnouts in the Riding Classes. "Leaping over hurdles and water" had become one of the public attractions in the Grand Ring. The military bands played, and the Army provided a large part of the Grand Ring attractions with musical rides, tent-pegging displays etc."[2]

In the pre-1914 days the coming of the Essex Show was a mark of importance, it would bring trade during the show and boost to the local economy. It was unlikely that the show would return for several years. Of the six visits to Colchester in the century the average gap was 10.6 years. Chelmsford also with six visits achieved an average of 9.6 years but at Braintree there was 25 years between the 1913 and 1938 shows. Waltham Abbey 29 years between 1885 and 1914. The chances of farm workers going to the Essex Show were probably no more than 3/4 times in a lifetime. The Royal Show went to Ipswich in 1932 and for farm workers it was the spectacle of a lifetime. A giant tented city and a mind boggling profusion of pristine farm machinery. The animals were superb, even if the longest memories were of the hospitality of the corn merchants. The relative merits of one beer against another seemed to be as debatable as the championship rosettes. It was a highlight not to be missed.

A local fund was launched and in the late 19th century sums of £800 were being raised from local tradesmen as a welcome. The money was spent trying to make the showground facilities better than the previous year. After the show was over there was an auction of the timber used in the construction of the Grand Stand, railings, stock accommodation and signposts. Each year local builders built the show from nothing. These were problems that would manifest themselves after the Second World War. After the first show the attendance crept up to around 20,000 pre-1914. Five shows were missed in the First World War. Despite the depression in the 1920/30s, the figure in 1938 was 32,390. By this time motorised buses were bringing visitors from all over the county.

The Suffolk Show lagged behind the Essex, and in the post war era that trend continued. In the last 20 years of the century the farmer content of the Suffolk Show was greater than the Essex although the total attendance was normally higher unless inclement weather hit the show, as it often did – whilst the Suffolk traditionally, two weeks earlier, bathed in glorious sunshine. In 1995 Essex achieved an attendance of 70,000 but Suffolk was 16,000 higher. The highest Essex figure was 101,634 in 1989. When the Show was revived in 1946, in a memorable quagmire at Hylands Park Chelmsford, it was the first single day event for 79 years, it seemed that it would soon be repeating its pre-war triumphs. When the animals were all county-bred there were fewer problems than when professional breeders took their animals, particularly jumpers around the shows. It was a change of emphasis, from a competitive county spirit to a shop

48 1946. Another champion. C.H. Cobbald's 5 year old Red Poll with 4 rosettes.

window for a largely urban populace, but a publicity event for the farming industry. The Essex Show rose to this new challenge.

It retained its popularity amongst the farm workers. In the immediate aftermath of the war, petrol was still rationed, although it could be used for bone-fide agricultural purposes. Workers did not have their own cars. Coaches were laid on from almost every village. There were still nearly 30,000 farm workers and there was a representation from every village in the county. The first day was traditionally the farmers day, the prices were lowered for the second day which was frequented by the workers and their wives.

The machinery agents and corn merchants dispensed hospitality on their stands. The workers would be given invitations by their employers and would proudly present these. The standholders, particularly the machinery firms, were anxious to ingratiate themselves with the workers in persuading their employers about the merits of the tractors which they drove. The hospitality became more and more lavish, with sit-down 3/4 course lunches, as merchants vied with each other to provide a more sumptuous feast. When tax embargos were imposed on corporate entertaining, the standholders vanished. The excess of entertaining had been their own downfall.

During the war the show ceased but a nominal AGM was held. Col.Guy Blewitt, Boxted Hall, the Essex representative on the Council of the Royal Agricultural Society reported that the RASE were making suggestions for amalgamation of certain shows. The difficulties of exhibitors in attending was a primary reason. "If shows amalgamated, then local shows would be encouraged and made to attract entries from farmers".[3] Essex was adamantly against losing its county identity. There was only one possible amalgamation – with Suffolk.

There had been some mergers in the 1920/30s but the formation of the conglomerate "East of England", did not take place until 1967 when five, later seven, county and local shows merged. Forty years after the Essex/Suffolk merger was mooted the spectre was raised again when the EAS was in financial trouble. The ESSEX WEEKLY NEWS commented in 1944 'a combined show is a vision, the Essex Show is a reality'.[4]

The 1965 Budget introduced by the Chancellor of the Exchequer James Callaghan introduced harsher rules for corporate entertaining. Like many other legislative measures its repercussions extended far wider than its original target. It was costing a machinery dealer some £500; the site cost £150, marquee £50, catering bill nearly £100, additional expenditure for haulage and the involvement of staff. Corn merchants in 1965 estimated it was costing them between £750 and £1,000 for the two-day show. One dealer commented "we get plenty of visitors, but very few actual farmers".[5] Said another "the Essex has already turned into a good old show for townies. All we need now is beach balls and bingo!"[6] It was a commonly held view. The ESSEX COUNTY STANDARD commented,

> "the show has tried to change with a rapidly changing rural scene, it has tried to integrate itself with the modern society ideas of gimmicks, slick salesmanship, TV ad's and high pressure business activities. But has it succeeded?"[7]

The fall-out from Callaghan's budget was swift. Already at loggerheads over the rents the machinery and most of the corn merchants perfunctorily withdrew. The 1965 showground was a dismal spectacle of overgrown grass in vacant lots.

Doe's, the Ford agents and Eastern Tractors the Massey-Ferguson were the two largest machinery exhibitors at the show. At Birch in 1947 Doe's had a line-up of Fordson Major Tractors that was unsurpassed. "The farmer has only to blow his whistle and the machine arrives in his farm for a personal demonstration. Therefore he does not need the show as he used to".[8] When these two major companies withdrew from the Show the farmer interest waned. The conviviality of the show took a severe hit. The manufacturers were exhibiting at the Royal Show, 2/3 hours by car for Essex farmers, or the Smithfield Show in December. There were plenty of opportunities for farmers to keep abreast of new developments.

The E.A.S. attempted to retain interest with a composite exhibition of machinery treated as museum pieces rather than aggressive salesmanship. They paraded around the Grand Ring to the interest of the urban crowds – but not for the farmers. Doe's and Eastern Tractors returned to the Essex Show in 1978 but it was never on the lavish scale of the immediate post war period.

49 1948 Essex Show at Orsett. King George VI and Queen Elizabeth. Col. Guy Blewitt (left). Sir Francis Whitmore, Lord Lieutenant (Right) and a Guard of Honour by Land Girls.

Permanent Gt.Leighs Showground.

The Essex went 'permanent' in 1958 when the society purchased 158 acres of land at Gt.Leighs. Land, without a house or buildings, it cost £92 per acre. An additional £7,000 (half the purchase price of the freehold land) was spent in draining the site. An investment of £21,500 or £136 per acre. The site was not without controversy.

Just after the war, in 1948 J.H. Strutt had observed [9] that the rising expenditure of removing the whole show across the county every year was becoming a burden and that a permanent showground might be a better solution. The 1947 Show at Birch Park had left a profit of £5,700. At Orsett in 1948 with a record crowd of 57,000, encouraged by the visit of the King and Queen the profit was only £100 more. Expenses were rising fast. But the ESSEX COUNTY STANDARD noted,

> 'It would be a heavy price to pay for economy if the itinerant tradition had to be abandoned, for not only would the Essex Agricultural Society lose much in local interest (and in local funds) if it ceased paying local visits; the Show itself would lose the richness which comes from variety, different grounds lending diverse characters to the annual events. The compromise of alternating between, say, Colchester and Chelmsford seems to make as much of the worst as of the best of both worlds'.

50 Gt. Leighs. Dignitaries presented to H.M. The Queen by President Sir Richard Butler (L-R) Peter and Effie Frost, Henry and Tina Ritchie, Michael and Ingrid Bendix, Tommy and Janet Matthews.

The Essex Weekly News commented in similar fashion

'From Place To Place

The Society would be ill-advised to adopt this idea. Never has the show been held in the same place twice in succession, and the interest which the whole County takes in it is largely attributable to the yearly change of venue. The County Cricket Club have no reason to regret leaving Leyton and going from place to place. Their visits to various centres multiplied membership several times and were responsible for increased public interest.'

Apart from the economies of permanency there were benefits which a static showground might bring.

'Once laid out and properly planned, with water, telephone, electricity and roads an enormous yearly bill could be saved. Stand-holders could build attractive features such as gardens and trial plots. At present their efforts are at best artificial. A permanent showground is a sound project.'[10]

In 1954 Lt.Col. James Round suggested that Birch Park could be a permanent show-ground. It was an offer that was not accepted. The arguments, however, continued. "I am firmly of the opinion that a permanent showground for the Essex Show would be a bad thing", said James Thom.[11]

As the post war swing got under way other problems began to manifest themselves. The pre-war habit of selling off the timber after each Show was not viable when wood was licensed due to post-war shortages. In 1948 the Society purchased tubular steel framework for the cattle lines. They were covered with canvas for the period of the Show. Cover was essential. In 1951 some pigs died at the Stisted Show due to the heat. The other eternal problem was the unpredictability of mid-June weather. Finding a suitable site around the county became more and more difficult as grassland was ploughed up, mansion houses were demolished and generous squires were less prolific on the ground.

Essex was in the vanguard of this new philosophy. The Yorkshire Agricultural Society had gone permanent in 1951, the Royal Highland Show bought its site the same year as Essex but the Suffolk Show did not go permanent until 1960 and the Royal Show continued its royal progress around the country until it settled at Stoneleigh Abbey in 1963. There was an ambition to make the new permanent showground an agricultural centre for the county. It was hoped that Gt.Leighs would attract meetings, trial grounds, experimental plots, discussion groups and a range of other activities throughout the year, but without any permanent buildings winter meetings were not a proposition. Independent commercial companies such as Haslers at Dunmow and Kings at Coggeshall were already establishing their own trial grounds. But in 1966 there were still ambitions to widen the usage of the showground.

51 Gt.Leighs. Essex Show. H.M. The Queen presents the Jersey Championship cup. Robert Orr in centre.

Jack Pollard, show secretary, announced a programme of agricultural interest.

'Four acres had been devoted to arable crops. Comparative plots showed the control of blackgrass in winter wheat by chemical methods. Weed control in winter and spring beans would be illustrated on six plots, while three grassland plots showed the effects of applications of solid, anhydrous, and liquid nitrogenous fertilisers after mid-May mowing.Fisons, ICI, and British Sugar Corporation were presenting demonstrations'.[12]

Ten years later the showground had become a venue for Braintree Round Table Rally with steam engines and a two day festival of youth event. Plans to create a permanent equestrian centre were not passed by the local planning authority. The ambition to turn Gt.Leighs into a focal point of agricultural interest with the NFU and YFC county offices in permanent buildings other county organizations ensconced similarly – simply had not transpired. Far from becoming a thriving centre, it remained devoid of the permanent buildings which it had been hoped commercial companies would erect. The gaunt structure of the grandstand stood bleak, gazing at the placid sheep which grazed the ground for most of the year.

By the end of the '60s there was a marked decline in the cattle entries. From a peak of 700 cattle in 1962 there were 235 in 1969 and only 40 sheep. In 1966 there were 209 pigs in the breed classes compared with 245 the previous year. The Suffolk show showed a similar decline from 180 to 140. The signpost for the future was contained in the 1310 horses, which had risen from 832 in 1963. No longer the magnificent Suffolks and Shires but equestrian events now began to provide the bulk of the Grand Ring entertainment.

The cattle parade, usually at 3.00pm, still provided a spectacle with a ring full of animals and their white-coated attendants. There were the spectacles of free-fall parachutists, the musical troop of the RHA, the Royal Corps of Signals motor bike display team and sheep dog displays. Farming interest in the trade stands were supplanted by lorries and cars with a multitude of other non-rural interests. The flavour of the show was changing. The Ministry of Agriculture, in an economy drive, withdrew from every show in 1972. The multinational BOCM/Silcock Ltd. withdrew in 1973 and the few remaining local corn merchants turned their backs on a showground presence

In 1967 the Essex broke new ground again, and for the first time in its history, and the first county show in the country, it was held on a Friday/Saturday. Shows had always been mid-week, allowing for the stockmen to prepare their animals, transport them, let them settle down, sleep for two nights on the showground and be home by the weekend. A weekend show presented new problems and additional expenses which also had its repercussions upon the hundreds of other staff required. Yet it was not opposed.

The Essex Farmers Union, given the choice of adhering to the Wednesday/Thursday for the 1967 show or a three day show, a week later than the normal date, or a two day show on the Friday/Saturday agreed that it would be preferable to hold it on the Friday/Saturday "but that provision should be made for livestock to be moved out of the Show on the Friday night. If this were done it would still be necessary to organize some kind of livestock exhibits as the general public would expect to see farm livestock at the Essex Show".[13] In the event there was a record attendance of 59,000 at the 1967 show – but a loss of £1,738. The EAS annual report said "this is the first loss on the Show since 1959 but in view of the success in attracting so many new visitors, must be considered as

52 1946 Hylands Park Chelmsford. First Essex Show after the war. A downpour and mud were the outstanding memories. Lord Rayleigh's bull, Ageous, (Right) weighed just over a ton.

an investment for the future". Losses from the annual show were to become a regular feature of life in the future.

The Show attempted to woo back Essex farmers – but to little avail. Token exhibits about Essex farming were mounted but the EFU found difficulty finding volunteer farmers to form a rota. Sunday was added to the two-day fixture. It was not received with applause by the trade standholders. Those with an agricultural interest were now in a minority – but it did bring in the crowds. How could you advertise a "family show" when it was held during mid-week? By adding the Sunday the attendance figures went up to over 100,000 in 1988, yet the Show produced a deficit of £18,286. The EAS, with considerable boldness embarked on a grandoise scheme for increased income, and to fulfil one of the laudable ambitions when the showground had been purchased. It was to build a permanent pavilion that could be used throughout the year.

It cost £250,000 but the land which the Society owned had risen a hundred fold from its purchase 27 years earlier. An appeal was launched, the building was built – but only around £40,000 was contributed. The interest charges on this debt were eventually to create serious problems.

Selling The Showground.

One of the planning stipulations from the Braintree District Council precluded letting the pavilion to outside interests excepting on a restricted number of days. The ideal usage would have been for wedding receptions but it had no resident catering facilities. It became a ghostly pavilion for most of the year, used occasionally for county meetings but never achieving the focus of attention for which its sponsors had hoped.

In 1988 the Essex Farmers Union pulled out. It was the first time since the EFU had been founded in 1913 that they had not played a prominent part at the Show. The A12 had been progressively dualled and farmers from South Essex could travel to the Suffolk Show at Ipswich in an acceptable time. They would also find themselves rubbing shoulders with their neighbours. The Colchester branch of the EFU had their own stand at Ipswich in 1988. The Suffolk Show was thriving and expanding with 1,372 horses, cattle (437), sheep (272), pigs (38), goats (236) and trade stands (612). In that year they made a profit of 50,707.

In 1989 the EAS was in financial difficulties. The showground was a millstone that could not be cashed. Any sale with a reservation to continue the annual show would have severely undervalued the true potential of 158 acres, with gravel deposits in the north west corner of the ground. Selling would put the future of the Essex Show in jeopardy.

At this time the National Farmers Union was reorganizing itself. The Essex FU agreed to sell the half acre property which they owned in a prime position in Chelmsford. The money was reinvested in purchasing the showground. The EAS would still organize the annual show and would pay a rent of £20,000 per annum. The showground would revert to the NFU for 11 months of the year. The NFU paid £450,000, which was half the amount Agriculture House in New London Road fetched.

The NFU, like the EAS, remained optimistic that the pavilion and showground could be transformed into a centre for Essex farming. They budgeted for a income of £40,000 from hirings and the offices of the EAS would become the new office for E.F.U. and the Essex Young Farmers organizer who had an office in the Chelmsford building. It was the start of the dream that had inspired the founding fathers 32 years earlier. In the event they were ensconced in two temporary buildings.

When the show secretary, Geoffrey Banham, retired he was not replaced. Philip Shaw recently retired EFU county secretary for 21 years took on the responsibility in a part time role. The secretariat and the administration of the Essex Show was taken over by the East of England Agricultural Society in 1991 at Peterborough when Banham retired. In 1994 the Essex County Council agreed to underwrite losses up to £30,000 per year for two years. They were called upon for the full amount.

There were two very wet years in the 1990s when over 30,000 people were deterred from visiting the Show. These and other factors gave the Essex Show a tenuous existence. The EFU was also looking to capitalize its investment and in 1997 John Holmes, a keen equestrian eventer bought the showground almost overnight. With a new landlord the EAS looked forward to relaunching the new image Essex Show. In 1999 gave up the administration and Holmes took over completely.

The Essex Show at the end of the century bore little resemblance to life in 1900. The childhood description by N.V. Crisp from 1905 paints a different picture to what a school boy would write 95 years later.

> "I enjoyed every minute of my visit. Naturally the livestock, sheep dog trials and the jumping all had their thrills, but before leaving we had to make a tour of the Trade Stands. The suction gas engine was being shown and its possibilities for farm use expounded, the threshing machine with the compound steam engine, which I thought was a great improvement on my Grandfather's old barn thresher, the motive power of which was four horses. The Trade Stands seemed to me to consist of a small show of goods with a back room where farmers were induced to enter for refreshment, and then place orders for stuff which they might or might not require'.[14]

The small boy became M.D. of one of the largest grain merchants in the county – Brooks of Mistley.

CHAPTER 12

The Essex Farmers Union

The EFU was formed in 1913 at a meeting at the Saracen's Head in Chelmsford. There were already six branches in the county, Braintree, Chelmsford, Colchester, Dunmow, Ongar and Romford. They had been formed in an outburst of activity in 1912/3. Romford 3 April 1912, Braintree in May. The Colchester branch was founded at a meeting on 14 November 1912. A branch had been founded at Sudbury in July of that year which embraced Essex farmers from the Bulmer/Belchamp Walter area. The Chelmsford branch was founded in May 1913. The Romford, or South Essex Farmers Union, declined to join the county Union but became affiliated in 1919. The intransigence of Romford to co-operate was stimulated by a judgement in the Romford County Court. (Ellis v Banyard). Initially the Romford branch had been styled an; 'Essex Farmers Union'.

Richard Banyard, Little Nelmes Farm, Hornchurch, was a dairy farmer and when some of his cattle strayed onto the road he was summoned for injuries by the aggrieved party. Banyard lost the case and judgement was given against him for £75, damages and costs. The general effect of this legal ruling was that if a farmer's gate was found to be open, although there was no evidence by whom it had been left opened the negligence of the farmer and his workers was adjudged to be the cause of any complaint.

The case went to the King's Bench Division of the High Court, but two of the judges disagreed. By this time Banyard was receiving letters from various parts of England when farmers realised the consequences even if the gate had been left open by a stranger. In a subsequent judgement in the Appeal Court three judges unanimously reversed the original decision and entered judgement for Banyard, with costs. This was inappropriate as Ellis was listed as a 'domestic servant', and had no funds. Farmers in the Romford area were aghast at the original decision and despite the later reversal realised that a Farmers Union was vital to protect them against any future law suits of this nature. Farmers were worried that, as isolated individuals they had no resources to fight such actions. 150 farmers from a large area of Essex attended a meeting at Romford on 12 February 1912 which later formalised the new Farmers Union on 3 April.

The provisional committee was chaired by Edward Winmill and the following were elected:

R. Banyard, Hornchurch	V.E. Castellan, Romford
J.C. Cole, East Horndon	W.S. Eve, North Ockendon
JAS. Fowler, Romford	I.M. Gay, Romford
J.R. Hall, Orsett	F. Harris, Brentwood
C.W. Hawkins, Stanford-le-Hope	R. Hilliard, Chigwell
R. Mallinson, Harold Wood	R.A. Manning, South Ockendon
T.J. Mugleston, Stapleford Abbotts	C.D. Parrish, Dagenham
A. Saltwell, J.P., Romford	W.H. Stone, Rainham
G. Strant, Upminster	J.S. Vellacott, Upminster

The first county branch, Lincolnshire, was formed in 1904 and in 1908 a national federation was created. The NFU Mutual Insurance Society was launched in 1910 and was the principal means of financing the salaries of full-time secretaries. It was not going to be a hand-to-mouth existence. The bedrock of stability was laid.

Attempts had been made in the 19th century to persuade farmers that acting in unison could bring more rewards than acting independently. There was a movement around 1839 when the repeal of the Corn Laws was a matter of concern. The Essex Agricultural Protection Society was formed by Robert Baker of Writtle and William Fisher-Hobbs of Boxted was his leading supporter. It was a county-wide organisation and at a dinner at the Shire Hall in 1845 there were men from 53 parishes across the county. Other 'protection' societies sprung up, but when the Corn Laws were repealed in 1846 there was little these organisations could exert to justify their existence. Some became Agricultural Societies and organised ploughing matches or local shows. In 1858 the Essex Agricultural Society was formed but had no political agenda. A Chamber of Agriculture was formed in the depression after 1870, had a 20 year life but did not appear to have any clear objectives. An Essex and Suffolk Farmers Defence Association was formed in 1873 with the purpose of forming a united farmer-front against the labourers who had started to form their own Unions. It resulted in lock-outs but it was a short-lived battle and the ESFDA quickly disappeared.

Over 30 years later the NFU was born with an intention to promote the interests of farmers with a non-partisan approach. It was to create a 'union' of like-minded farmers which, with numerical strength could exert pressure on governments to alleviate the distress which had been prevalent for over 30 years.

At a formation of the Epping Agricultural Society in 1834, the rules were agreed "that at meetings of this Society no subject of a political nature should be discussed".[1] This sentiment was not carried into the new farmers union and it stuck to its lobbying policies thereafter, despite occasional ferments that the NFU should dabble in commercial activities. It only did this once, with the formation of the nation-wide 'NFU Seeds', with its own logo and based in Essex at Witham. It was not successful and was quickly wound up.

The NFU stood aloof from commercial activities although there was surreptitious support in organising buying groups. The NFU sympathised but did not overtly become involved. The non-involvement reserved the role of political lobbying to the Union, a role it filled with great distinction, much to the chagrin of other pressure groups in the UK. The NFU was always regarded as exemplary in its activities, and its results. These things were far from the minds of the early pre-1914 founders who were linking themselves together in a last ditch attempt to reverse a trend that had been ruinous.

> "Farmers organisation in the period before World War I was a very piecemeal affair...But until the outbreak of war there still existed in many counties local societies of farmers that had not federated with the Union, and there was in practice no body that could speak with one voice for the farmers of the country".[2]

Farming was prosperous during the war and new branches were formed. Southminster started in 1917 and in 1919 the South Essex Farmers Union (Romford) decided to join the now well established county federation. The following year George Raby, Tillingham

53 Essex Show at Harlow, 1923.

Hall, who was chairman from inauguration for 16 years until 1929, reported that new branches had been started at Maldon, Stansted, Halstead and Waltham Abbey. The membership rose from 1,000 in 1918 to 2,081 two years later. The income to support the Union was on a sound footing.

> "My father, George Smith of Great Burstead Grange Farm, had hired a farm for me from the estate of Lord Petre, and I took possession on 25 March 1919. My brother Arthur who farmed at Mountnessing looked after the farm for me until I arrived home (from service with the Essex Yeomanry). In April I was approached by Mr. J. Milbank of Ingatestone to join the Farmers Union and he collected my first sub of 10s.0d. which was for 120 acres".[3]

On the basis of 1d. per acre subscription the 1918 income of £547 represented 13,128 acres. In 1919 income had risen to £1,227 which equates to 29,448 acres or under 4% of the farmland in the county. The creation of new branches went on apace and by 1923 there were 17 with Colchester the largest (494 members) followed closely by Romford. Saffron Walden, the smallest, had only 11. The membership continued to rise. By 1923 it had grown to 2,562. The following year 3,739. It spiralled upwards reaching 3,813 in 1927, with a slight drop of 102 in 1928 although 195 new members had been enrolled from tenant farmers, many from the West Country, Lancashire and Scotland. A decade later in 1936 534 members were enrolled from amongst the newcomers. Colchester had 582 members and Saffron Walden had grown to 87. There were small branches at Great Yeldham and Thaxted but only just over 100 members.

The Great Yeldham branch brought the total to 18 and by 1927 the county structure was completed with 19 branches. The last to be founded was the Lea Valley Growers some of whose members were in Hertfordshire. In a post-war reorganisation Saffron

Walden left the county to become part of the Cambridgshire Farmers Union. In 1944 the small Waltham Abbey branch linked up with Epping. It had a membership of 38 and could not support an organisation of its own.

In 1944 membership topped 4,000 for the first time. In 1923, 309 farmers had been enrolled onto the executive committees of their local branches. They remained representative of farmers who were predominantly tenants. The involvement of the gentry was small. In 1923 less than 1% of the executive committee members came from the squirearchy. Charles Round, Colchester, James Tabor on the Rochford committee, one of only four JPs who were branch chairmen. Brig-Gen. R.B. Colvin MP was a member of the Epping committee and also president of Waltham Abbey. Miss Courtauld was president of the Halstead committee and had been a founder of Braintree branch. At a later date Charles Gooch, Wivenhoe Park was chairman of Colchester 1946/8.*

Amongst the early members John Garton, Hatfield Broad Oak was president of the National Farmers Union in 1929, Stanley Ratcliff was national president in 1933 and treasurer 1955/9 and Miss Courtauld's relation, Sir Richard Butler, was NFU president 1979/86. The numerical strength in the county can be seen in perspective by the following comparisons;

Kent	4,063	Hertfordhire	2,459
Essex	3,700	Cambridgeshire	1,600
Suffolk	2,945		

The Essex membership hovered just over the 4,000 mark until the early 1960s when, with the amalgamation of farms the number of farmers in the county dropped. In 1968 it was 2,814, the following year 105 members had gone. A report in 1969 said,

"A drop in membership is bound to be a continuing trend; amalgamation of farms accounts for a good deal of this loss... it is estimated that those farming approximately 85% of the agricultural land in Essex are members of the NFU. A further attempt is to be made in the coming year to enrol the remaining 15%".[4]

The trend of falling membership continued but the coverage of farmland remained high. Philip Shaw who was EFU secretary 1969/90 said,

"when I came here there were 2,700 members and when I retired 21 years later there were about 2,000 we had lost farmers but not land. The bulk were amalgamated and some new blood came in. We still had 95% of the farmland in the county farmed by our members".[5]

The NFU had two levels of activity. The first was its involvement with the annual Price Review, which from 1947/90 gave it a high profile. The second sphere was at the local level giving individual farmers assistance. These became more manifest, more complicated and more legalistic as the years progressed and the structure supporting and controlling agriculture became more complex. The NFU needed strong local branches where the salaries were sufficient to attract high calibre men who could, with occasional county assistance, suggest remedies for farmers' problems. The more difficult ones were referred to county level, and to London if necessary. The legal department became a very active one.

* See also page 97

It was also the system of financing itself which forced the smaller branches to amalgamate from 1965 onwards. The bulk of the secretaries' salaries were acquired from commissions of insurance policies executed through the NFU Mutual. A separate organisation but with crossover representation on both sides. The county secretaries survived on a modest salary.

I think mine was £350 a year when I started in Essex but a small part of the branch secretaries' commissions was earmarked to support the county HQ. We had 13 full-time staff but finding enough to pay them was never a problem. Essex farmers were always very conscious about insurance",

said Philip Shaw.[5]

From its formation in 1913 the EFU required a county secretary and an office. George Knowles was the first Hon. Secretary. He farmed at Lordships Farm, Writtle, now part of Writtle College, and the secretary's office was a small room in 17 Duke Street offered by Fred Taylor and Co. Knowles was the first County Branch Secretary but he was also a full time farmer, later moving to Stacey's, Broomfield. With the launching of new branches during the Great War and the increasing work load it was decided to appoint a full time secretary in 1918. The formation of this post was marked with bad luck. Leonard Fitch was appointed the first 'full-timer' but died in the influenza epidemic only a few weeks later. Walter Farthing stepped into a temporary position and later that year John

54 1948 Chelmsford Branch NFU Executive Committee. Outside the old County Offices King Edward Avenue.

55 1912 Romford. Calling farmers to unite. The first branch to be formed in the county was at Romford.

ESSEX FARMERS' UNION.

General Meeting

OF

MEMBERS, AND FARMERS

DESIROUS OF JOINING THE ABOVE-NAMED UNION

WILL BE HELD AT

The "White Hart" Hotel, Romford,

ON

WEDNESDAY, 3rd APRIL, 1912

At 3.30 p.m,

The Rt. Hon. LORD O'HAGAN

will take the Chair (pending the election of the President),
and will be supported by

Major F. H. D. C. WHITMORE, D.L., J.P. (President-Elect)

T. ATKINS, Esq., J.P,, C.C., AND OTHERS.

ALBERT H. SYMONS,

Hon. Sec.,

68 South Street, Romford.

55 1912 Romford. Calling farmers to unite. The first branch to be formed in the county was at Romford.

Gill was appointed. He was to hold this position for 19 years and in the period 1918/90 there were only three county secretaries. The appointment of Gill prompted a move by the county office from 17 Duke Street to Castledon Farm, Downham where he had a market garden farming operation. Miss E.C. Yeomans wrote; "The office looked out across the garden of the farm...the beauty of this was somewhat marred in my opinion by the farm bull, who on occasions seemed bent on showing me an even nearer cut across the fields". Executive and committee meetings were held in the Board Room of Chelmsford Corn Exchange. "Gill used to drive me over (from Downham) in his trap. I liked this. The trap was put up at the Saracen's Head, we lunched at Cannon's Old Restaurant in Duke Street".[6]

Branch secretaries throughout the county operated from a front room in their own homes. The larger branches rented offices such as Victoria Chambers close to Colchester

Town Hall. The EFU, at that time did not own any property of its own. The increase in the activities of the Union particularly for improvements in the farmers lot during the 1920s, and the implementation of policies in the 1930s, such as the formation of the MMB, and the administration of the new Wheat Production Act, as well as problems with tithes, and farm workers threatening to strike. The importance of unity was strengthened by an office in the heart of the county town. From an office in the Corn Exchange it moved in 1936 to 1 King Edward Avenue, now part of the County Hall complex. John Gill also fulfilled the dual role as secretary of the Essex Agricultural Society with the annual task of organising the Essex Show. He was chairman of the Essex Agricultural Education Committee and served on a variety of other bodies including organising help for the destitute poor of the east end of London. "It may be said that no good cause in what he always regarded as his native county failed to find a sympathetic and very capable helper"[7].

Ensconced at 1 King Edward Avenue it combined with a small office for the fledgling, Young Farmers organisation. John Gill laid one of the Foundation Stones at the new Institute of Agriculture at Writtle and Frances Dent laid another in 1938. It was Gill's last public appearance. He was succeeded by John Walker who remained as county secretary for 31 years. The organisation was growing and before the Second World War was over Leslie Clark was appointed horticultural secretary in 1944 and John Feltwell as poultry organiser. Twenty years later the office moved again. A property known as Brierley Place on New London Road, Chelmsford, with an acre of land was purchased and renamed 'Agriculture House'. It cost the County £12,750. 33 years later in 1989 it was valued at £1.2millions. Due to a property recession the eventual sum received was £900,000. It had proved a good investment for the EFU.

Additional accommodation was added and it became the county centre for the Young Farmers Clubs, Potato Marketing Board, NFU Mutual and Chelmsford Branch. When Essex was amalgamated into the Eastern Regional structure in 1989 the EFU, whilst making a contribution for the purchase of a regional HQ at Newmarket, jealously guarded the proceeds of the sale of Agriculture House as rightfully belonging to Essex. Half of it was invested, short term, in the purchase of the Great Leighs Showground but the rental showed a poor return and in 1997 the showground was sold and the capital returned to the trustees.

John Walker remained county secretary until 1968 and from January the following year Philip Shaw, a Yorkshire farmer's son who had considerable experience in NFU circles and had recently been county secretary for Surrey, was appointed to Essex. His tenure in the office was 21 years. He extended his working life to oversee the sale and reinvestment of the capital proceeds from the Chelmsford property.

There were only three county secretaries in 71 years and around the local branches long service was a hall mark. At Colchester there were only two secretaries in 62 years. Frank Folkard (1924-61) and Michael Pearce (1961-86) who was succeeded by his son David. At Braintree there were only two secretaries in 72 years. Percy Hasler served from 1922-64 to be followed by Malcolm Jones 1965-94.

The only other property owned by the EFU in the county was 'Agriculture House' on the Mile End Road in Colchester. It had been the office accommodation for Cant's Roses and was bought for £9,000 with a mortgage from the NFU Mutual in 1972. The mortgage was cleared and the freehold remained with the EFU.

56 Chelmsford Agriculture House which the Essex Farmers Union bought for £12.750 in 1956 and sold for £900,000 in 1989.

The EFU adopted a lobbying strategy in the second half of the century. They were against Hanningfield Reservoir, Stansted Airport, the extension of Witham and wherever there were threats to the rich farmland of the county the EFU, and the public face of John Walker, and later Philip Shaw, were prominent at public enquiries where they presented well constructed, and deeply researched documents and arguments. When members' interests were threatened the EFU took up the cudgels. When the last gap in the upgraded A12, the Chelmsford bypass, was completed the EFU had to fight hard to get payment for the land which had been compulsorily acquired by the Ministry of Transport. They adopted a close liaison with all the Essex MPs giving them a lunch once a year, usually at the Farmers Club in London which was within walking distance of the Palace of Westminster. Wrote Henry Ritchie about the 1977 meeting,

> "we entertained to a working lunch the Conservative Members. Of a possible 15 members who have constituencies in Essex, no fewer than 13 were able to accept our invitation. In fact, they out numbered our own delegation. On the second day [of the NFU annual London Conference] we had an equally good response from the Labour members and, of a possible nine in Essex, seven came along to meet us".[8]

The EFU found the MPs, even those without a single farm in their constituencies, were eager to learn about farmers' problems. Some were of a wider nature such as injustices under employment legislation and unfair tax concessions which were available to pension funds and were pushing up land prices.

At a lower level branches were encouraged, and successfully succeeded in maintaining close relationships with their local MPs inviting them to meetings once or twice a year and not always whinging about problems. The objective was to keep the MPs informed. The Executive Committee hotly debated the advent of Britain's entry into the EEC during the run-up period pre-1973. They organised demonstrations throughout the county in 1965 and 1970 when tractors, with suitable posters, paraded through the streets of Colchester and Chelmsford.*

In 1965 the NFU rallied farmers from throughout the county to an eve-of-poll Labour rally at Saffron Walden to confront the Minister of Agriculture, Fred Peart.

EFU organised Essex farmers who attended the Countryside protest when a quarter of a million country people, of all political shades, attended the great London March in 1998 and organised the bonfires which were lit on almost every farm at this protest against the insensitivity of a new government which appeared to be anti-farming.

Towards the end of the century the EFU were conscious that the farmers voice must be heard and spokesmen were deployed on the multitude of local radio stations which had swept the country. They also instituted and encouraged farm visits by school children, 'opinion formers' and local councillors, particularly those with planning interests, to give them a greater understanding of the problems of the farming industry.

The first to amalgamate were Great Yeldham and Halstead in 1955 and later joined Braintree. With hindsight the prolification of small branches throughout the county was necessary in the days before the roads had been improved, or cars became an essential part of life. Farmers did not want to travel long distances at night after a hard day on their farms. Easier transport facilitated the amalgamation of branches without opposition. The Maldon and Southminster branches amalgamated and then joined up with Chelmsford. Epping, Ongar and Harlow came together to form South West Essex. Stansted, Dunmow and Thaxted – North West Essex; and South East Essex and Wickford covered an area from Rochford right across the southern swarth of the county to Epping including Brentwood.

By 1998 there were six branches in the county, with the addition of the Lea Valley growers, They were reminiscent of the same number that had formed the County Union in 1913. The EFU had ceased to exist by this time. The requirements of specialised experts had forced the NFU, nationwide to adopt a policy of regionalisation. It stemmed from a study in 1971. Some counties quickly joined their neighbours. Essex stuck out for independence. With a substantial membership it was able to maintain its identity until 1990 when it became part of an eastern region embracing seven counties. There was no longer an office in Essex. The impressive Agriculture House at Chelmsford was replaced by a portacabin on the Great Leighs show ground. There was no longer a county secretary, but a 'Regional Director'. The office was first at Ely and later into a newly built Agriculture House at Newmarket.

The Essex Farmers Journal was born in 1922 and had gone through its difficult times. "All the advertisements in the first number were given away to advertisers to bring the paper to their notice. And they did notice it, and it succeeded"[9] In 1973 Essex joined an 18 county company called NFU County Publications Ltd. which gave umbrella assistance from professionals to help county journals survive in difficult times.

* See also pages 282/3

Perhaps the greatest cause for pride in the EFU story of the 20th century was the magnificent response to the wartime Red Cross Sales. It was a glorious chapter in its history.* See page 79

CHAIRMEN
ESSEX FARMERS UNION

1913-1929	George Raby	1971-1972	Peter Frost
1930-1938	John Garton	1973-1974	Alan Hunter
1938-1945	Hollis Clayton	1974-1976	Peter Philpot
1946-1949	David Gemmill	1976-1978	Henry Ritchie
1950-1951	Herbert Hayward	1978-1979	Tony Bosworth
1952-1953	Ralph Sadler	1980-1981	Peter Holmes
1954-1955	Pendril Bentall	1982-1983	Richard Matthews
1956-1957	Harold Philpot	1984-1985	Robert McTurk
1958-1959	Robert Padfield	1986-1987	Richard Carter
1960-1961	Horace Juniper	1988-1989	Tom Howie
1962-1963	John Hawkes	1990-1991	Jim Padfield
1964-1965	Gerald Curtis	1992-1993	Tony Evans
1966-1967	Victor Gray	1994-1995	James Padfield
1968-1970	Robert Percy	1996-1997	Dan Squier
	1998-1999	Jonathan Dixon-Smith	

COUNTY SECRETARIES

1913-1918	George Knowles	1918-1937	John Gill
1918 (Died)	Leonard Fitch	1938-1967	John Walker
1918 (Temp)	Walter Farthing	1968-1989	Philip Shaw

CHAPTER 13

Essex Young Farmers

The impetus for Young Farmers Clubs came from the USA encouraged by Lord Northcliffe, owner of the Daily Mail who thought the American 4H clubs could have a British counterpart. The first club in the UK was founded at Hemyock, Devon in 1921. In 1925 Henry Phillips who was farm bailiff to John Balfour at Mayfield Farm, Harlow, was optimistic that with the backing of the Ministry "we may be able to start a few clubs in Essex"[1]. Five years later, in November 1930, J.C. Leslie principal of the Institute of Agriculture voiced his disappointment.

"It is an alarming fact that there is not a single Young Farmers Club in the county of Essex...membership is not confined...it does not matter whether they may be the sons or daughters of a farm labourer or of a country squire. The Young Farmers Club movement recognises neither class distinction nor creed and is open to everyone".[2]

The first YFC in Essex was started a few months later. "Most young people keep pets of some kind, either rabbits or poultry, and one of the chief aims of these Clubs is to stimulate the interest in the care and management of such livestock" was the principle outlined by the North West Essex District Agricultural Organiser, R.P.Hawkins.

They were known initially as 'Calf Clubs', and the rearing of young stock was their prime activity. The impetus came through the Agricultural Education Committee and was under the aegis of the Institute of Agriculture. The Essex County Council regarded these clubs as part of the educational system. In 1930 the EFU appealed to public spirited people who would lend money, free of interest to help start up a Young Farmers Club in their district.

The money was required to purchase young stock, and to ensure that the proper rules of livestock husbandry were observed. The young people were given advice and allowed to elect their own officers. It was a rule, however, that a member must keep an animal. Records of feeding etc. were to be kept and when the animals were ready for market they were to be sent to a local auction to be judged before they were sold. There would be prizes for the winners and the return from the sale would repay the promoter and the profit would go to the member.

The criteria was wider in Essex and J.C. Leslie outlined the qualifications for membership as; "looking after something that lives and grows. It may be an animal such as a calf, a pig, a hen or a rabbit, or it may be an allotment or a few fruit trees".[2] In reality nearly 100% of the members did keep livestock – and they were nearly all farmers' sons and daughters. In some clubs one tenth of the profit was paid into the Club funds.

Soon after J.C. Leslie said; "this is a state of affairs which much soon be remedied", the formation of Clubs throughout the county commenced. The wave of enthusiasm was not as widespread as its sponsors hoped. There were only three Clubs formed in the county in 1931. It would seem that Finchingfield and Thaxted could jointly claim the honour of being the first. The Great Bentley Club was formed the following month. The Clubs were firmly under the wing of their elders. Great Bentley had a farmer as its president and the District Agricultural Organiser as its leader.

Within a month they had decided to purchase 10 heifer calves, "these have been ordered and are expected any day".[3] Fired with enthusiasm they asked the Tendring Hundred Farmers Club to create a special class at the annual show. "We look forward with interest to see the youngsters parading their animals in the ring"[3] and two months later the EFJ said "the owners of calves are occupied in getting their animals fit for the show-ring, and there is every prospect of keen competition. It is unfortunate that owing to the difficulty of obtaining good Shorthorn heifers, a few of the boys are still without them".[4] The emphasis on boys was misplaced when the first prize at the Tendring Show went to Elmstead Market farmer's daughter Mary Pryke with "Frosty". Vivienne Pryke got third prize with "Babs". The influence and participation of the girls had not been foreseen, although few became club chairmen in the early days.

The spread of clubs was tentative. They flourished in the Colchester and Tendring areas where in 1932 six of the ten were located. Ralph Sadler DAO for South Essex said "visitors to the Essex Show at Colchester will, it is hoped, see a string of beautiful Shorthorn heifers, the property of the Great Bentley Calf Club. It is a matter of deep regret to me that not a single club has been started in the south of the county.[5]

A club was started at Wickford County School in March but it was October before one was launched at Southminster. There was a club at Kelvedon and one at Dunmow Council School. There were main clubs and school clubs and in the Essex returns the numbers were kept separately. The clubs formed in 1932 in the north east corner of the

57 Young farmers, Ralph Sadler, Hugh Hawkins and Brian Carter

county were: Old Heath, (Colchester) Ardleigh and Bromley in February, Langham and Boxted in March and Tendring in October. Another club at Shrub End (Colchester) was formed in late 1932 but its exact inauguration is obscure. By May 1933 there were 11 clubs with 200 members.

Clubs decided what sort of stock they wanted to keep. At Finchingfield and Thaxted in 1931 the members decided to start with a sitting of eggs and a broody hen although many decided to start with day old chicks. Some wanted to keep pigs but those without accommodation undertook to cultivate a small allotment.

The Dunmow club was entirely a poultry club. In its first year the Thaxted club had only eight members, five kept poultry and three kept pigs. There were lessons in economics to be learnt by the fledgling farmers. The hens did well and each one reared five/six pullets. The cocks were sold and the club was repaid for the initial outlay. The pigs, on the other hand, had been bought when prices were high – and sold when they were low. They showed a small margin but it was a marginal margin. The young farmers had to learn the harsh facts of farming life in the '30s.

The common mode of transport was a bicycle and for this reason clubs sprang up in adjoining villages. Great Bentley, Wix and Tendring all adjoining parishes. One at Bromley completed a link-up with the clutch of clubs in the centre of the Tendring Hundred. Wix was formed on 29 September 1933 and Tendring merged with it in 1935. Great Bentley, one of the first three to have been formed in the county merged during the war. The Shrub End club closed in October 1936 and although a club was formed at Tolleshunt D'Arcy in May 1936, and had 14 members, it had a short life and despite attempts to form clubs at Peldon, Berechurch and Bures, these were not pursued. There was a very heavy concentration of clubs in the north east corner of Essex.

Goodmayes was formed on 4 May 1933 with an emphasis upon allotment keeping. A year later it was recorded "that there is hardly a club in the county, carrying on against more difficulties than this club at Goodmayes. Opportunities for stock keeping are practically nil, the allotment worked by the members last year was small and not on the best land".[6] They did start an amateur magazine. In 1936 Goodmayes members had given up the allotment ground and decided to carry on in their own gardens. "A competitive show of members stock seems out of the question",but later that year they entered some poultry for the local horticultural show and the comment was made "the variety and numbers of livestock that can be kept in an ordinary garden is really amazing".

Whilst Goodmayes in metropolitan Essex managed a tenuous survival there were more new clubs, Chelmsford, Shalford (1934), Great Yeldham (1935) were but a small proportion of the potential.

Showing the animals was as important as making a profit when they were sold. Great Bentley YFC had Shorthorn yearling heifers at the Essex Show in 1932 and the following year there were classes for Essex Young Farmers with heifer calves under 9 months, and those 9/18 months. At the Braintree Agricultural Show in 1934 Shalford club exhibited Aberdeen Angus Cross and Red Poll heifers. Thaxted had six Shorthorns but Kelvedon had broken new ground.

"The Kelvedon Club was the first in the County to keep beef calves, and the first two were sold at Witham. They were reared together by Lilian Harvey and her brother Thomas. The calves arrived on 5 April 1933, and were weaned on 48 gallons of new milk, a dry meal mixture being fed as soon as possible: the mixture used was as follows: equal parts of the following – linseed 'cake', crushed oats, maize meal, bran and fish meal. The cost of the ration worked out at 9s.4d per cwt., the mixture being made on the farm. In July the cost dropped to 8s.3d, while in March 1934, the fish meal was omitted, reducing the cost to 7s.9d per cwt. The following is an extract from Tom's book:– "I have omitted fish meal from my calf meal this month as I hope to make him into a baby beef animal, and by cutting out high protein food from the ration I hope he will stop growing so fast and put on more flesh.

These calves were on view at the County Rally and at the Braintree Show, in each case Lilian's heifer 'May' won first prize and Tom's steer 'Archie' second.

Charging a shilling per gallon for the milk and 3s.0 a cwt.for hay, the total rearing cost of these animals to the date of sale was 16 18s. 0d. An extract from Lilian's book states:- "My father gives me the straw for litter in exchange for the dung!"

These animals were sold at rather less than 15 months of age and weighed over 7.5 cwt. The price realised in the open market, one of the animals being bought by a butcher, was £17 5s. 0d. a head, a profit of 7s.0d" (35p).[9]

The young farmers movement was still firmly under the wing of the educational section of the County Council. An out of doors activity that was encouraged – with strings. It was led by lecturers from the Institute of Agriculture and there remained an attitude of teachers and pupils which perpetuated into the 1950s.

Following the prolification of clubs in 1932/3 it was decided to form a County Committee; it was de facto, the first County Rally. The morning consisted of a resolution to form a county structure, a tour of the dairy, chemistry, bacteriology and botony departments then the poultry station in Beehive Lane, and a picnic lunch. Afterwards the events followed the typical pattern of a school sports day.

Young farmers were not allowed to run their own affairs. The constitution suggested 10 members representing various official bodies, 11 were from the advisory committee established farmers, and out of 32 members only 11 were club members.

The role and attitude which a young farmer should adopt was outlined by J.C. Leslie in 1936. "The time has not yet arrived – though it is coming quite rapidly – when every farmer's son considers it part of the normal training of his life to attend one of these organised day classes, or to become a student at the Institute.[10]

At the end of the war the Young Farmers Clubs in the county presented a different picture. Many of the small village clubs had disappeared. The YF rules stipulated an age range of 14–25 years. Many of the older ones served in the forces. Feedstuff rationing curbed livestock keeping and of necessity the activities were scaled down. In 1939 the Board of Education recognised Clubs in a circular entitled 'Service of Youth'. It was estimated that the national membership was 15,000. By 1945 the figure was 60,000, a 400% increase, and the same pattern applied in Essex.

A new club was formed at Ongar in 1941 and within a few months had attracted a membership of over 100 with an average attendance of 80. Two divisions were created in the Ongar club, both organised by the Education Committee of the Essex County Council. One evening a week was devoted to a class on agricultural engineering and

58 YFs were known as 'Calf Clubs'. Joan Garner, Wix YFC

another to 'dramatics'. The Education Department appealed to the EFU asking them to find suitable leaders to start Young Farmers Clubs. Three organisers were appointed from the Institute of Agriculture. The County Organiser was Dr. F.E. Kenchington. David Ewing, who had replaced J.C. Leslie was county president.

A county 'Federation' was constituted in 1944.[11] There were 13 active clubs and 31 a year later. Twenty of them 'senior' and 11 school clubs. Five others had started "but they are not yet on active service. This is good progress."[12] A county rally took place during wartime in 1944 and in 1945 it was estimated that there were 1,300 members in Essex. In the immediate post-war period there were School Clubs formed at East Ward, Colchester, Ongar Secondary Modern, Brightlingsea Secondary, Felsted, Ashdon School, the Bachad Farm Institute and Henry Ford Institute. During the last half of the century the School Clubs had an average of 25% of the county membership.

The Young Farmer of the post-war period was a very different animal. Farmers had made money during the war and they wanted to return to happier times. Many farmers' sons had cars of their own for the first time. Petrol was rationed but farmers had a generous allowance, and attendance at a YF meeting was a bona fide excuse. There was more money and a greater sense of fun. The pre-war movement had been a very serious organisation. A lightness of touch ran side-by-side with the serious business of stock judging and technical talks.

An annual public speaking competition was organised. Inarticulateness in the pre-war period had been partly blamed for the lack of conviction with which farmers had put their case. Bringing up a new generation with public speaking prowess was vital.

The doors were opened to non-farming members. Robert McTurk of Brentwood, county chairman said, "try and get members from the towns to join your club. Both the townsman and countryman can benefit from each other's views and company. This will also foster a better understanding between town and country people which is so badly needed".[13] McTurk was the first Young Farmer to become Chairman of the Federation. The president and a majority of the County Executive Committee consisted of older people.

There were still clubs in villages such as Great Tey and Earls Colne but with the founding of a major club in Colchester in 1947, the smaller clubs disappeared and a strong nucleus of town based clubs took their place. There was a Labour Government in power the Conservative Party was reorganising itself. Part of this was the extension of the Young Conservatives. The Young Farmers and the Young Conservatives sometimes created a dichotomy to young people. Those without any interest in farming joined the YCs but a nucleus of members, mainly girls, had no farm connection. The YF movement was accused of being a marriage bureau!

To some extent this was true and the considerable Scottish element amongst Essex farmers gave their offspring the opportunities to meet. With county and inter-club events more common the opportunities to foster liaisons were greater. Behind the scenes the clubs were rated, by the male members, in order of the beauty of their girl members.

Dual membership was not uncommon. In 1948 the abolition of the basic petrol allowance did not affect meetings but it was not allowed for social events and a commentator suggested that clubs hire coaches to get them to county events. "Quite a novel form of transport".[14] The County Council still regarded them as an off-shoot of the Education Department. Youth Clubs were being established supported by organisers whose salary was paid by the County Council.

The YFCs had a county organiser, Donald Sutherland. His energy saw the establishment of a clutch of new clubs and the co-ordination of county events such as the public speaking competition, county quiz and annual Rally. The Carnegie Trust in the USA had given grants towards YFs in Britain. Now the Kellogg Foundation took over that role.

The County Council were reluctant to lose control of the YF clubs and only agreed to give them full independence if they became self supporting. By 1950 this had been achieved. The jealousy did not diminish and in 1949 Young Farmers Clubs were denied the use of school premises as meeting places unless they became affiliated to the local Youth Centre. The Wickford Club was re-launched (originally started in March 1932 it had become defunct) in October 1950 and used the Runwell Youth Centre for its Monday meetings. It was not an easy transition to become self supporting.

In 1957 a Subscribers Scheme was launched with a target of 400 interested adults who were asked for a Guinea each (£1.5p). This would guarantee 50% of the organiser's salary. The remainder would come partly from the clubs and from help that was being received by the Joseph Tucker Foundation, and other Trusts. The ECC gave a small amount but had in reality absolved itself of any committed liability. In 1978, 21 years after the Subscribers Scheme had been launched it was still only £2pa. Michael Pearce, past county organiser and president said, "the tradition and future of Essex Young Farmers is at stake. Whilst our current financial position is sound, it remains vulnerable. I hope existing subscribers...will change that £2 Bankers Order to £5 now!"[15] As the Advisory Members had given their knowledge to select calves for the pre-war 'Calf Clubs'. They had underwritten any losses the YF Federation might make when they broke with the County Council. Salvation was at hand from an unforeseen source.

59 1991. Dunmow YFC and a sponsored tractor pull.

From its immediate post-war high the county membership dropped by 20% between 1951 and '67. It started to rise again and in one year jumped by 115 members. Braintree had a 112% increase and Thaxted and Wickford both went up by 50%. The Ongar club had boasted of 100 members in 1942. Colchester had a similar total in 1951, three years after its foundation. Thereafter both these clubs showed some decline. By 1974 the membership was falling again and this had its repercussions upon the grant from the Essex County Council which was fixed at £1.50p per head. The cost of the secretariat did not fall commensurately, although they were ensconced in the EFU Agriculture House at Chelmsford.

The County Council grant rose in 1974 from £364 to £942. In 1974 there were 926 members of both senior and school clubs. In 1979 it was 1,033 and remained over the 1,000 mark for the next decade. It reached 1,145 in 1982 and the ratio of school clubs remained constant at 20%–25%. In 1979 it was proposed to form new clubs at both Tiptree and Mersea Island. Mersea club was formed but nothing more was heard about Tiptree. In 1981 a club was formed at Elmbridge School, Fyfield and soon had a membership of 40. There was another small club at Ramsey School, Halstead and at that time there were eight school clubs in the county. There were 18 senior clubs but Harlow and Wickford clubs later closed. Mersea after its late start, had 80 members in its first year and nearby Colchester, which might have seemed in competition had 76 members.

The highest club at that time was Dunmow with 81. In 1997 the county membership of senior clubs was 500. Throughout its history the ratio of boys to girls remained roughly level. The original principles of stockmanship never disappeared but was not as paramount as it had been pre-1939. Elmbridge School became the owners of a small flock of sheep in 1984. "They have a very handsome young Suffolk ram and five ewes. The ewes are two Clun Forests, two Polled Dorsets and one Colbred."[16] The erstwhile future farmers were to discover the hard facts of farming life. The Colbred ewe gave birth to still born twins. "This was a great disappointment to the members, it made them realise that farming is not always easy".[16]

In 1991 the Elmbridge boys, with sponsorship from Lloyds Bank and the assistance of Chelmsford auctioneers Tom Whirledge and Nigel Nott, decided to rear beef cattle. They were sold on 20 September 1991 at Chelmsford market. The champion was Jennie Inkster's Belgiun Blue but Clive Rowland's Simmental cross steer and David Wright's Limousin cross heifer also took awards. The Belgiun Blue made £530, Rowland's Simmental £500 and they calculated afterwards that the best calf had made over £100 profit. This was in stark contrast to the 35p profit made by Kelvedon members in 1934.

Sponsorship was also being attracted and the Essex Hunts and Barclays Bank combined to sponsor an annual farm management and replanning competition. It involved a practical, hands-on visit to a farm and detailed, and strictly budgeted plan to re-organise it on the most profitable lines.

The 1983 farm management competition started with a farm walk on P.H. Wheaton and Co.'s Slampseys Farm, Black Notley with a visit to the off-hand Lodge Farm, Witham in October. The final was held at the Queen's Hall, Halstead the following March. The exercise was divided into two. The boys had the task of recreating a dairy herd on a farm, which still had its parlour, dairy and cattle yards, but had ceased milking five years earlier. The competitors were allowed to enlist the knowledge of local ADAS officers. The amenity/domestic section was aimed at re-designing two cottages on this 109 acre farm which had no farmhouse. It was a criteria that the only labour to run the farm would come from the family and the two semi-detached cottages could be converted into a family farmhouse. They were given a budget of £20,000.

The idea had evolved from a 'Valuation Day' when Young Farmers were asked to value a farm. An annual event, this alternated in the Hunt areas, including the 'Essex and Suffolk' which allowed YFs from Hadleigh, Suffolk to participate.

Saffron Walden School Club went on the Internet in 1997 and when a new sports centre was built at the school, the 'farm' had to be moved with the support of the school governors; "we are probably the only school in the country having a new farm built. Most have had their farms closed down".[17] The club had 50 members between 11 and 16 yrs.

County Rally.

After the first clubs had been established the instigators launched an annual County Rally. In 1933 it attracted 90 members and supporters. The supporters outnumbered the members. The principle objective was running races and a hearty tea. In 1936 160 Young Farmers took part in this annual event. They visited Falconer's Hall, Good Easter; "when Mr. J.A. Matthews explained his system of farming pointing out that practically the whole of his 500 acre farm was under the plough and that livestock was a minor part of his enterprise".[18] They went on to Little Hallingbury Hall and looked at the crops which, that year had been badly laid by storms. The sports programme was cancelled when the rain returned. In pre-war days the County Rally's were orientated towards sports and could have been mistaken for any school sports day.

It was estimated that between 400 and 500 from 12 clubs participated in the competitions which included one for cake-making for girls. There was some embarrassment when a boy hoaxed the judges and beat the girl entrants "confessing the deception when the time came for the award".[19] There were acts of prowess commensurate with the brute strength required to be a farmer. Such competitions as pitching a sheaf over a high bar and the very practical job of 'Pacing Two Chains' (44 yards). The EFU presented a silver cup for annual competition to be awarded to the club scoring the most points at the annual event.

As new clubs were formed in the immediate post-war years the success of the annual rally increased. By 1956 the attendance was 4,000 against the 450 a decade earlier and 300 for the last pre-war Rally in 1939. The '50s were a high spot of enthusiasm and support. In 1967 the attendance dwindled to 1,500 at Langford and the first time it went to the Essex Showground at Great Leighs the attendance was 3,000 (1969). By 1974 it was becoming popular again and 6,000 attended. Into the '80s it had been relabelled a 'Country Show', had firmly rooted itself on the Essex Showground and figures of 10,000+ were normal. In 1997, 14,500 were estimated to have passed through the gates.

In 1983, after a wet day restricted the attendance some of the senior supporting farmers; John and Roger Norris, Peter Frost, Henry Ritchie and John Speakman appealed to Subscribers to give an extra donation to make up the deficit. The annual profit had been in the region of £4,000/£5,000. As running costs increased the profit from the Annual Rally kept pace with them. It gave the Federation the financial independence which it had struggled to achieve. By this time individual clubs were organising fund raising events for a multitude of charities.

The EFU commented after the 1945 Rally; "there is probably a case for closer liaison between the YFCs and the Union".[20] The Young Farmers Federation remained staunchly independent but in 1961 the Southminster NFU and YFC branches combined in an Annual Field Day. There was no agricultural show in the Dengie peninsular as there was at Orsett and Tendring. The Southminster event became a smaller version of an agricultural show but with a greater emphasis upon practical farming, such as planning farm buildings, than competitive exhibits of livestock.

The YFCs provided part of the Guard of Honour for HM King George VI and Queen Elizabeth when they went to the Essex Show at Orsett in 1947, in company with the WLA. They were dressed in white milking coats. In 1978 they staged a 'battle' in the Grand Ring on the second day of the Essex Show which was a crowd stopper! The range of activities of the Young Farmers had widened. From prehistoric and futuristic themes on gaudily decorated farm trailers, they progressed to fast revving 'buggies' which raced around a circuit and were just as gaudily painted.

The Essex Show always came about a month after the Annual Rally and, having put all the efforts of stock exhibiting, cake making, flower arranging and other competitions it was a repeat performance. The EFYFC relinquished their stand at the Show and, ironically, the EAS took a Stand at the YFC Rally.

A favourite competitive sport at that time was to allow competing teams to smash up a piano into very small pieces. Since a piano was an intricately made piece of equipment, with an iron frame behind the veneer teams were cheered on by their supporters. A motor mower grand prix. 'Dwile Flonking' an ancient Suffolk rural custom involved drinking ale from a decorated chamber pot. A hovercraft demonstration, motorised oil-drum raft races on the reservoir at Great Leighs in 1969, radio controlled model aircraft, a pony rodeo, motorised wheel barrows, fancy dress on horseback, a three-man pram race.

In 1971 they staged a miniature 'Highland Games', complete with a pipe band, hammer throwing and caber tossing. That year a pram race with grown up 'babies' and a gruelling course of one and a quarter miles at Marks Tey was an energetic spectacle. A hot air balloon, when these were still an unusual sight.

Despite the lively nature of the Annual Rallys the principles on which the movement had been founded remained strong. The tug-of-war had been a feature of the pre-war events and it remained part of the programme until the end of the century. Calf rearing and animal keeping still featured and Young Farmers proudly displayed their animals. But it was the audience that changed.

As the merchants withdrew from the County Show they turned their attention to the YFC Rally. Once the machinery companies were present, it paved the way for the farming community of Essex to find a substitute Essex Show. It became part of the calendar of the County – and boosted the attendance figures to around 18,000, It was a large success and put the finances of the County Federation onto a secure foundation.

The Essex YFCs organised an annual 48-hour non-stop ploughing marathon when tractors and ploughs were loaned by Essex machinery dealers, relay teams of Young Farmers ploughed day and night at a weekend. The dealers were happy to see their models working side by side with others. Farmers were encouraged to view the progress, and at the end of the weekend the Young Farmers collected a cheque for the normal cost of ploughing. It was another exercise in balancing the Federation finances.

Writtle College

Writtle Agricultural College Higher Education Corporation, to give its full title, but known as Writtle College, started life as the 'County Laboratories' in 1893, and in 1903 the word 'Technical' was inserted into its nomenclature. It played a vital part in spreading new ideas and teaching farmers' sons and daughters the principles of farming to a greater depth than their fathers had been aware. Educating farmers, at that time, was ridiculed. It was commonly said, at least until half way through the 20th century that farmers' sons went to an agricultural college – to learn about the mistakes which their fathers had made, earning enough money to send them there! The scepticism, and the wide gulf between a classroom and a muddy field in winter was all too stark.

This uphill task was tackled by educationalists with practical demonstrations, and research was always an important part of its role. The idea of teaching by example. At the turn of the century early field experiments were carried out at six centres; Burnham-on-Crouch, Gosfield, Ramsden, Roxwell, Tendring and Saffron Walden. A range of soils with a cross section of Essex fields initially aimed at assessing manurial effects on wheat, mangolds, permanent pasture. There was a natural disaster in 1897 when 50,000a of Essex coastland was inundated. The investigations into the effects of salt water on plant growth, and clay deflocculation was usefully imployed again after the East coast floods in 1953.

A horse-drawn travelling dairy had been set up before 1893 which visited 18 venues

60 Writtle College finished in 1939. Many more extensions were built later."Dig for Victory" spread everywhere including school sports fields. Brussel sprouts were growing on the lawns.

throughout the county. 264 pupils attended these ten-day courses. There were 15 classes in bee keeping, 35 in agriculture and 152 in cookery.

In 1903 the County Technical Laboratories had become an important part of the county educational system and £14,000 was spent building a new home in King Edward Avenue, Chelmsford. The Institute, as it was known, occupied these premises until Writtle College was opened in 1939 where it remained but, large though the college buildings were, they became only a part of an ever growing campus. Residential tower blocks in the '60s the Hubert Ashton Building 1963, the Strutt Hostel, a new dining room, a library building. The expansion was vital to accommodate the ever growing number of students.

Financed by Essex rate payers, the college aimed to educate men and women who would, one day, be responsible for Essex farms. This principle was abandoned as the number of farmers declined and as agricultural colleges throughout the country developed specialised departments. Writtle became known for its horticulture and fruit courses, and for its machinery. In 1988 the college decided to develop its equine studies, a strange departure when the days of horses were over. Never-the-less the British love of the horse ensured that riding a horse was available to a wider section of the population.

Equestrian events, riding centres, and more leisure created a reversal of habits. The previous necessity of horse transport and horse power had been usurped by the car and the tractor. Horses became an object for leisure and sporting pursuits and the college was responding to a need. "It is said that Essex has the highest population of horses of any county".[21] A riding school was developed and from only 52 students studying equines in 1990 there were 493 in 1997. It was the fastest growing department in the college.

Pioneering work was carried out at Writtle, with a wider application than the county of Essex. Amenity horticulture – particularly landscape and design work as well as floristry with courses available on a part-time basis gave the college a new impetus and an enhanced reputation. The full-time equivalent students more than doubled from 1990 and quadrupled from 1980.

In terms of the development of the College, the later areas of growth were Animal Care and Animal Science. In Animal Care there was a massive increase of students coming forward. In 1993 Writtle left the County Council and became independent as a Further Education Organisation, then transferred to the Higher Education Funding Council and became a University Sector College. With 2,000 students it was the largest College in the country – and a very diverse Higher Education Institution still looking after the practical needs of Essex Farmers.

Writtle College Principals:

T.S. Dymond (Acting)	1892	C.A. Ealand	1909
J.G. Stewart	1910	A.M. Smith	1911
R.M. Wilson	1912	H.M. McCreath	1923
D.B. Johnstone-Wallace	1924	J.C. Leslie	1930
B.H. Harvey	1949	A.E. Maddison	1974
	M.D. Alder	1986	

CHAPTER 14

The Decline of Farm Workers

In 1901 there were 41,306 people 'engaged in agriculture'. In 1997 there were only 11,468. or 28% of those previously involved. The figures are, however, misleading. The 1901 figure represented 3.81% of the population of the county.[1] But this was sharply reduced by the 25% of the county's population who lived in West Ham. The 1997 figures also included; 'sleeping' partners, farmers' wives and seasonal workers such as fruit pickers. To measure the downturn in the labour force on Essex farms a clearer analysis is formed from the 25,827 regular full-time workers in 1925 (the first date they were classified seperately) and the 2,637 in 1997.

Livestock workers could not be assessed on an acreage basis but this criteria suggests that, overall, one worker was required for every 30a in 1925. A figure which, despite the increase in farm machinery, hardly changed for 30 years. In 1955 the labour force had gone down to 3,800 but immediately after the Second World War it was higher than it had been in 1925.

In 1960 there was one man for every 42a, in 1970 one for every 96a, 1980 one for every 146a, 1990 one for every 234a and in 1997 one for every 285a. This is a much more accurate measurement of the replacement of men by machines. On non-livestock farms, which were rare in 1900 but commonplace in 1990, there were many 500a arable farms where the work was done by the farmer and his son, or wife. Others of similar size employed perhaps one man. The role of the worker had changed but the role of the farmer had become a more active one in working his land.

An addition to the labour force was the advent of farm secretaries spending one day a week with several different farmers. Not only were they more knowledgeable in form-filling and general accountancy, including the complexities of PAYE and VAT but the hands-on farmer no longer needed to manage his staff, and spent his time on a tractor or a combine.

The role of the labourer had not materially changed for centuries. Growing crops and tending livestock still employed the same techniques that had been used in Tudor times. The clod-hopper village-yokel were caricatures of the velvetene coats and corduroy trousers, the smock and the crumpled headgear as part of the traditional image. "The head horseman was *somebody* among his fellows. His knowledge gained from casual contact with folks in the market town often stood him in good stead on the Saturday night, when meeting his confreres at the village pub".[2] The farmer talked to the shepherd about *his* sheep, the cowman of *his* cows, the horseman of *his* horses and later it became normal to the tractor driver about *his* tractor. The pride of custodianship remained in farming, when jumbo jets had a rota of pilots.

Farm workers had always lived in farm cottages. The odium which the 'tied' accommodation engendered was a deep dissatisfaction. Towards the end of the century it was not unusual for farm workers to live 20 miles away from their employment and some in towns. The tied cottage agitation was used by the Workers Union as a lever to increase

61 1947 Terling. Charlie Emery 'fiddling' seed corn.

wages. In reality most cottages were rent free but the spectre of homelessness in retirement remained a nagging fear. It was expected that the cottage would be required to house the replacement. This did not occur as the march of mechanisation continued and redundant cottages were still occupied by retired workers. On the Terling Estate they had nearly as many cottages occupied by retired workers as by active employees, and they built retirement bungalows in the centre of Terling for widows. The paternalistic traditions remained strong.

The Tied Cottage Controversy was no longer an issue during the last quarter of the century. The release of workers was accompanied, firstly by the continual upgrading of machinery which needed injections of more and more capital, some of which was realised when empty cottages were sold. It was a mistaken policy. Cottages which were worth £1,000–£2,000 in the 1960s were attracting an annual rent of £4,000 in the 1990s. More than twice the freehold value as annual income. The retained properties proved an excellent investment and the £1,000 cottage was worth £60–£70,000 within 25 years.

Wage levels lifted the farm worker to a respectable level. Pre-1914 workers received 75p per week. "Despite rising wages during 1900–14 the lot of Essex farm workers remained one of poverty and, for families of any size, acute poverty".[3] During the First World War wages doubled to £1.50p in 1918. This trend continued to a peak of £2.30p in

1921 but with the onset of the agricultural depression wages down to £1.40 in 1923/4 and thereafter remained around £1.50 until the Second World War when they were £1.71 in 1939 and reached £3.79 in 1945. In 1925 farm workers over 21 years received an additional £5.25p for their harvest efforts. They were not expected to work more than 11 hours on any day, and not on Sundays. On farms with less than 60a of corn there were lower rates. In 1933 workers were trying to make the best deal they could.

'At the annual rally of the South East Essex Branch of the National Union of Agricultural Workers outside the Memorial Hall, Southminster the Chairman, alluding to the Essex Agricultural Wages Board, said that for this year's harvest the workers had applied for a flat rate of pay of 11d. per hour. He believed this was a better arrangement than giving the men an annual bonus of £2 2s. for a period which might be anything from three to six weeks'.[4]

The second half of the century saw an annual increment that was normally ahead of inflation. A declining labour force and the prosperity of agriculture enabled farmers to meet these increases. The reduction in the working week from 44 hours in 1960 to 39 hours in 1990 bedevils a strict comparison, but with this caveat workers received £8 in 1960, £13.15p 1970, £58 1980, £122 1990 and £190 1997. The advent of heavy hp tractors, costing £50,000 upwards prompted the farmer to expect longer hours of work to utilise the full capacity of his machine. This was an extension of the age-old tradition of

62 Thorpe-le-Soken, muddy tumbril wheels, workers with inverted sacks for weather protection.

harvest bonuses. In 1997 average earnings were £261.40p and the average hours 47.3. These figures were for the whole year and indicate that they were higher at certain periods. In 1985 the farm workers' rise was 8.3% or double the rate of inflation and in the five years up to 1996 they achieved an increase of 23%.

Not that the workers were always satisfied and in 1975 70 men and women from all over the county marched through Chelmsford to highlight their demands. "The march through the town, which was quiet and orderly went along Duke Street through the shopping precinct and up the High Street before stopping outside Shire Hall. The demonstration passed off without incident".[5] With cottages worth £70 per week and most rent free, the workers were no longer amongst the poor.

When the Community Charge (Poll Tax) was introduced, Essex farmers were advised to give their workers a commensurate net wage increase, after tax, and that the worker should, with a sense of responsibility, hand over the money to the local Council.

From a bucket full of oats for his horse, the farm worker progressed to setting his computer or satellite communication in his air-conditioned tractor cab. A new breed of younger workers, although often the descendants of the 'clod-hoppers', they embraced the new technology with acumen.

In the first half of the century, although steam power had appeared in the 19th century, and tractors were making a tentative incursion onto Essex fields, the bulk of farm work was still manual and required physical stamina and uncomfortable working environment. The Second World War induced the need to increase food production and the main worries of the Essex Farmers Union was a shortage of labour. The Womens Land Army was created and P.O.W.s were drafted onto farms from detention camps such as at Berechurch. There were 22,300 regular full-time workers in 1939, and 25,972 in 1949. The numbers had dropped to just over 17,000 by 1960, 7,031 in 1970, 4,550 in 1980, 2,815 in 1990. Farm workers were assured of continuous wages throughout the year being employed on indoor maintenance work when outside conditions were unkind. This was a security that few other employees were experiencing.

The substitution of horses for horse-power is clearly shown in the decline of the number of horses used for agricultural purposes. In 1901 the 41,306 people working on farms, including the farmer, shared 39,285 horses. The horseman retained a seniority amongst the farm staff. With the downturn in arable farming there were 7,000 more horses than workers in 1925. The horse, despite it key role was an expensive animal to keep. It required a meadow for grazing, oats for feeding, hay for fodder and straw for litter. Horses required nearly two acres each to support them and in the pre-war depression the number of horses in the county dropped by 12,000. In 1939 there were still 19,367, by 1946 there were 5,000 less but despite the proven ability of tractor power there were still 3,000 horses in 1960. They finally became redundant in the following decade. The extinction of the horse took nearly 20 years, to the time when combines and tractors had fully taken over. Tractors were, by the standards of the times, fully capable of performing the tasks for which they were required but when Ben Harvey retired as Principal of Writtle Agricultural College in 1974 he commented that the greatest change in his lifetime had been the deterioration of timeliness in farming operations. Farmers had dispensed with horses, but had not yet fully become mechanised. Only when elderly men retired did the farmer replace them with a machine.

Typical of the prevailing policy was Cecil Harvey, Heath Farm and Keelars Elmstead

63 1900 Burnham. Threshing cabbage seed.

who, in 1953, when most farmers were buying combines, bought himself a threshing drum. Asked if he would buy a combine he replied "not likely! not while these silly fellows all around me have got combines and nowhere to put their corn! I shall buy, and stack mine for threshing after Christmas".[6]

Harvey still had a team of horses which he used for drilling and cultivations. He admitted; "if it were not for the fact that I have a keen horseman I would probably have to go the way of the times and turn over entirely to tractors".[6] J.R. Tinney at Rickling, amongst others, adopted this not uncommon policy. There were many farms that were over-stocked with labour, farmers admitted it but said they would not sack any men, although when they retired, they would not be replaced. In 1950 John Walker, EFU secretary wrote "mechanisation, in fact, has not had the effect of displacing man-power. What it has done is to increase productivity".[7] Since 1939 the labour force had increased. Between the start of the war and 1950 there was an increase of 2,500 adult males, which only brought the figure back to where it had been in 1925. Yet, with casual workers included there were 1,500 more workers on Essex farms in 1950 than a quarter of a century earlier. Clearly John Walker's remark was accurate. The substitution of men by machines gathered pace in succeeding years.

Four wheels Replaces Four Hooves
Farmers needed convincing and the age-old method was to promote comparative trials. In 1902 two Canadian, and one English plough were tested on Arthur Cant's Reed Hall, Colchester. Joslin's of Colchester exhibited the Cockshutt, which came in two sizes, the

'Kangaroo' and the 'Kangaroo Kid'. J. Brittain Pash, the Chelmsford engineer and machinery dealer sent two 'Verity' ploughs made in Canada. Williams & Co. of Colchester demonstrated a plough made by Ransomes Sims & Jefferies, Ipswich. It cost £5.5s and was the cheapest of the three. Diplomatically the Essex County Standard concluded that the trial was; "a dead heat".[8] In 1917 a prototype four-furrow plough was tested at Foulness in a bid to prove that the cost of ploughing by steam was competitive with a tractor operation. This prototype was the 'Suffolk Punch' like many of the early tractors it was labelled an 'Agrimotor'. It did not have a successful launch and was inferior to the Fordson tractors which Henry Ford was selling for £225 in 1919. The unreliability of the early tractors made farmers reluctant to consider them seriously. In 1918 there were 127 tractors in Essex – but 31 of them were broken down.

Farmers were not convinced and S.J. Perrott, a salesman for J. Brittain Pash Ltd. wrote in 1923; "during the war all kinds of tractors and tractor implements were commandeered, including many which were totally unsuitable for Essex soils and which have since become more or less extinct"[9]

Despite the depression the enthusiasts continued to promote them. John Steel, Rochford, suggested in 1923 that steam tackle could do a better job for deep ploughing, sub-soiling and heavy cultivations. "I have noticed this year in moving about the county far fewer tractors standing about the fields in a dismantled condition"[10] and he gave the credit to the drivers although lamented their lack of knowledge of mechanical problems which he described as "irritating delays", but concluded "I hope the confidence of the farmer will return to the tractor, as I am sure no farmer with 100 acres of arable land can afford to be without one".[10] Two years later S.L. Bensusan put a different interpretation on the progress of mechanisation when he wrote "many of the men who had bought tractors and were using them for ploughing, reaping, haulage and the rest, have gone back to horses and say that they find this is the better way".[11] The wartime boom in machinery did not develop as its promoters had hoped. Farmers did not look after their machines and the men, reared with livestock, regarded tractors as another farm animal which could be cajoled by shouting, and a stick! When a tractor was discovered in a ditch the driver looked sadly at it as he would a cow that had sunk to its udder. The prevalence of this attitude was endemic.

In 1928 figures were produced for Essex which showed that although tractor ploughing and cultivating was cheaper, the cost of harrowing, rolling and harvesting was greater with tractors. Essex farmers were advised that; "there seems no possibility of reducing, and every likelihood of increasing cultivation costs by using tractors instead of horses".[12] It was argued by the protagonists that the tractor did not eat when it was idle, but the lack of mechanical skills by tractor drivers meant that the smallest malfunctions would require the services of a skilled mechanic.

In 1931 orchard tractors were demonstrated at Toppinghoe Hall. W.P. Seabrook considered the baby caterpillar machine ideal for working between orchard trees. Fordson had withdrawn from this trial.

At the Steeple Bumpstead Ploughing Match and Machinery Demonstration held at George Colman's, Garlands Farm in 1933 there were classes for tractor ploughs both paraffin and crude oil but emphasis was already being placed upon the wheels.

The traction between spade-lugs and cleats was debated. Pneumatic tyres were disparagingly taboo. No self respecting farmer would allow a rubber-tyred tractor on a

64 1910 Kelvedon. Farmer W. Moss with his staff of 56 (including young boys) at Threshelfords Farm.

field. It was considered that the weight would kill the soil. At Steeple Bumpstead R.P. Hawkins, DAO said "the subject of tractor wheels is an important matter on the heavy clay land of this district and arrangements are being made to demonstrate track laying tractors, and a number of different types of tractor wheels, so that farmers will have an opportunity of comparing the different types".[13]

Despite all these misgivings and forebodings and although the number or horses increased during the First World War, the Second World War had an opposite effect. In 1944 there were 2,000 less than there had been in 1939. 11,430 was considerably below the 25,384 in 1918. The horse remained as an adjunct for the running of the farm but tractors had come into their own. Nearly 70% were under 50hp, 3.7% were 4-wheel drive. In 1942 6.3% of them were track-laying machines. Although the numbers increased slightly they only represented 5.2% in 1944 and 6.5% in 1969. The ousting of the track-layer was accomplished when 4-wheel drive tractors became common in the later years of the century.

The "iron-horse" was an epithet that tractors embraced. They replaced horses – but not men. Later the combine became a replacement for men. It accomplished, in one operation all the work of the binder, the travers, carters, stackers, thatchers, threshing gangs. The acquisition of a combine did not immediately deplete the labour force. There were still such labour consuming jobs as sugar beet and root crops. In the 1970s, as wages started to increase more rapidly, farmers often made the decision to drop out of sugar beet because they were keeping an excessive staff for a very small part of the year. The breed of massive tractors that traversed Essex fields during the last quarter of the century was a complete revolution. By this time not only had the horse disappeared but tractor drivers' output had quadrupled (at least).

The combine needed a back-up investment in hydraulic tipping grain trailers, a new grain-barn. The traditional Essex barns were too narrow and too low to accommodate grain storage. There were grain driers to incorporate, elevators and conveyers with storage bins. Carrier's of Braintree, Bentalls (later Wooley, later Acrow) at Maldon, Crittall at Witham were in the forefront of designing and supplying this new equipment. They established design and installation departments. On average the combine could achieve with 3/4 men what had been done by 20.

It's introduction was tentative and controversial. Many had regarded the tractor as a temporary innovation. The shaking of heads over combines was greater. The better sunshine in the U.S.A. was conducive to their usage, but in Britain they would never work, said the pundits!

In 1943 the North Essex Discussion Society debated the motion "that there is a great future for the combine harvester in East Anglia". The arguments against the combine related to the additional capital investment and this was set against the cost of wages. Combining was assessed at a charge of £1.70p per acre. Cutting with a binder and threshing in the field at £2.40p but taking home to the stackyard and threshing later cost £3.30p. Against this argument the additional capital for silo storage outweighed the financial advantages. The audience were tepid in their response.

There were reputed to be three combines in Essex before the war. Robert Davidson had one at Beaumont, James Barbour at Stanway Hall another. In 1944 there were approximately 120 in the county and 25 years later, in 1969 there were 2,360, of which 90 were still tractor drawn. The self-propelled harvester had come into its own but there was still a substantial 520 that were under 10ft. in width. The largest majority, 1,740 were between 10–15ft. and only a miniscule 10 over 15ft. Twenty years later the majority were over 15ft. and in the 1990s the 24ft. monster had appeared on the scene. Combines had taken over the harvesting role.

One of those who held onto the traditional methods until 1966 was 78-year old Reginald Pudsey, Griggs, Coggeshall. He was selling his straw to the racing stables at Newmarket. The loss of the straw after combining had been a serious argument in opposition to them. Pudsey gave up because he retired from active farming. The machine was operated by Bert Blackwell, Herons Coggeshall, a 15-year old Ransome threshing drum powered by 25-year old Marshall diesel tractor. This example was not untypical. The older farmers did not like the new ideas but as they retired the younger men embraced combine harvesting with enthusiasm. Steam engines had entered the realm of preservation societies and annual rallies for enthusiasts.

Spiralling wages encouraged mechanisation. At the Essex Show every year, farmers went along to see what was new. In the world of potato harvesters, balers, hedge cutters and a multitude of new-fangled machinery the inventors had got to work. It soon became possible for every job to be done from a sitting-down position. Hoeing, the most unlikely candidate for mechanisation was obviated by the development of selective chemicals. Singling sugar beet became unnecessary with mono-germ seed, and placement drills. The inventiveness of the designers was comprehensive.

If all the combines in the county had been lined up side-by- side in 1969 they would have cut a swarth 5 miles wide. The average 12ft. combine was required to cover 192a in the season. As reliability improved there was a trend of replacing two combines on the larger farms, with one giant. In the 1980s machines were combining 1,000a in the short harvesting period.

CHAPTER 15

The Granary of England

Essex was always a major wheat producer. John Walker called it "The leading cereal-producing county in the whole country...and Essex yields are much above national averages. This is the heart of the 'granary of Britain'".[1]

The predominance of wheat is not easy to explain. It was a crop which exhausted the soil, and one that came at the end of a four course rotation. In earlier days everything seemed to rotate to a culmination of wheat after a three year preparation period. Farm leases stipulated that white-straw crops should not be taken in succession. In 1949 David Gemmill who was managing the LCS farms in Essex advocated grazing wheat in the spring. He estimated it could increase the return by £2 per acre and pointed out that although cows appeared to do more damage than sheep "cows will graze upon the blade of the plant and leave the stem and heart untouched, whereas sheep will graze a patch of wheat down hard and as soon as the green shoots appear, will graze the same place again".[2] Apart from additional income by grazing forward- looking, wheat crops, the actual sale of grain was not encouraging. The straw was unsuitable for feeding cows but was used for bedding and thatching. The greatest demand was to thatch all the corn and hay stacks on every farm – every year. It required considerable quantities.

During the most prosperous period of Essex agriculture, the price of wheat briefly touched £28 per ton in 1812. A dizzy height that it did not achieve again until after the Second World War. The low point was 1934 when it was only worth £4.80p. The lowest price since the 16th century and from 1931–52 the average price of barley was higher than wheat.

The popularity of wheat was such that in times of depression, both 19th century and in the '30s farmers refused to realise that it was a noose that was dragging them down. A reduction in the wheat quotient on the farm was required.

It was considered a lazy-man's crop. Long before technical methods became routine, the scathing comments of livestock farmers about their neighbours' wheat growing habits, was that "they drilled the field, closed the gate, and went back at harvest time". Many wheat crops were hoed and dock-pulling was carried out. They were a dirty crop and poppies grew in profusion on the lighter soils, whilst thistles, charlock, wild oats and black grass polluted the clay lands. Root crops were cleaning crops. Corn crops brought back the weeds. Permanent, or semi-permanent grass was the only real alternative when fields became excessively polluted.

After the widespread application of selective herbicides the position became reversed and cereal crops became the clean ones, and continuous cereals became a possibility – excepting where tenancy agreements precluded this practice, but more farms had become owner occupied and this restriction less of a constraint. It enabled the cereals acreage to expand.

There were 18 years when the barley acreage exceeded wheat. These were wet autumns, not a price differentiation, although in 1940 the equal balance of wheat/barley

*65 1908 Harold Wood.
Matthews new steam
driven mill built in
1905.*

was induced by a drop in the wheat acreage, and a consequential make-up of spring barley. A period of 11 years from 1959 saw barley higher than wheat. In 1961 by a margin of 74,036a. The price of wheat had stagnated, barley was in demand, and the introduction of Pioneer, a winter hardy barley variety induced farmers to plant a crop that would take less out of the soil, and came to harvest earlier. This was a considerable advantage since the previous slow maturing wheat crops which had been suitable for the binder delayed harvesting. From 1971 the barley acreage never exceeded wheat and in 1984, when wheat achieved its peak of nearly 308,000a it exceeded barley by a massive 196,061a. The escalation of wheat had developed.

The lowest ebb in wheat plantings was in 1931 when the area was only half of that grown in the last year of the First World War. The decline throughout the '20s/'30s was a matter of serious concern. In 1923 William Hasler, Dunmow, reported; "the supply of Yeoman...has been noticeably heavy this season, but not withstanding its recognised superiority in quality it is difficult to command a premium in the matter of price. This is probably largely due to the increasing demand for wheat by poultry feeders".[3] Whilst Alan Gifford, Fingringhoe Hall, put forward a plan that would regulate the supply of wheat coming onto the market – and hopefully stabilise prices. He suggested that permits should be issued to farmers limiting the threshing in any one month. They relied upon contractors who travelled a circuit, threshing out one stack at a time on each farm, reducing the problems of barn storage and giving a balanced money supply.

Gifford suggested that, for example, "the Colchester manager finds that the total acreage of wheat in his area is 12,000a; therefore in one month he must limit the threshing to 1,000a. Each farmer who wishes to thresh, say in September, will apply in August for a permit to thresh so many acres".[4] Gifford pointed out that the value of one quarter (4½ cwts) could be borrowed from the bank for four months 'for ninepence'.

In 1931 Wilhelmina was one of the most popular. It had been grown in Essex for many years and in 1910 the Essex County Standard reported "threshing wheat this week from poor heavy land, taken after long fallow, steam cultivated, with no dressing whatever since a coat of dung in 1903, we were surprised to find a yield of five quarters per acre (22.5cwts) (Wilhelmina), which speaks volumes for this variety".[5] This was an outstanding yield.

In 1925 the County Crop Testing Station was established at Good Easter, a farm of heavy calcareous clay, a boulder clay subsoil. "Wilhelmina (or Victor) is the most reliable high yielding variety. Yeoman, chief prop of the all-English loaf is a safe variety Little Joss should be grown on lighter wheat soils. Square Head's Master; and this will come as no surprise to most corn growing farmers, has been proved to be a good all-rounder".[6] Yields from a small group of progressive farmers gave average wheat yields of 26.2cwts. but the official estimate for 1938/47 was only 18.7cwts, and until after the war the more average crops could be expected to produce around 17cwts.

In the '70s/'80s wheat yields almost doubled. It was a phenomenal increase. In 1974 W.V. Hutley, Pond Park, Felsted, achieved a yield of 72cwts. Three years later Andrew Smith, Wigborough Wick, St. Osyth, achieved 80.9c, Tony Clarke, Lawns, Langley, got 83.4c and John Muirhead, Eastland, Bradwell-on-Sea got into the Guiness Book of Records with 87.12c. That record was broken the following year by Tony Clarke who harvested 89.8c and took over the mantle of the champion wheat crop in the UK. It was a record that stood for four years when Clarke beat his own yield with a 109c crop but lost his place in the record book to a Mid Lothian farmer who achieved 113c.

Essex farmers were leading the way but in 1967 George Barrows, agronomist for Pertwees tackled the concern of farmers that the top had already been reached. Essex crops that year were 36c wheat, 31c barley, 34c oats with the 10-year average of Essex wheat crops at 31c. George Barrows refuted the pessimists. "This is a view to which I am not prepared to subscribe, since I feel it to be about as valid as that once held by the medical pundits – namely that the human body would not be able to withstand speeds much in excess of 60mph".[7] In 1974 Essex farmers grew 6 cwts an acre more than in 1970. The first time the two-tons barrier had been broken. Due to inclement seasons, particularly the drought years, 1975/6 and a bad autumn, the yields declined to only 30.6 cwt per acre in 1976 but picked up with a new record in 1978 and continued to climb.

Despite the exhortations and efforts of the War Ag's the First World War saw a peak of 162,201a of wheat and in the Second World War 144,058a in 1943. The increased area

66 *1950? Mistley. International 10/20 and McCormick Binder cutting wheat. Seed crops were still cut this way long after combines had been proved to work.*

of cereals in Essex rose by 27,000a between 1914/8 and by 61,000a between 1940/4. The wheat area exceeded the 1915 162,000a, in 1965 and with minor fluctuations reached a higher area every year with a peak of 308,000a in 1984, more than double the highest achieved during the war and without the coercion engendered by a wartime blockade. There were a combination of factors at work, not the least being increases in the margin of profitability.

Pre-war the price of wheat had been below the cost of production. It is surprising that the area did not decline to a greater extent. Although not as high as in 1914-18, there was over 100,000a in Essex from 1933 onwards, with 115,129a in 1938. It was a traditional crop in the granary of England and farmers grew wheat out of habit.

Interest in wheat growing spiralled. At Spain's Hall, Finchingfield, the 328a Home Farm owned by Sir John Ruggles-Brise saw a radical change of policy. The family had been pioneers in many areas of agricultural development. A prize winning herd of Jersey cows that had been there for 80 years was sold in 1958. The last of the livestock, a herd of Large Whites being bred for bacon was sold in 1967, "it left the farm without livestock for the first time since it entered the family". A grain dryer was installed and the future was orientated towards cereal production. In 1969 25% of the farm was in wheat and there was a rotation of; beans, barley, sugar beet and wheat. A second-hand combine was bought and grain storage was increased from 160 tons to 400.

The EFU and ADAS combined to promote an 'Essex Wheat Conference', it was one of many winter conferences that filled the farmer's calendar. Scheduled for the Marks Tey Hotel the organisers were taken by surprise when more than 400 farmers tried to get in.

It was an unprecedented demand and they organised a repeat performance a month later at Chelmsford. It became a regular fixture at the much larger Marconi Centre, Chelmsford and throughout the years the numbers of farmers remained high. In 1989 there were 230. Joe Matthews, Divisional Head of Essex and Herts. ADAS said, "I've been here now for five years and it was well above average".[8] During those years wheat went through a revolutionary change.

In 1980 Henry Ritchie, Marks Hall, Margaret Roding, said that his whole farm had been in continuous wheat for the past five years and he predicted that continuous wheat was a serious option. The old taboos about white-straw cropping, disease carry-over, soil impoverishment and disease build-up had been countered with antidotes from the chemical and fertiliser industry. A record of increased yields seemed to prove the point. Ploughing was traditional but direct-drilling, minimal cultivations, cleaning the fields with stubble burning and a greater emphasis upon soil-testing were ingredients of the new era. The wheat acreage expanded rapidly.

Long riverside meadows were ploughed up, many Essex marshes were drained, with new laser techniques, and drilled with wheat. The area of fallow land declined as 'fallowing' was no longer considered essential for the well-being of the land. The permanent pasture of the county which had stood at nearly 183,000a in 1950 dropped by 50% in 1975. The area of wheat was 55.7% in 1900 and 59.2% in 1996. It reached a level

67 1950s Mistley. Corn in sacks in the days before bulk carriers. Grain from combines was delivered in sacks. A sack of barley weighed 2cwts, wheat 2¼ cwts. Men carried them on their backs.

of 77.8% in 1979 which was the end of the first decade of the wheat revolution.

There was an urgent need for a farm to have its own grain store, with conveyers, elevators, a reception pit, and a grain dryer to combat the irritability of wet harvests. In the forefront of supplying these needs was Crittall's of Witham. The company produced grain bins which were square and reinforced to withstand the pressures of a weight of bulk grain. In the early days tipping it into old fashioned barns, the grain pushed out the walls! These bins could be bolted together in a long line with added strength. They became nationally known. 'Crittall bins' were as famous as 'Tiptree jam'. In the vanguard of producing the accessories for this system was Carrier at Braintree who produced steel conveyers, elevators and a grain dryer. Bentalls at Maldon produced wooden conveyers and other equipment, also several models of their grain dryer. Swift at Ardleigh, founded by farmer John Latta, produced another range of equipment. Marconi at Chelmsford produced a farm-sized moisture meter which both farmers and workers soon learned to master. It was an essential piece of equipment when corn was no longer stored in a stack.

The increased enthusiasm of grain growing and increasing yields produced larger and larger harvests. Moving these massive amounts gave the merchants some marketing headaches. Britain had traditionally been a grain importing nation. The wave of prosperity which hit Essex farmers, and made the Napoleonic period the most prosperous ever experienced, was engendered by the closure of the continental ports. The Crimean war helped to delay the onset of the great depression in the 19th century when the Black Sea ports were closed. At that time Britain was importing large quantities from the Ukraine. There had been a period of grain exports between 1715–65 but for over 100 years, with scarcities in wartime, there was a necessity to make up the shortfall with imports. The situation was now reversed.

This produced a considerable increase in the volume of traffic going from the port of Colchester. In 1966 Witham company Richardson & Preece exported 30% more than in 1965. Three years earlier they had averaged six vessels a year. In 1966 they aimed at one a day, Medium quality malting barley being exported to Holland and Spain. Feed beans, tic beans and 1,000 tons of other commodities produced an increase in activity but in the same year Maldon NFU branch was warned "we are in the midst of the biggest slump in livestock production for years".[9]

There was an excessive production of barley, which had topped the wheat acreage for eight years. Farmers had reduced their livestock because they were unprofitable and then proceeded to swamp the cereals market.

A far sighted look into the future convinced Len Ratcliff of Halstead merchants Newman & Clark Ltd. that they should become involved in exporting grain. In 1963 they bought the maltings at the Hythe owned by Associated British Maltings, and carried out conversions to give a loading capacity of 500 tons a day. Exports of barley from the Hythe Quay, Colchester, shot up from 1,317 tons in 1955 to 113,222 in 1967. Wheat showed some decline in that period but beans, which 6,675 tons went through the port in 1965 rose to 37,863 tons in 1967. In 1966 the largest outgoing cargo to leave the port, 740 tons of feed barley exported in bulk by Hasler & Co., Dunmow was loaded through the 2,500-ton silo which E. Marriage & Son had built. It went to Copenhagen. At Mistley, Brooks set up shipping facilities for grain exports and to a smaller extent at Brightlingsea. In 1968 the Hythe became the fourth busiest barley exporting port in the UK.

68 1966. Ardleigh contractor, Bill Earle and his fleet of Claas combines. Many farmers relied on a contractor.

At Tilbury the Port of London Authority built a new Bulk Grain Terminal. The loading facilities were operated by Thamesgrain Elevators, a Division of Mardorf Peach & Co. Ltd. with a clutch of mills owned by Allied Mills Ltd., Spillers-Milling, Rank Hovis Ltd. and Cargill UK Milling. Tilbury had been developed as a terminal for grain importing. Now it became a major exporting port which with Southampton created a new industrial, quasi agricultural industry. With conveying equipment capable of handling 1,000 tons per hour, and a deep water facility that could export grain in 50,000 ton lots.

Marriages had developed the Hythe as it was below the road bridge which only allowed barge traffic to their East Mill. Newgrain became part of Spillers, which became part of Rank Hovis McDougall when Coldock, as a subsidiary company was created, and later taken over by Associated British Ports who expanded the Rowhedge Quay and warehousing. The narrow river and the short period of high water put constraints upon the usage of the Hythe. Something that did not apply to Tilbury.

Barley exports were pushed into second place when a new variety, 'Golden Promise' was bred in Scotland, which closed the traditional destination for much of the Essex grown malting barley. "Now even the Scots have become self-sufficient in their own malting barley requirements...This has reduced the reliance upon the sun-drenched barleys from the tender soils of Eastern England", said the Essex County Standard. Wheat had been transformed from a Cinderella crop into the King of Essex fields.

Prices
It would be an over-simplification to suggest that the price of wheat stagnated for 30 years, and then increased by £10 per ton, per annum in the '70s, but it sums up the

surprise which Essex farmers felt about this development. No longer the poor relation in the cropping sequence, wheat, in particular became the cash generating crop in a way that was unprecedented. It came at a time when the dairy herd was diminishing.

In 1948 the price of non-millable wheat was fixed at £19.25p. The actual market price was lower but a deficiency payment was calculated to make up the difference. The most advantageous price was £24 per ton for milling wheat if it was kept in the stack until the following June. The increments were tightly fixed by MAFF but barley was fixed at £14.50p as a 'maximum' price. The pricing structure was designed to encourage wheat at the expense of barley, but did little to augment farmers' plans although in 1948/9 the barley area was greater than wheat for only the fourth time in the 20th century.

In 1952 the price of non-milling wheat was £23.50 rising to £32.50p on the same basis Barley, by this time was on a level with wheat. For the next 20 years the price hardly moved, and costs were rising every year. There was a period between 1955/69 when the average level was £21.50p per ton. Yields were increasing slightly. The gross return from wheat crops barely rose above £32 per acre, and in 1961 was only £29.66p. There was some slight improvement in 1969 when a good harvest produced £36.28p an acre. A better harvest the following year gave farmers a gross return of £39.49p. At an average price per ton in 1970 of £23.23p, but in 1980 the acre return was £102.97p and a decade later had risen to £245.6p. Three years later it had gone up by another £80 per acre.

The advent of Britain's membership of the E.C. and the implementation of the C.A.P. were regarded as the major influence. When membership had been mooted cereal farmers had looked forward with greater anticipation than most livestock farmers, and fruit growers. A scheme had been devised to give Britain a 'transitional period' of five years. Continental wheat prices were £5-£10 higher than UK prices and the prospect of attaining these levels was alluring. There were sceptics who said that it would be like running after an accelerating train. It had been anticipated that the average £23.23p in 1970 would reach £35 by 1975. In the event the actual price was £57.65p. And it was not the result of the C.A.P.

World prices produced a rapid escalation. The oil crisis in the Middle East. The Russian grain raid. The Essex County Standard commented in 1971; "last year, due to the failure of the American maize crop, and to other world influences, we saw cereal prices rise to heights that bore some resemblance to the Common Market level...and the restoration of the fortunes of the American farmers has contributed to push our prices almost back to the pre-1970 levels".[10]

In early 1972 the same source commented "prices which were static for months have moved forward with confidence, and farmers who have played the poker game with silos and bins full of grain are smiling at last".[11]

In 1974 farm economics were in turmoil. Pigs and chickens which relied on reasonably priced cereals found they could not compete. Pigs were losing £4 each. The cost of producing chicken meat was $21\frac{1}{2}$p per lb and the return was only 20p. Diesel fuel trebled in price, baling string rose in six months from £180 per ton to £700 per ton. Cereal prices made handsome gains. Average levels of £25 per ton in 1972/3 doubled to £50 in 1973. In January 1974 Essex farmers were receiving £70 per ton. Soya beans, protein for livestock, went up to £240, and plummeted to £80 per ton. All of these violently moving prices were the result of world adjustments to a new level of oil prices and a realisation that the world was still short of food. The enhanced prosperity enabled farmers to combat the rapid inflation in the '70s. Workers' wages increased at a faster rate than previously. Machinery costs escalated but farmers still purchased the latest models. Other farm improvements such as concrete slabs for dumping sugar beet, and upgrading many of the pioneering efforts of grain handling and storage and a capital investment programme, put Essex farms on a sound footing to face whatever might occur in the future.

Other Cereals
The area of rye was never high in Essex whilst durum wheat was tried by some farmers in the 1980s it was never pursued. "Rye was far less grown in the south than in the north of England. In Essex, Dagenham had the largest acreage 250a. This crop was normally used for early feed; at Grays Thurrock it was 'in general fed off, but very little any year standing for a crop'".[12] The peak year was 1919 when over 2,700a graced Essex fields.

Mixed Corn, a composite crop of wheat, barley, beans and sometimes oats was sown when the resultant produce was destined for grinding into animal food on the farm.

Mixed corn gained popularity in the Second World War when wheat had to be sold off the farm to feed the nation. Feeding compounds were rationed and there were shortages of animal food.

AVERAGE WHEAT YIELDS			
	Yield Per Acre	Best Year	Worst Year
1807	13.5c		
1927–9	26.2c*		
1930–39	17.0c		
1938–47	18.7		
1950–59	24.8c	28.8c(59)	22.6c(52+54)
1960–69	30.8c	34.0c(67)	28.2c(69)
1970–79	36.9c	42.4c(78)	34.0c(70+72)
1980–89	51.4c	62.4c(84)	47.4c(81)
1990–96	59.4	65.6c	55.2c(92)

Source: MAFF returns. In general Essex crops were 1–2cwts above these figures.

Selected records of 4,069a (out of 90,101a) top farms analysed by J.B. Gill EFU secretary for NIAB from farmers:_ 200/300a Group (329 Fields). [See EFJ October 1933, p.406]

ESSEX CROPPING CHANGES: BALANCE SHEET (%)			
	1900	1950	1996
Wheat	14.1	17.5	40.4
Barley	10.5	13.5	9.9
Oats	7.8	7.3	0.3
Fallow	4.0	2.9	9.3
P. Pasture	33.9	21.8	10.8
R. Grasses	12.2	9.5	2.9
Potatoes	1.2	4.3	2.0
Sugar Beet	—	3.0	1.7
Turnips	2.5	—	—
Mangolds	3.3	1.0	—
Peas	2.3	—	2.3
Vegetables & Fruit	0.3	7.7	1.7
Beans	3.0	0.8	3.1
O.S.R.	—	—	7.2
Others	4.9	10.7	8.4
	100	100	100

CHAPTER 16

Old Crops and New Ones

Many attempts were made, mainly in the second half of the century, to launch new crops. They were hailed as an 'alternative'. Some of them failed.

The story of grain maize growing in Essex began in the mid-'60s. Although there were some misgivings that the Essex climate was not hot enough for the maize to ripen. There was great optimism and it was hailed as a new 'wonder-crop'. The Essex County Standard recorded its birth in 1965.

> "Passengers on London main line trains are intrigued by regimented rows of maize plants, many of them festooned with paper bags, in a three acre field at Rye Mill, Feering. As the trains roar past Dr. Andrew Pap, an eminent plant breeder who left his native Hungary during the 1956 uprising, methodically continues his quest for improved hybrid varieties at Hurst Gunson Cooper Taber Maize Trial Grounds".[1]

The following year a variety 'Kelvedon 59' was grown in a 3 acre field by Tom Harvey at Scrips Farm, Coggeshall. It was the first time that maize had been mechanically harvested in Essex. The following year it yielded two tons per acre but was 37% moisture when combined in November, and had to be dried down to 18%.

A Maize Development Association was incorporated as a limited company with Tom Harvey as chairman. They set a target of 1,000a of grain maize to be sown in 1968 – and more the following year. "Essex is a leading county in maize development" said Andrew Pap.[2] In 1972 grain maize was being grown on 2,418a in Essex. There were 80 farmers in the Essex and Herts Maize Growers Group. Bill Dixon-Smith, Houchins, Coggeshall grew 45a of Kelvedon 59, and Michael Wright 20a at Great Bentley which he used to help feed his 1,200 pigs. 1972 was not a good season for maize plants, and the following year the acreage was reduced by 50%. The best areas had been around Halstead and Ongar. Newgrain Ltd., Halstead merchants conducted detailed surveys and in 1972 MD Len Ratcliff commented "on the importance of home-grown grain maize in the light of our impending entry into the E.E.C."[3] After 1974 the leading protagonist, Tom Harvey, gave up growing maize. He considered that it was suitable as an adjunct to a livestock unit and needed the proper machinery to ensile it. The acreage dwindled to only 526a in 1975 and by 1978 there was only 167a grown and it was not recorded thereafter although maize growing for sileage remained an option for dairy farmers and played a useful part in supplementing the ration.

With precision-chop forage harvesters it was possible to utilise the luxurient growth with its and high nutritional value. The third National Forage Maize Demonstration was held at Dengie Manor Farm, Southminster where Guy Wilsdon had grown an acreage for his herd of 350 Friesian cows, and 330 following stock, with a beef herd of 200 head. Wilsdon grew 120a of forage maize which had spread to many areas in Britain and doubled its area in 1973 to a figure of 20,000a. Forage maize lasted the century out – but grain maize became a slice of history.

69 1910? Feering. Ladies in Edwardian hats picking lavender grown by school teacher John Orst to produce oil of lavender.

Paramount amongst new crops was the devotion which King's of Coggeshall put into the promotion of Navy beans. Baked beans had become a staple part of the British diet mixed with tomato sauce, but named because they had, supposedly, been the main diet and salvation for a contingent of U.S. marines on an isolated Pacific island. They were only grown in a small area around the Great Lakes and were also known as Michigan pea beans, Canadian pea beans and Phaseolus Vulgaris. Now they came to Essex.

The first crop to be harvested in Britain was in 1972. Kings had introduced them to England and Goldhanger Fruit Canners promised to take the resultant crop and produce sample tins of the first English grown baked beans. It was hailed as a breakthrough that would reduce the stranglehold which American imports had developed into a monopoly. David Ashby, Insteps, White Colne, Harold Fairs, Great Tey, Richard Manning, Feeringbury, Feering, Eric Hobbs, Honeywood, Earls Colne and F. Percival & Sons, Great Tey were amongst the farmers who planted trial acreages in 1972.

Encouraged by Francis Nicholls of Kings who had promoted the experimental work before Navy beans could become acceptable. They also needed a set of husbandry rules which had to be developed by trial and error. In 1972 Nicholls said "we had a small trial area about the size of a billiard table growing on our trial grounds last year [1971] but in 1972 nine Essex farmers are carrying out trials. The last thing I would want to do is paint an optimistic picture for this as a possible break crop".[4] Two years later Kings offered contracts to pliant farmers. "This is a new and profitable break crop, although at the moment we don't have all the answers", said Nicholls and added that the UK was the biggest, per capita nation of baked bean eaters in the world. 1,400a were contracted.

There were severe problems including; late frosts, slow growth, and unfamiliarity of harvesting techniques. They were so short that a normal combine knife could not cut the beans low enough, thus leaving many of them behind. Yields were also variable.

Soya beans had been tried on the Fordson Estates at Boreham in 1935. The first time they had been grown as a field crop in Europe. The main purpose was to produce grain that was rich in oil and made good hay after the oil had been extracted. It was primarily grown for livestock feeding.

They never quite succeeded in the way that was expected. In 1989, 17 years after the initial launching, there was a small come-back. A new British bred variety called Albion from Cambridge University was launched together with a stripper harvester that could cope with them. It was another optimistic – but short-lived revival. Navy beans did not achieve the prominence which was expected but they were a pioneering effort in the range of alternative crops, and one of many which promoted the name of Kings.

Other crops in which they played a leading role were tobacco, of which some illicit fields were grown during the Second World War. Rev'd Hugh Cuthbertson at Tilty operated the Tilty Tobacco Centre and Curing Co-operative. Cartoonist, Zak, designed a label. It was active in the 1939–45 war and carried on by his daughter into the late 1990s. In 1973 Tom Harvey grew four acres. After tobacco, Kings went on to encourage lentils in 1976, and sunflower trials in 1979 by which time they were also trying a revival of coriander, and caraway which had disappeared in the 19th century.

Fenugreek had a dual role as a source of flavour for curry powder and steroids for medicinal use. Triticale, a genetic combination of wheat and rye. Quinoa whose origins were in Peru and was a welcome ingredient in game cover mixtures when sown with kale. Kings sold it to 10 European countries. Chick peas Meadow foam grown as a substitute for sperm whale oil, Evening Primrose and Borage, noted for its bright blue flowers were two more crops which attracted interest from the pharmaceutical industry. In 1991 the Essex County Standard reported "within a dozen years we shall find the Essex summer vista is much more colourful and varied than it has been under a blanket cereal regime".[5] It was predicted that linseed, often confused with flax, would become widespread. Due to a high EU subsidy payment many acres were grown. It was not successful for its yield until the arrival of a winter hardy variety, Oliver in 1995, linseed crops did not pay for themselves. The subsidy, and the European shortage of linseed oil made it viable to grow.

Miscanthus, Spartina, used to produce fuel for road vehicles, Cuphea, a genus containing over 40 species and a range of other crops were grown on an experimental scale.

Lavender, although grown on a large scale in Norfolk, never became popular in Essex. The other company which was in the forefront of developing these new crops was Hursts at Feering who helped to encourage lupins as a farm crop in 1976, but did not see their optimism rewarded.

Hursts invested £400,000 in a plant breeding station at Great Domsey, Feering, which was opened by Sir Henry Plumb in 1978. The company could claim that its antecedents were a Mr. Field and a Mr. Child who were in business in 1560. Of the four names in the title; Hurst, Gunson, Cooper and Taber, Hursts had originated at

Houndsditch, and when the last Hurst died Nathaniel Sherwood became the proprietor. R.W. Gunson, a refugee from Hungary, initially went to New Zealand to become a seed merchant with his father but in 1920 came to England and founded R.W. Gunson (Seeds) Ltd. Robert Cooper, who died in 1884, had built up a seed business in London having become sole proprietor after the death of his two partners. The firm had an ancestry that dated back to 1771. George Taber was of Essex stock and was head gardener at Braxted Park in 1848, although a few years later he was making a reputation as a market gardener and seedsman. He lived at Rose Cottage, Rivenhall, but moved into Matchyn's as a tenant of Sir Samuel Brook Pechell. His assistant was Thomas Cullen who was made a partner in 1881 and the name changed to 'Taber & Cullen'.

Three years later he injected capital into Robert Cooper's ailing company. George Tabor's only son, James, farmed Little Braxted Hall but his grandson farmed at Matchyns. The seed business was conducted from an office and warehouse at Witham. Cooper-Taber, Gunson and Hurst remained independent companies until 1962. Hurst had trial grounds at Boreham but moved to Feering about 1890. Great Domsey was bought in 1942 and Broom's Farm adjoining in 1948. They eventually acquired 1,000a of land which was suited for seed production being well drained and friable. It was from here that they embarked upon an explosion of activity in the 1970s.

By a link with a Swedish company, Weibull's, they entered the world of cereal varieties, which was already over-crowded but at the same time grew 10a of lupins in trial plots. The Essex County Standard said in 1976, "this year, if the seed is available, it could expand to 100a; next year to 1,000a; and after that it could become a fast expanding new crop".[6] From this pioneering work they introduced the first British bred maize variety. 'Kelvedon 33 and 59A'. They developed various strains of thousand head kale, and dwarf giant rape.

Backed-up by a 7m litre reservoir and rabbit-proof fencing, the Domsey Complex was able to sustain a rotational programme which allowed varietal purity to proceed within the rotation. They introduced 'Garden Pride' seeds and a 'Gourmet Vegetable Collection'. "This was produced after painstaking research carried out from inquiries to their stand at an Ideal Homes Exhibition...It is also of note that in 1982, to help repair the war damage in the Falklands, Hurst's re-stocked these islands with seeds free of charge".[7]

Gipsy Pickers to Mobile Viners

Peas were a traditional crop which expanded as the railways were extended, but as Arthur Wilkin at Tiptree discovered, the produce was often spoilt before it reached Covent Garden. Lorry transport from the 1920s established a quicker route to the market. Bags of fresh peas could be picked up in the field and taken, overnight, whilst they were still fresh, to be shelled and eaten within 24 hours.

The pea crop was centred, and its most famous heartland, around Marks Tey and Kelvedon, with other growers at Greenstead Green around Halstead, and in the Rainham area. These were not exclusive homes. Peas formed a useful preparation for wheat, being cleared early, in June/July leaving time for a barstard fallow before drilling the autumn cereals. The demand declined in the 1950s. Dried peas and canning became alternatives but the days when convoys of lorries traversed the overnight road to London were drawing to a close. The laborious task of shelling peas became less popular with house-

70 1950s Coggeshall. An old swarth cutter (1947) dealing with a cocksfoot seed crop for R.W. Dixon-Smith.

wives when they could be obtained, ready shelled, in a can, and could also be enjoyed throughout the year, and not exclusively in the 'season'.

With an extension of women occupied in full-time employment, and bringing-in a regular source of income, there was less compunction to embark upon the seasonal work which had previously been a necessity to supplement cottage, and village, incomes.

The hand picking had been done, until 1950, by hundreds of women and children. School holidays were often, and officially, arranged to comply with the requirements of the pea picking season. It was not unusual to find fields with 200 pickers at work. An army of gipsies descended to reap some of the rewards and encampments of gipsy caravans were regularly deployed along the only stretch of dual carriageway that existed on the A12 before 1959 (Kelvedon-Marks Tey). The gipsy pickers were itinerant and many of them were ensconced in Cambridgeshire and the Midlands during the winter months. Their favourite occupation seems to have been making the wooden clothes pegs which were in common use.

Peas had the propensity to leave a deposit of nitrogen in the soil and the succeeding cereal crops were usually of good quality, and excellent yield. In 1900 there was 17,362a in Essex. It rose to a peak of 25,059a in 1913 and declined slightly during the war years only to rise to a new peak of 28,000a in 1924, the highest ever recorded. It remained high until the Second World War but in the 1950s a more average county acreage was around 3,500a. The days of picking fresh peas were over but the introduction of a new variety, Harrison's Glory, which could be swathed and combined, or combined direct, put a new emphasis upon dried peas as a useful break crop in the arable rotation. This declined in the face of imported peas and the invention of the pea viner.

An innovative enterprise was launched in 1959 when Richard Butler brought the first Mather and Platt mobile pea viner to Essex. The problem of freshness was still paramount and it required quick transportation to a canning factory. Goldhanger Fruit Farms had established a canning facility and there was a good demand. They were already producing shelled peas from static viners but the mobile viner was advantageous to them. In 1959 Golhanger Growers contracted 156a, of which seven acres were seeded, 36a were vined by the static viner at the factory and 113a was done by the mobile viner. They were put into 28lb trays and as Sir Richard Butler recounted; "they were stacked in our horse box trailer until lorries came to collect them. It was jolly hard work".[8] The demand for canned peas was catching the popular imagination. They had to be delivered to the factory at Goldhanger, having already been washed and cleaned, within four hours of vining in the field. It was a tight schedule and the factory operated nearly 24 hours a day. There was a problem with the 28lb trays and they were replaced with 5cwt bins.

Butler had formed Essex Pea Viners Ltd. but in 1968 it was changed to Butler's Peas Ltd. and was part of a larger co-operative named Essex Peas Ltd. There was a contracted acreage of 3,500a grown by the five members. Lord Rayleigh's Farms 950a, Strutt &

71 Feering. Hege Forage Plot Harvester designed to harvest large numbers of trial forage plots quickly and accurately. Peas being harvested prior to threshing. Hurst also used the machine in its grass and clover work and in the evaluation of its other forage breeding activities.

Parker Farms Ltd. 200a, Butler Farms 1,000a, Rankin Farms 600a and A.H. Philpot & Son 750a. Michael Parris was appointed the pea vining manager and it became an all absorbing and hectic operation.

The peas had to be drilled in sequence. There was a strict discipline which dictated that certain soils, and particular varieties were drilled in a batting order. Parris kept in constant communiction with the contracted growers to ensure that the peas were drilled, in a timetable, from February onwards, which would ensure that the eventual vining could be done when the peas were at their optimum quality. The 'season' was usually about six weeks. A succession of lorries carted the vined peas to Goldhanger but they were soon swamped by the seasonal influx and the static viner could not cope. Mobile viners were the answer but they required an intermediate plant between field and canning factory.

This was achieved when Essex Peas Ltd., by then with six mobile viners in the county went back to a static viner at the old Rivenhall aerodrome in 1962. It had been used as a Displaced Persons refuge after the war and there was a useful sewage disposal plant. The excess water after vining was toxic. It was vital to have a good supply of water and the septic tanks were 'Re-charged' by the local council with genuine sewage once a year – to enable the bugs to grow. The water could not be recycled.

The Rivenhall plant was operated by Butlers Peas Ltd. but included shareholders from the other large growers in the county. Butler's Peas expanded from Sir Richard's own farm to an operation which agreed contracts with other farmers. There was a proviso. They had to be within a 10 mile radius of Rivenhall so that the peas could be transported in the minimum of time. After vining, washing and re-loading they had to be at the factory at Goldhanger within four hours. It was a tight schedule, but there was no shortage of contracting farmers within the prescribed catchment area.

The static viners at Rivenhall and on Philip Green's farm at Writtle operated on a system of return loads. After the pea rice was stripped of its produce, the trash was returned on lorries and was ensiled for cattle feed.

At its peak about 5,000a had been absorbed by the vining boom. It was encouraged by the entrepreneurial skill of some of the leading farmers in the county. The compliance and proximity of the Goldhanger cannery was of paramount importance. At this period in the 20th century farmers were still cognizant of the need to produce break crops between cereals, but wheat was becoming the money-maker. Most break crops lost farmers money, or at best, gave a small return, with the prospect of an enhanced wheat crop the following year. Peas, and in particular vining peas, provided an attractive crop alternative.

Having a long tradition as the birthplace of quality seed Essex fields produced seed that was used throughout the UK. The soil and sunshine were conducive to the production of reliable products, and the farmers adept in the husbandry techniques.

Coggeshall Peas Ltd. was formed by Tom Harvey, and Michael Parris joined him after leaving Butler Peas. The prime business was to supply seed peas for the farmers growing the crop for vining and to trade generally in peas. Eventually Parris took over the business and continued with a Plant and warehouse at Curd Hall. This business existed between 1970–90. Semi-leafless peas were developed and enhanced the appeal of this crop. In 1977 Pulse & Commodity Traders Ltd., Coggeshall, was founded in a unique consortium of three independent companies; Church of Bures,Coggeshall Peas Ltd. and

72 1950 Burnham marshes. Bob Cole and a Hulme pea cutter. Fordson Major driven in reverse all day.

John K. King & Sons Ltd. £100,000 worth of equipment was installed with an annual capacity of 3,000 tons. A new word was added to the farmer's dictionary – 'Decorticated', a process of taking the skin off the pea and splitting it in preparation for the up-and-coming new trend of 'mushy peas'.

The development and sustained growing of peas in Essex, after fresh picking peas became outdated, was the establishment of Goldhanger Fruit Farms, as it was originally named, later Goldhanger Canners. A combination of three farms in Goldhanger which Jack Cohen bought as he already owned the neighbouring farm, Little London. The founder of Tesco (named after his wife Tessa Cohen), the first branch was opened at Maldon and it later became a nationally important chain of supermarkets.

When Cohen came to Goldhanger farms were losing money and he copied Wilkin & Sons and went into fruit farming, but put in a freezer unit at Hill Farm and produced goods for his shops. The cowshed was turned into a jam boiling plant and there were two horizontal retorts for steam cooking and cooking cans, from which developed a cannery. He pulled down a barn and expanded the warehouse.He installed a large steam boiler and started to can fruit and made pulp out of the surplus. More warehouses were built and, apart from processed peas during its hectic season, he also canned peaches, apricots, pineapples, plums, gooseberries and strawberries. Later expanded with rhubarb, black-currants and plums. The rhubarb came from Scotland. To find sufficient water a pipeline was constructed from Tiptree to the factory. Cohen was fast expanding his retail businesses and Goldhanger, which had once been the name of a famous plough, was sold to Chivers Hartley. Chivers' factory at Peterborough was sited on a disused airfield which the government wanted to derequisition and Goldhanger became busier. In summer, with students, there were 600 people employed. In winter 300, mainly women, continued to find a job. The business eventually went bankrupt when a heavy capital injection to double the output of cans proved unsuccessful.

Chivers Hartley amalgamated with Schweppes, later Cadbury Schweppes. It was part of the chequered story of Essex farming and, in its day had a useful input for farmers within its prescribed radius. The factory eventually closed and the site became the Beckenham Industrial Park.

Essex Wine

Grain maize had not been a success because of the northerly position of the UK. Corn-on-the-cob was largely a product of the United States and grain maize was also grown in Southern France. The Essex climate was not good enough to compete. The same was said about vineyards.

Wine growing was not seriously attempted until the 1960s when Robin Leslie at Langham, with his partner, Dick Pissaro, founded the Langham brand. There were vineyards in the county in the 12th century. Sir Godfrey De Mandeville had a large establishment at Great Waltham. There was another at Castle Hedingham. It is likely that the Romans were cultivating wine grapes in various parts of Essex up to about 300AD. Viticulture was almost certainly practised in the Blackwater valley towards Braintree during this period. The south facing slopes at Coggeshall would have been an ideal site. Following the early Roman wine production, Cistercian monks were recorded as having vineyards at Coggeshall, probably from the mid-14th century up to the dissolution. In Roman times wine was exported from Colchester until the Emperor Provus removed a ban on the setting up of local vineyards in Italy. The Dissolution of the monasteries played its part in the cessation of English vineyards. It was a cultural fact that wine could be produced in Essex – but the consumption was mainly personal.

In 1969 the first commercial crop of grapes was harvested by Mr. & Mrs. James Barrett at Crickes Green, Felsted. The Barretts had commenced planting four years earlier with up to 30 varieties to test their potential. The wine, marketed as 'Felstar' was a white wine of the Riesling Sylvaner type and there were 1,900 vines to the acre with a potential output of 2,000 bottle of wine.

In 1970 the Essex County Standard commented; "if the blackbirds, thrushes and wasps can be kept at bay there's going to be a bumper grape harvest at the only commercial vineyard in Essex".[9] In the 1980s other profitable vineyards were established at East Mersea and New Hall, Purleigh. In 1980 Kings looked at the possibility of grapes for wine production. The area and soil (within the constraints of the British climate) proved to be good. In 1981 one acre was planted with grafted rootstock (of Faber grapes). The first harvest was taken in 1984. 700 bottles were produced and the wine was entered into the English Vineyards Association annual competition. It won the gold medal for dry white wine for small vineyards. Production from 1984 to 1998 varied from zero to 3,300 bottles. The 1994 production was made into sparkling, the dry acidity of English grapes making an excellent 'champagne'. The final year of production was 1998. Following King's acquisition by A.B.F. in 1995, the vineyard was eventually sold and so with it Coggeshall's third period of wine production in two millenia. In the 1990s a vineyard was established at Great House, Great Bardfield, by Alan Jordan producing three tastes; sweet, medium dry and dry from his 1994 crop. It was marketed under the name 'Bardfield' and was first exhibited in the Food Hall at the 1997 Essex Show. Carters Vineyard at Boxted commenced production in 1995.

Marshland Grasses

Hailed in 1969 as "Britain's rarest crop"[10] 16 acres of Sorghum grass was grown by Sidney Hull, Turncole, Southminster. "It was a fantastic crop and no trouble to grow", Hull commented. The Sorghum seed was imported from Kansas and it was the first time it was grown on a field scale in the UK. It's purpose was to supplement the feed of a herd of 300 cows at Turncole.

Six years later Spartina Townsendii a wild grass and a native of the Essex marshes was identified as being in the C4 category. Plants in this bracket "are elephantine, almost prehistoric jungle plants related to other climatic regions. Now scientists are investigating the Essex marsh grasses".

Townsendii only grew in three places in Britain. The others at Southampton and in Scotland. The scientists became convinced that the genes from this plant could be crossed into other species which would produce an explosion in yields. Cereal crops were being bred shorter, but with longer heads, fodder crops relied on bulk matter and although the Essex experiments did not bring a dramatic revolution, it was another pioneering experiment.

A Sea of Yellow

Of all the new crops that were launched with a fanfare – but never sustained themselves, it was oil seed rape that became the only truly innovative crop to transform the Essex countryside in the second half of the century. Sugar Beet was the major introduction in the first 50 years but farmers choices were constrained with the demise of oats, red clover, mangolds, swedes and turnips which had together been grown on 206,480a (25.7%) in 1900.

Like many innovative crops, launched with optimism, rape was slow to spread into Essex. When the first MAFF returns separated rape for oil seed, from forage rape, there was only 148a. Twenty-three other counties were growing more and nearly 47% was grown in Hampshire, Dorset, Wiltshire and Berkshire where the greatest stimulus had emanated. The Essex contribution was less than 1% of the amount being grown in the UK. To prove that Essex farmers were not enamoured with this 'fancy' new crop, the year after (1969) there was only 32a! It took until 1973 for it to become accepted, and only on a modest scale. It had been rumoured that it would not grow in the Eastern Counties, and certainly not in the North of England or Scotland. Later events, and new varieties were to disprove that philosophy. The bright yellow fields became a curiosity. Farmers discovered that the profitability was good, it did not need additional capital and could be handled with ease. There was a husbandry stipulation that it could not be grown on the same field without a gap of five years. Another sacrosanct rule that was broken by intrepid farmers' persistence.

As the barley acreage gently declined farmers were looking for a new crop. Throughout the '70s the rape acreage grew. It reached 2,185a in 1974 and 13,300a in 1979. but was now established and farmers had acquired the necessary skills to manage it. In 1988 it covered nearly 53,000a and peaked in 1991 with just under 65,000a. This was in line with the UK peak and Essex was producing 6.8% of the UK annual output.

73 1950 Hatfield Peverel. Strutt and Parker (Farms) Ltd. static pea viner at Whitelands. Capacity was one ton of graded, vined peas per hour.

It had started as a spring sown crop yielding 17 cwts per acre. Autumn sown it was a swede rape, spring sown a turnip rape. The first varieties were high euricic acid which restricted its usage for human consumption, and limited the market. By 1987 winter hardy low euricic varieties had been introduced. The 'double zero' varieties followed these. The profusion of cross pollination problems resulted in the establishment of the Essex Seed Zoning Committee, a statutory scheme which required isolation distances of 600 metres between forage rapes and swede and turnip seed crops. In an extreme case the ESZC could apply to have an offending crop ploughed up. This power was rarely exercised.

The rape acreage would have expanded faster but it coincided with the expansion of wheat and although rape was a highly profitable crop towards the end of the 1980s, it declined after its peak in 1991 as the CAP payment structure was reformed, and, despite subsidies the market price plummeted. By 1996 there was 18,000a less than at the height of its popularity, but it remained a substantial crop, and when stubble burning was banned the continuous cereal farmers found that they needed a cleaning crop to carry out the work which the annual burning had achieved. At one time root crops had been the cleaning crops and cereals the dirty ones. For 40 years cereal fields had been kept clean by a combination of improved herbicides and scorching the stubbles. Needing a combinable break-crop farmers continued to grow rape.

One of the best success stories initiated by Kings in the early 1980s was the promotion of high erucic acid rape (H.E.A.R.). It was used as a 'slip agent' for polythene sheeting and polybag. (Without HEAR the polythene would stick like 'clingfilm').

However nearly all the production was based in Communist countries, East Germany, Poland etc. The U.K. manufacturer came to Kings who were perceived as innovators in new crops. It began with a very small trial in 1983 (25mm x 1m approx). Over the following 13 years the contracted acreage throughout the UK rose to 45,000a of which about 15–25% was grown in Essex. The other main industrial use was for bio-fuel. High erucic rape for the plastics industry remained a much sought after crop particularly suited to the Eastern half of the UK, from Scotland to the English Channel. The largest single European contracting company for HEAR was Kings.

The decline was exaggerated in the figures, which only applied to rape being grown for vegetable oil. There was another use. It had industrial connotations, although there were no facilities in the UK capable of converting it into fuel never-the-less under the CAP rules, it could be grown on set-aside fields for industrial purposes. Many, but not all, the area of statutory set-aside was planted with the same varieties that were grown for vegetable oil, treated in the same methods, but deployed under a strict contract with a merchant who directed the produce of these crops into a fuel producing factory. It is not possible to compute any figures for this thesis but it would be reasonable to assume that the total area in the county growing rape in the last years of the century was approaching 100,000a.

The bright yellow fields for almost two months in early summer enlivened the vista of the countryside – but was debated, and opposed by many of the new villagers who had occupied housing estates in rural parishes. They complained of the smell, and it could induce asthma related problems from the sweet aroma, and they complained that it was not a 'natural' colour for the countryside in summer. It was the same colour as the much heralded, and beloved daffodils which announce the end of winter and the beginning of spring!

CHAPTER 17

Spuds, Sugar and Mangel Wurzels

Turnips and swedes were grown as vegetables for the London market and for sheep feeding. During the century the area of potatoes averaged just below 10,000 acres until 1905. It more than trebled to over 35,000 acres by 1948, and the average for the five year period (1992/6) was 12,628a or a 26.7% increase from 1900. Mangolds were a favourite for cattle feeding occupying over 26,000a – but dwindled away to a minuscule area by 1970. The pattern of swedes and turnips was not dissimilar. From a 1900 area of over 20,000a there was only 79 acres in 1986.

There would appear to be no correlation between the increases and decreases in the sheep population of the county. The lowest sheep population 35,000 in 1953. Turnips were only grown on 696a. By 1958 the sheep population had more than doubled but the turnip area continued to decline. There is evidence that the acreage of mangolds monitored the number of milking cows, which rose steadily from 1940–44, when the area of mangolds rose from 6,872a to 10,112a in 1944 and remained above its pre-war levels until 1952 although cow numbers had declined by over 1,000 in the same period. The eventual unpopularity of mangolds was caused by the introduction of alternative feeding stuffs, notably lucerne cubes.

By 1970 many farmers were questioning the relative juxtaposition between sugar beet and potatoes. They were both high in labour demands. The price of beet was fixed by the factory and when the crop was poor there was no compensatory increase. This did not apply to potatoes where a poorer crop usually ensured an enhanced price. Thus the gross return per acre was either unaffected, or rose. It was the dry summers of 1975/6 which convinced farmers that they must make a choice, and it was sugar beet which became less popular. There was an increase in the number of farm reservoirs which were constructed. Irrigation, pumps, and pipe work had improved, and irrigation in a dry county like Essex became a viable proposition. It was an economic benefit for potatoes and the economics were matched by the acres which were grown. It was not feasible to install irrigation solely for sugar beet. Apart from specialised market garden crops, or as frost protection for vulnerable fruit, the main purpose of irrigation was potatoes. The areas devoted to these crops preserved a rough balance with the potato area between 20-30% above that of sugar beet.

Sugar Beet

The sugar beet factory at Felsted was opened in 1926 when there was 5,598a grown in the county. It was closed in 1982. Beet was being grown in Essex before the factory was built. The first commercial attempt to produce sugar from beet was launched by Robert and James Marriage at Ulting in 1832. The enterprise failed after two years. In 1868 a factory was established at Lavenham to extract sugar from beet, and factories in Essex at Silvertown for the extraction of sugar from imported cane.

In 1910 there was a determined effort to encourage Essex farmers to grow this new

74 1906 Smithfield Show. The Golden Tankard mangels which yielded 94tpa.

crop. Roger Carr of Mundon grew a trial field and Sir Valentine Crittall took a photograph to prove to MPs that it could be grown successfully. In January 1910 it was reported; "the sugar beet industry is reviving, and although, as far as our own neighbourhood is concerned, our experience was by no means encouraging. I suppose we should have no objections to start afresh on this line provided we were sanguine as to the result".[1] Advertisements were published in Essex newspapers during the summer of 1910 proclaiming that the yields of sugar beet would range from 15 to 18 tons per acre and it was rumoured that a Dutch firm had acquired 26a of land in Essex to grow beet and build a factory. It was prepared to invest £200,000.

A meeting was held at the Moot Hall in Colchester to hear more about the proposed new factory. It was to be built at Maldon and the site would be,

"so situated that they can easily ship their stuff in the sprit-sail barges and so have it conveyed to the factory at extremely low rates, and therefore one of the great difficulties which was presented in many new industries, mainly, the cost of carriage by road or railway, disappeared by reason of the location".[2]

William Hasler, one of the leading protagonists and a director of the East Anglian Sugar

185

Co.Ltd., told the farmers that whatever quantity they grew in the first year they would grow more in the second and more still in the third. Hasler explained the practical methods of dealing with the crop; "it was usual to use a short handled two-pronged fork, which could be put under the root with one hand and the aid of the foot, and with the other hand the root, thus loosened, could be pulled out of the soil".[2]

Essex farmers dabbled with sugar beet – not always encouraged by the results. At Terling, Edward Strutt decided to grow a small experimental acreage in 1910.

> "When the crop was ready for lifting a Dutch man came from Cantley and said that the roots must be hand-dug with short three-pronged forks to avoid bruising and bleeding. Twenty-five of these forks duly arrived from Holland and the work began.
>
> However suitable these forks may have been for friable Dutch soils, they were quite impracticable for Essex. Within a few hours every fork was bent or broken... The roots were satisfactorily ploughed the next day, but the yield was barely six tons and the sugar content low. The crop was not tried again for some years".[3]

At the annual show of the Witham Root Club in October 1910 Sir Fortescue Flannery MP in an effort to popularise sugar beet offered to remit the rent of five acres of land on each of his farms [at Wethersfield] provided it was grown with sugar beet. He thought that local farmers should seriously consider the possibility of this crop.

The Cantley factory was built before the First World War. In the four years 1924/8, 15 factories were built in England and Scotland. But Essex farmers had grown sugar beet in a small way since the pre-war experiments. 158a in 1913, 222a in 1921 and 1,631 in 1925, the year before Felsted was built. The beet was processed at Cantley and one of the objections rested on the fact that the crop was worth 17s.0d. (85p) per ton but would cost 5s.0d. (25p) for transport. In 1924 the rail rates to Cantley from 10 railway stations in Essex ranged from 6s.6d. (32½p) at Manningtree to 8s.6d. (42½p) at Chelmsford. Of the 10 stations quoted [4] it is noteworthy that half of them were in the Tendring Hundred, two in the north west corner, one each at Maldon, Witham and Chelmsford.

Before the Felsted site was finalised there were suggestions that Maldon would be a good location. Another idea was Manningtree but the response from farmers was disappointing. There was another proposal in 1924 to build a factory at Colchester if farmers would guarantee at least 4,000a or up to 6,000a. "That guarantee was not forthcoming and the Colchester scheme was dropped".[5] The Felsted factory was built in a centralised position which would attract beet from farmers in Cambridgeshire, Hertfordshire and parts of Suffolk as well as Essex. The Ipswich factory took beet from the Manningtree area and some farms in the north sent their beet to Bury St. Edmunds

Felsted did not meet with approval from everyone. The vicar of Dunmow and a rural dean wrote; "the sugar beet factory at Felsted is a blot on the landscape visible for many miles, typical of the utter soullessness of modern industrialism which thinks only of profits and tramples ruthlessly on beauty, even on the beauty of a countryside like ours. It is an outrage".[6]

The manager of the Cantley factory told Essex farmers that he would prefer a smaller acreage from a number of growers rather than a small number of growers with a large acreage and suggested that the ideal area for a farmer was between 4 and 10 acres. He anticipated that 75% would be delivered by rail. Lorries were commonplace in 1925.

FELSTEAD SUGAR FACTORY

SUGAR BEET

IS STILL

THE MOST PAYING CROP

TO GROW

THE NEW Two Year Contracts 1929=30

Are now available giving you the following

GUARANTEED PRICES.

Beets with 15½% Sugar Content	... 46/- per ton.
,, ,, 16% ,, ,,	... 47/6 ,, ,,
,, ,, 16½% ,, ,,	... 49/- ,, ,,
,, ,, 17% ,, ,,	... 50/8 ,, ,,
,, ,, 17½% ,, ,,	... 52/4 ,, ,,
,, ,, 18% ,, ,,	... 54/- ,, ,,
,, ,, 18½% ,, ,,	... 55/8 ,, ,,
,, ,, 19% ,, ,,	... 57/4 ,, ,,

Apart from Direct Cash Returns you receive Handsome Indirect Profits by Heavier Yields in Cereal Crops following Sugar Beet.

GIVE SUGAR BEET A TRIAL,

It will convince you of its worth and pay you well.

APPLY NOW TO:—

Second Anglo - Scottish Beet Sugar Corporation, Ltd.,

FELSTEAD,   ESSEX.

75 1928. Prices to encourage sugar beet growing.

Within a short time 75% of the crop was arriving by road "we find ourselves with excellent rail silos but with all too few rail beet to put in them, and with totally inadequate road reception facilities" lamented F.E. Thornhill, the factory manager.[7] The Felsted authorities were surprised by the interest taken up.

Growers demonstrations were well attended. In 1930 Arthur Lodge, Roxwell, held one on his farm. Fraser Ruffle who farmed at Gestingthorpe and The Nunnery, Castle Hedingham, had a beet 'investigation' demonstration on his farm. "In spite of the uncertainty of future beet prices the events were attended by over 160 farmers, and it was very evident that the interest in the crop was being maintained".[8] Sugar beet singling, a new job for farm workers, was required because each seed had the propensity to produce three shoots and when 'doubles' were left they did not produce sizeable bulbs. By 1930 sugar beet singling competitions were annual events. 77 workers competed at Maldon, Good Easter and Wethersfield. The competitions started at 6.30pm and there was a target for the plants of 8ins. apart. The prize winner at Maldon completed just over 300 yards in an hour.

In 1936 plots were laid down to test the effects of lime on Bernard Speakman's farm at Danbury. At Gilbert Baker's farm at Mundon there were tests with potash and phosphates. It was confirmed that a heavy coating of farmyard manure was vital. "The result on these low manure plots is, perhaps, more marked than one would expect. The crop on these plots being practically a failure".[9] Little by little both farmers and the Anglo-Scottish Beet Sugar Corporation evolved a compendium of husbandry criteria which helped to increase the yield and profitability of the crop.

It was recognised that Essex beet had a high sugar content. From a starting price of 15 % sugar content there was, in 1928, an increase of nearly 25% if the sugar rose to 19%. In 1971 the Felsted level was the highest in the country at 17.23% and in 1972 at 17.66% was equal top of the UK list with Bury St.Edmunds.

Was sugar beet the cash crop that would be a life-line to Essex farmers? The tempting advertisements in the Essex Farmers Journal convinced many.

The crop held out the promise of a profit of £2 per acre. Ten acres of beet could produce the equivalent of a labourers' wages for three months. On an acreage basis the profitability of beet was four times as good as cows. It was a temptation and a salvation, albeit that there were limited contracts, it was an unknown crop, and it was labour intensive. The factory had no problem in contracting sufficient to sustain its slicing capacity.

In 1924 John Wilkes, Elmdon Bury, Saffron Walden grew a crop of 16½ tons pa. He made a profit of over £9 per acre. It was statistics such as these which encouraged farmers. In the first year, 1926, the average Essex crops were 8.9 tons per acre and a sugar content of 17.9%. The following year the acreage nearly doubled to just under 10,000a but only produced 5.5 tons per acre. Farmers lost money on a crop that had been heralded as a salvation. The following year the area halved and was below the 1926 area. It later started a slow recovery. In 1928 it was recorded that;"sugar beet has been a most profit-able crop on the continent for many years and has considerably improved agricultural conditions there. The most hopeful line for improving the beet crop is in increasing the yield per acre, as we are well behind the average yield of the continental countries".[10]

Yields varied widely from year to year. Having achieved 10.9 tons per acre in 1936 the two following years were drought prone summers. 1937 (6.70 tons), 1938 (5.80 tons). In 1939 the crop yielded 11 tons per acre. Average for the first five years at Felsted was under 8 tons per acre. In the five years 1936/40 it was nearly nine tons and in 1950/4 it was just under 12 tons. Improved varieties, farmers' expertise and favourable seasons were producing crops above those grown in the initial years. The factory had been

76 1947 Dunmow Martels Farm. Unloading sugar beet by hand. Throwouts on the left were 10%.

designed to take 500 tons of beet per day. Within a year this capacity was doubled and by 1949 there was a limit of just under 2,000 tons. In 1949 there was a target of 17,000a in Essex but it was anticipated that the area could expand to 20,000a.

It topped this figure during the Second World War when beet produced the total sugar ration for the UK. In 1948 just over 21,000a were grown within the county and this figure remained very constant until 1973 and thereafter declined. This belies the fact that yields had increased and in 1954 Felsted was achieving a throughput of 2,400 tons per day. In the years since it had been an innovative, and rather strange crop there had been; "a six-fold increase in acreage which produced, in a record year a ten-fold increase in tonnage".[11]

Felsted was the southern most factory to be built in the UK although farmers in Hampshire/Surrey campaigned for a factory. Considering that the sugar content was assisted by the sunshine quotient it might have been expected that the British Sugar Corporation, as it later became, would have encouraged the growing of sugar beet in the southern counties. By 1980 the Essex area had declined to 15,412a because world, and sugar politics were exerting pressures. Farmers found themselves being offered smaller contracts. The area was down to 10,500a by 1984 and remained constant for the remainder of the century. Felsted was closed in 1982 and the Bury St. Edmunds factory was enlarged. Built in the year when Britain went on strike the factory had a life of 55 years.

The problem of 'doubles', which were the bane of growers' lives was solved with the introduction of mono-germ seed. It was researched and developed in Essex.

"High above Maldon, commanding magnificent views of the Blackwater, down to Mersea Island, and with not a sugar beet field in sight, stands Woodham Mortimer Hall, an unique house where they live, breathe, and sleep sugar beet. Research work being carried out there will have effects as far away as Colorado, Pakistan and India".[12]

Sidney Ellerton operated this research station for Bush-Johnson Ltd. who were the only wholly British sugar beet seed producers of international renown. The station was founded in 1942.

The crop contributed to the survival of Essex farmers. Its labour requirements were replaced by mechanical harvesters. Sugar beet remained important.

Potatoes

Exactly when the first field of potatoes was grown in Essex is not known. In 1664 farmers were being urged to consider, what had been an 'exotic' plant grown in the gardens of mansion houses, as a commercial crop. A native of Peru the potato took a long time to become a popular British food and in the poorer households its place was taken by turnips or swedes. By 1767 Essex farmers were growing potatoes on a large scale but it was in a restricted corner mainly around Ilford. "The profit is exceedingly great. The landlord of the Red Lyon Inn at Ilford sold three rood as they grew, without any expense of taking up...for £9 and some Irish men who had hired about two acres took up 40 sacks which amounts to above £20 per acre".[13] Young ascribes the introduction of potatoes to Irish growers and commented "but of late the farmers have got pretty much into the culture themselves". Although the land was suitable in many parts of the county, excepting the heavy clay, Young pin-pointed a very small area within 3/4 miles of Ilford.

Messrs. Griggs, Hill House, Messing wrote in 1794 that although they were a lucrative crop when sold in Covent Garden they could not be grown with success except; "in light lands where the situation is such as to afford a constant supply of town or other good manure".[14] The expansion of potato growing occurred in the final years of the 18th century. In 1796 it was recorded that there were 300a in Barking, 450a in East Ham, 120a in Little Ilford, about 200a in Leyton, 50a in Wanstead and about 500a in West Ham. "Fourteen years later (1811) there were then about 600a in the parish of Barking, about 80a in Walthamstow, about 200a in Wanstead and about 420a in West Ham".[15] Young also noted that potatoes were more largely cultivated in Essex "than perhaps in any other southern county".

By this time they were grown at Hornchurch, Averley, Ingrave. In the north west corner of the country at Saffron Walden, Chesterford and Birdbrook. In central Essex at Terling, Gosfield and Hedingham, and near Colchester at Ardleigh. They were often used for animal feeding – but not sheep. Farmers had to be wary that cows did not choke to death. At this time Tom Pittman, Barking, was growing between 200/300a every year. The constraint was the lack of manure from London, which was transported by barge down the Thames, and only reached a restricted number of farms. Chalk, was unavailable if the distance was more than a horse and tumbril could travel. Potatoes remained an 'exotic' crop.

By 1867 there were 9,345a, just over 1% of the farmland in the county. In 1900 the area was still the same as it had been 33 years earlier. In 1958 potatoes covered 4.6% and an area of 33,000a. It was the peak. In 1970 3.6%, 1980 2.2% and 1990 2.0%. The constraint was the licensing system administered by the Potato Marketing Board. This prevented any rush into potatoes after a good year, and was a safeguard against ruinous dumping in glut years. The balance of production and demand was achieved and there was very little criticism from farmers about this system.

Throughout the years the ratio of earlies to main crop remained constant with 25% of early potatoes. Essex could not compete with Cornwall and Cyprus in the days before new potatoes were available all the year round. Prices were high but the yield low. A wet day in the West Country could restrict lifting, Essex farmers with a drier day could 'steal' the market. Early potatoes were good money and despite its percentage of the farmed area of the county, the fluctuating fortunes of the potato crop were the barometer for re-investment, particularly in sales of new tractors and other machinery. Potato growing was always regarded as a very profitable occupation. It had echoes of Young 200 years earlier; "the profit is exceedingly great".

The 1975/6 drought years persuaded Essex farmers that they could not continue to grow the crop without an on-farm irrigation system. In 1966 it was estimated that 400 farms in the county had irrigation with a potential of around 14,000a (2%). The potato area was around 25,000a. In 1977 it was just under 19,000a and still a short-fall in the irrigating capacity on farms. The introduction of polythene covering entire fields was an innovation that sparked a new phase in potato growing from the late 1980s.

Yields had averaged 7 tons per acre in the period 1938-47. There was a steady increase in the immediate post war years as new and more prolific varieties were introduced. In the five years 1978/82, the average yield of main crop was 14.7 tpa and in the succeeding five years, to 1987 it was 15.5. These levels continued to the end of the century but there was a greater emphasis upon 'quality', which was not always commen-surate with enhanced crops. Lifting techniques and plastic film, coupled with the scientific usage of irrigation contributed to these improvements.

From earliest times potatoes had been labour intensive. Before the turn of the century fields had been planted in the same manner that were used in gardens. A labourer had a bag of chitted seed strapped around his waist and a hewn 'dibber', usually elm which had been cut from the hedge. A foot position was etched out and the end was pointed. By pressing his heel on the notch the dibber was then twisted and the potato dropped in the resulting hole. They were normally sown eight inches apart and the rows were 12ins. Before 1900 a system had evolved on the most progressive farms of opening up the ridges with a 'double-tom' and muck was spread into the bottom of the furrows, the potatoes were dropped at intervals and another double-tom split the ridges, covered the seed, and left the land in baulks. There were attempts at automatic, but hand operated potato planters by 1945 but the operation was not fully mechanised until the 1960s.

Harvesting was similarly expensive. The initial method had been to use a graip, a stubby three-pronged fork to lift them. They were then collected in baskets by women and children and put into tumbrils.

"Potatoes were planted by machine – two of us either side with the box of potatoes in the middle – but harvesting was by hand. The women had opened-out hesian sacks tied around their waists which, when full of potatoes, were emptied into hundred-weight sacks. I only managed buckets. At the end of the day they were usually weighed in the field and then two men with a strong stick between them would toss them onto the trailer or lorry".[16]

77 1965 Langham. Majestic potatoes being riddled at Messrs. E. Halsall & Sons' Little Hall Farm, before despatch to Smithfield market.

One of the first harvesters to be successful was produced by Salmons whose factory at Great Dunmow constructed a self-propelled model. It was later improved and amalgamated with the Armer machine from Eire and became known as the Armer-Salmon. They also produced a beet harvester which was the first to be produced in the UK. It was the introduction of successful machinery which counterbalanced the spiralling costs of labour.

In 1907 it was remarked that; "the cultivation of early potatoes is now generally unremunerative in Essex, owing to the home-grown supply being anticipated on the London market by supplies from abroad. These changes ruined many Essex growers".[17] Despite the speed of transportation there was still a market for early potatoes which Essex farmers, with their less frost-prone climate could produce in time to catch the early market. Potato growing developed into a highly specialised operation including washing and polythene packing on the farm. The enterprise of Peter Rix at Great Horkesley was in the forefront of this on-farm vertical integration.

Mangolds

Mangolds, or mangels, or mangel-wurzels was a crop which was grown on over 26,000a in 1900 and was a substantial part of the diet for cows. It declined to the point of extinction but was an important crop for dairy farmers.

Young in 1807 [18] despite his comprehensive assessment of all crops, did not mention mangolds. Other 19th century writers equally neglected any mention of mangolds although turnip cultivation, as a supplement for winter cow feeding, and later cabbages for the same purpose both received considerable attention. In 1850 Caird related the mangold growing technique of William Hutley at Witham. "He manures highly for his mangold-wurzel, the yellow globe variety, using 30 loads of dung, four cwt rape dust, and two cwt guano, per acre. The result is a yield of 35 tons an acre over his whole crop, and that he is now selling at 15s.0d. (75p) on the spot, to be sent to London which is equal to £26 5s.0d. an acre (£26.25p). The green crop thus appears to be much more remunerative than the corn crop when it can be disposed of on such advantageous terms".[19] Caird concluded by urging farmers to consider mangolds as a useful crop. It is evident that they were not widely grown.

Despite the silence from some leading authorities there was over 26,000a in 1866, the earliest MAFF returns, and it was coupled to nearly 29,000a of turnips and swedes. Some of the latter were used for human consumption but many were fed to animals.

There was an ancient belief that the shortage of winter fodder necessitated a ritual autumn slaughtering, a belief that has been questioned by historians. It is certain that the difficulties of winter feeding reduced the milk output from cows.

Mangolds came into popularity many years after turnips and were largely restricted to the east and south east of Britain. They required a higher mean temperature whereas swedes and turnips were more widely grown in the north of England and Scotland. Essex, with its large dairy herd was an ideal proving ground for this 19th century crop and, despite Mr.Hutley selling his mangolds in London, they were quickly adopted by as an addition to the winter rations. The crop at Witham in 1850 was an outstanding one. But in 1907 Kings of Coggeshall quoted several growers with yields over 70 tons pa.

Mangolds had an attribution which enhanced their popularity. As opposed to potatoes, and certainly sugar beet, the mangold grew 75%/90% out of the ground.

Supporting itself by a tap root with a luxuriant foliage. They were easy to harvest, unlike sugar beet, and by a gentle rocking could be pulled up with a firm hand-grip on the dying leaves in late autumn. The leaves were then twisted off, not breaking the skin and the mangolds clamped by covering with straw until after Christmas. They lost some of their moisture and prevented the animals from scouring. Small mangolds could choke a cow and they were normally sliced by a root pulper and mixed with chopped straw. Cottis at Epping, Hunt at Earls Colne, Whitlock at Great Yeldham and Bentall at Maldon were local companies which produced root cutting and chaff chopping machinery. The typical ration for cows was described by Sir William Gavin;

> "The usual winter maintenance ration for cows as sliced mangolds mixed with straw chaff and a little rice meal, middlings and flaked maize, the whole being allowed to heat for a few hours in the heap before use. Wet brewers grains were fed whenever available and the production ration made up with decorticated cotton and linseed cake. Hay at £4 per ton was considered an extravagance"[20]

This was a better ration than most dairy farmers would have given their cows in 1914. But mangolds and chaff with a light addition of a concentrate was the average feed.

CHAPTER 18

Apples and Orchards

Commercial fruit growing expanded rapidly in the 1930s. Farms solely devoted to producing fruit were established all over the county. The peak was reached in 1955 when there were over 13,000a of orchards. The story of the century was of an increase of orchards, mainly apples, for the first half, and a decline in the second half. There were 2,501a in 1900 and 2,699a in 1996. The graph had gone up and come down again.

The rise was engendered by the enthusiasm of newcomers. When Thomas Ridgwell died in 1926 his orchards on the Orsett Estate were taken over by Sir Francis Whitmore and became known as The Orsett Fruit Farm. They were grubbed up in 1964. With the ease of transporation, and the lack of urgency with apples, London fruit merchants such as Samuel King, 73 Carnarvon Road, Stratford E.15 Bought the 94a Glebe Farm at Abberton in 1922 and planted apples and plums on its south facing slopes near the coast. The expansion of fruit growing in the county and its suitability was recorded by Lawrence Taylor, Galleywood.

> "Essex seems very free from frost...a good water supply is most necessary, either ponds or running water in ditches...In the earlier days nearness to the railway was considered a great asset, but in these days of motor transport it is not necessary to study this point so much. One big reason in favour of fruit-growing in Essex is that land is cheap; suitable land with good house and buildings can be bought for under £20 per acre".[1]

Samuel King paid £28 per acre.

Roger Edwards, Fontenay, Wickham Bishops, wrote; "Essex is largely a dessert apple county...the soils and climate are admirably suited to growing high quality dessert apples with Cox's and Worcester's second to none, as we believe anywhere in the world".[2]

Essex hop growing disappeared in the 19th century. Cherry orchards too had an antiquity in Essex which was marked on Chapman and André's 1777 map with orchards at Mucking, Southminster and Rainham. Every farmstead had its orchard filled with ancient trees. They provided the needs of the family. Apples, pears, cherries and bush-types such as gooseberries and currants were grown. There were few attempts to commercialise or capitalise the fruit as a crop, usually given away after a bumper season.

The D'Arcy Spice is reputed to have originated in Tolleshunt D'Arcy at The Hall but in 1848 John Harris, a nurseryman at Broomfield propagated from these old trees and sold them under the name, 'Baddow Pippin'. The Fruit Manual (1884) recorded them as 'Essex Spice'. Abbotts of Ardleigh held stocks of the variety for over 100 years and in the 1960s they were still receiving orders for them.

In the 1930s there was competition from Californian fruit, and English growers swamped their own markets with inferior products. Essex farmers were advised that the

78 1900 Tolleshunt D'Arcy. Picking a heavy crop of pears.

best outlet for small apples was to use them as pig food. "There are no marketing expenses attached to this method of disposal, it is economically worth considering".[3]

In was in the spririt of upgrading standards that the first Essex Commercial Fruit Show was held in 1928 and in 1936 *'Associated Fruit Growers of Essex Ltd.* (hereafter AFG)' was founded. The annual Fruit Show was held until the war, revived in 1947 when it was staged at the Kursaal Southend and again in 1948 at the Corn Exchange in Colchester but Leslie Clark lamented; "it is evident that in present circumstances and in its present form it is not successful. It does not attract the general public and nothing like enough support is given by entries".[4] Despite attempts to amalgamate the autumn Fruit Show with the Essex Agricultural Society's annual match. The EAS complained that there was "an apparent lack of interest on the part of growers"[5] who had not supported the Essex Show at Saffron Walden in that year. The EAS said they would not support a second show at Colchester although they would support classes at the Ploughing Contest at Boreham.

The 1950 Show was held in a hangar at Boreham airfield "the lighting was but a tangle of wires and cardboard boxes, the stands for the boxes looked bleak and skeletal and the general background of sausage-like corn sacks and heavy machinery was not ideal...The Show, as usual was difficult – almost impossible – to find in the vast open spaces of Boreham airfield".[6] It was never revived in its traditional format.

AFG had twin objectives. To co-ordinate marketing and also to provide a co-operative method of obtaining supplies such as cardboard boxes and plant protective materials. There were 32 members at the outset with 2,000a under an Association label, 'Essex Fruit', and imposed quality control. A year later, in 1937 another company, Fruit Packers (Essex) Ltd. was formed and a fruit packing station was erected at Witham which was designed to deal with the apple and pear crops by packing them in identical boxes under one trademark, and promising wholesale merchants regular quantities; "one of the serious criticisms which has been directed at the home producer by the wholesale distributors will be overcome by this system".[7]

79 1912 Tiptree Hall Farm.
Ladies hoeing strawberries.

Packing equipment to deal with 1,000 bushels a day and a refrigerated gas storage plant for 200 tons was constructed. During the war cheese was stored in this pack house for the Ministry of Food. The fruit was marketed under the trademark 'ECO' (Essex County Orchards) and in 1941 marketed 2,400 tons. The following year this increased to 4,600 tons. The seventh AGM of AFG reported that "spray manufacturers had enlisted the collaboration of the Association in investigating the life history and control of Red Spider".[8]

Arranging discounted prices for requisites became more difficult in the post-war period and in 1972 AFG was amalgamated with Nursery Trades (Lea Valley) Ltd., formed in 1922 and had itself amalgamated with Glass-house Growers Sales Ltd., a marketing co-operative society at Waltham Abbey. After AFG was absorbed by its new parent the depot at Witham continued in use. Competitions to uplift growers standards were taken over by fruit discussion groups which arose at Witham and Chelmsford, and in Colchester which finally amalgamated with East Suffolk but fruit growing was a rapidly shrinking industry in Essex.

Another development was the foundation of the *'Land Settlement Association'* (hereafter LSA) in 1934. Started under the auspices of the Carnegie U.K. Trust to relocate distressed miners from the north of England, they bought two estates in Essex, at Great Yeldham and at Ardleigh. At Great Yeldham the farms were split up into small holdings with a newly built, but modest, house, a piggery and between a half and one acre of land. Forty holdings were provided at Great Yeldham with others at Little Yeldham and Tilbury-Juxta-Clare. Manscroft, and Change with Hyde and Mashey all came under this new estate which initially had 100 small holdings. At Ardleigh the estate covered 393a with 59 small holdings between four/seven acres. It became known as the Foxash Estate, Lawford. The LSA was geared to providing packing and marketing on a co-operative basis.

Foxash built a packing station, a propagating unit, offices and stores. In 1970 the propagating unit was supplying 300,000 tomato plants, 8,000 cucumbers and 1m celery plants annually.

The LSA collected the produce from each holding, transported it to the packing station, at Lawford, where it was graded and packed. In 1970 the output of the Foxash tenants was £306,370. They were marketing lettuce all the year round, tomatoes from March to October and celery from May to December.

Typical of the tenants was Ron Smith, a former farm worker from Felsted who was helped by his wife and a full-time worker. He grew 30,000 cabbage lettuce in his glasshouse and followed these with tomatoes, then another cabbage lettuce. He had an acre of celery. "Ron Smith is one of the tenants who earns a very good income from his holding and is proud of it".[9]

Some of the County Council smallholdings were purchased with the objective of reinstating soldiers from the First World War, which they had been promised would give them "a land fit for heroes". These were around 5/7 acres each, the returning servicemen were settled on holdings where the primary occupation was the production of soft fruit, vegetables and some orchards, notably the Boxted estate, near Colchester and Eastwood adjacent to Southend airport.

The Boxted estate was purchased for £10,499 in February 1919. The sale of produce that year amounted to £2,290. In 1920 a further 252a were bought at Romford, Braxted,

80 1930 Tiptree. Well-dressed schoolboys picking apples.

Great Oakley and Beaumont. The land was divided up into holdings of under 10a. Timber homes with thatch or pantile roofs were built at a cost of £575 each. More permanent brick built houses were costing £1,000 each in 1920.

The applications from ex-soldiers came pouring in. They were disillusioned and felt betrayed for their wartime exertions. It was government policy to placate them with the offer of a smallholding. By 1920 1,507 men had applied for land in Essex, there was a shortfall in the land which the County Council was able to buy. Inevitably the number of ex-servicemen settled was lower than the number who applied.

At a meeting of the Small Holdings Committee of the C.C. Capt. L. Cranmer Byng asked for the number of ex-servicemen who were smallholders. Alderman the Hon. E.G. Strutt replied that the Committee had approved of 400 and got 97 on the land. "In the next three or four months they would probably approve of another 100, and they hoped by Michaelmas to get another 100 on the land".[10] (See also p.110)

There were no centralised facilities for marketing, unlike the LSA 14 years later. Faced with this problem, and an unfamiliarity with the technical aspects of commercial growing, the fall-out rate was high. Eventually a nucleus of hardened survivors, or their descendants, remained. The holdings were mainly bought outright by the tenants from the 1960s onwards. The Ministry of Agriculture took over the LSA estates in 1948 and these were sold, at advantageous prices, although the LSA marketing operation at Lawford continued to be successful to the end of the century.

The Tiptree Jam Factory

Probably the most world renowned product of Essex farming was simply known as 'Tiptree'. The output from Wilkin's jam factory spread into every country in the world. In 1911 the Company was awarded a Royal Warrant. The receipt of this award was recorded by Maura Benham;

> "The two 'gentleman of official standing' who brought this news were shown some Tiptree jam setting out for Khartoun, Zurgeru (Nigeria), Rangoon and the Falkland Islands, and were told this was due to the fact that where young English men go in quest of enterprise, whether it be rubber, coffee, tea, diamonds, gold as Military men or as Civil Servants, some of them send for 'Tiptree jam'".[11]

Arthur Charles Wilkin (1835–1913) was the son of a Tiptree farmer and when farming became unprofitable in the 1880s he started growing fruit, raising fruit trees and roses. Strawberries were particularly successful on the very light Tiptree soil but there were difficulties in the transportation to London, often being carried in coal trucks covered with black tarpaulines. The crop was ruined before it arrived at its destination. He continued the traditional pattern of Essex farming, but as prices declined he increased his fruit. What Gladstone called "infant undertakings"[12] soon grew to a large commercial undertaking. Wilkin's first overseas contract was with a merchant from Australia who suggested that the name on the label should be; 'Britannia Fruit Preserving Company' because it would find a better trade in Australia. It became a limited company in 1888 and the name was changed to Wilkin & Sons Ltd. in 1905.

H. Rider Haggard visited Tiptree in 1891 and wrote "we walked over the Tiptree Farm that is planted with strawberries, currants, gooseberries, raspberries and ordinary crops sown to the rest of the land".[13] By that time the jam was being sold to over 8.000 customers. Three hundred acres were planted to various soft fruits including cherries, damsons, quinces, bullaces, crab apples, cranberries, dessert plums and greengages. Strawberries remained the centrepiece of the Wilkin's fame and, with an area around Dagenham, strawberry growing expanded in the county.

In 1911 Wilkin's had 18,000 customers and there were agents in India, Africa, America and "demand was springing up in Germany, and at more irregular intervals, shipments were being made to every part of the world".[11] Selling his fruit as jam Wilkin bought more land to keep his factory supplied. He bought back Trewlands, Tiptree which had been sold by his father in 1880. In 1900 he bought Feering Hill and Brook Hall 600a where, amongst a choice variety of quality fruit he introduced the loganberry from California, a cross between a dewberry and a raspberry. They were also leasing fruit farms at Tolleshunt D'Arcy, Beacontree Heath and Dagenham.

After his death in 1913, there was a disagreement between his two sons, one wanted to expand the factory, and the other the farms. Stanley Wilkin took over the farms and built up a herd of Guernsey cows and a milk round in Tiptree. He specialised in Large Black pigs and a boar was named 'Tiptree Conserve'. This pig was four times champion at agricultural shows in 1922. There was a flock of sheep producing both mutton and wool. There was also a poultry business utilising 11a. Fruit growing remained the prime interest of the farming operations. The Dagenham farm was hived-off to another brother and Tiptree became the focus of the family interests. In 1951 there was over 1,000a. Later Wilkin's purchased 400a at Tollesbury and then 102a Hunts Farm in that parish. Six

81 1920 Tiptree. 8 Young men picking Victoria plums.

hundred acres was under fruit with 100a of strawberries including the famous Little Scarlet. Four hundred acres was growing general farm crops.

At Wivenhoe J. Worsp built a small cold fruit storage unit. A Kelvedon company sent over two workers to Tiptree to mend torn sacks. In 1961 the traditional pattern of production had changed. It was becoming less commercially attractive to grow plums and cooking apples. Government grants encouraged grubbing up old trees and replanting with young ones. The Guernsey dairy herd, the retail milk business and a farm in Suffolk were sold in 1963. They increased the cold store at Wivenhoe with a ground area of 9,000 sq.ft. With decimalisation and metrication the company kept abreast by introducing jars with twist-off caps instead of the previous push-off ones.

Picking strawberries at the peak of perfection required an army of people to gather the crop in six weeks. Pre-war there had been little shortage of women and children to do this, but as more of them acquired full-time employment the Tiptree enterprises began to suffer. The same problem affected all fruit picking until a blackcurrant harvester was developed by NIAE (National Institute of Agricultural Engineering) at Silsoe, which involved shaking the berries from the bush and this was the saviour of the continuation of blackcurrant growing in England. Pea viners were a success and achieved the almost impossible task of shelling peas.

In 1958 Wilkin's established a summer camp for young people. Overseas students, many from Eastern European countries were offered working holidays in Britain. Wilkin arranged the work permits, accommodation in a camp on the outskirts of Tiptree and daily transport to the fields. The average was about 120 students annually. It became an answer to the hand-picking problem. In the 1990s Wilkin were producing 43 jams and

82 1910? Tiptree Wilkins Jam Factory. Girls (left) sorting fruit into pans, then taking off jam. Empty pan in front is ready for next batch.

marmalades but the Tiptree Little Scarlet Strawberry Conserve remained the mainstay of the business.

The Wilkin story put Tiptree and Essex firmly on the map. They were not the only company involved in jam making. William and Charles Volckman had a jam factory at High Street, Stratford, in 1890 and the Burnham Preserving Co. at Burnham in 1929. Chivers, who had originated their jam production at Histon and Trumpington in Cambridge also ventured over the border. "The working men of Histon, in numerous cases, do not hesitate to pay 50s. to 60s. an acre for land; whilst a few miles off, in the adjoining county of Essex, land cannot even be let rent free in numerous parts. On the other side of the Colne Valley is a farm which, a few years since, could not be let or sold to anyone. Mr. Chivers, however, has now transformed it into a veritable Arcadia". [14]

W.W. Bull, Ramsden Bellhouse, was another of the early pioneers seeking to preserve, and conserve the fruits of the summer for all-year-round use. Jam was a method of fruit conserving, Bull built an evaporator "for the purpose of drying plums, apples and pears... he is able to dry seven bushels of plums at one time, and has kept for two years plums dried by himself".[15] This was a small but enterprising preserving experiment.

Elsenham

Sir Walter Gilbey of Elsenham founded a jam factory in 1893 which continued to produce 'Elsenham' jam during the 20th century. Sir Walter was an eminent agriculturist although he had founded his wine merchanting company W & A Gilbey as a result of profits when with one of his four brothers they obtained commissions in the Pay Corps, went out to the Crimea and set up a business selling refreshments – mainly port and brandy. He was of a Bishops Stortford family and bought a country estate and became a baronet in 1893. He involved himself with his fruit farm at Elsenham and bought Great Sampford Hall 1,800a.

Gilbey bred cart horses and was a prolific writer on agricultural topics he endowed a Lectureship at Cambridge in the history and economics of agriculture. Although the name of Gilbey exists in the wine business the name of Elsenham is equally famous. The factory was built in 1893 "because it was found unprofitable to send soft, perishable fruit to market".[15] Copying Wilkin's example Gilbey produced 'table-jam' using the best and highest quality fruit he could produce. "Sir Walter Gilbey states that the factory has not yet paid interest on the capital invested in it...He believes that the enterprise will pay eventually".[15] In 1901 produce from Elsenham was being sent by railway to 50 retail shops. Gilbey promoted a light railway from Elsenham to Thaxted in 1911.

Abbotts

Abbotts of Ardleigh was founded by Edward Abbott in 1850. Starting with half an acre, specialising in seed production and propagation of trees and shrubs, the business expanded until to covered over 1,000a and included seed growing, general farming, specialised nursery sections for fruit trees, specimen trees, choice herbaceous plants and quality vegetables such as asparagus, globe artichokes, gourmet peas and beans.

Before the 1939 war Abbotts had built a reputation for trained fruit trees, specimen standard trees and bush and standard roses. They were responsible for maintaining stocks of the choice D'Arcy Spice. The company was taken over by Notcutts of Woodbridge in 1966. It continued in business and concentrated upon the new, and expanding, business of garden centres.

Seabrooks

In the history of fruit growing in Essex the name of Seabrook predominates and the fame of the family outshone their rivals. The story of Seabrooks mirrors the fortunes, and misfortunes, of fruit growing throughout the century. With a peak of 1,150a of orchard and nursery around 1950 and 200 regular staff supplemented by seasonal workers. The decline of the industry reduced Seabrooks' orchards to about 100a. The old orchards were grubbed out; wheat and barley crops took their place.

Seabrooks had been at Boreham for many generations. It was the Victorian downturn in farming which persuaded William Seabrook, in the early 1880s, to embark upon fruit growing. When land in British Columbia and the United States was £200 per acre. In Essex it was £15. English costs were considerably below American costs. Pests were more virulent in the United States and controlling them more expensive. There was scope to increase the consumption of home-grown produce which was only taking 30% of the market.

W.Seabrook & Sons was established in 1886. Brent Hall, Boreham, was sold and 12a was bought in nearby Springfield. It was planted with fruit and nursery stock. The Cordon system was introduced which lasted for 70 years. Whilst the orchards were maturing, brassicas and tomatoes were grown on the spare land. In 1900, 60a of brick earth land on the south side of the A12 at Boreham was bought and planted. The first underground fruit store was built and a packing shed. Lord Rayleigh whose Terling estate bordered the Seabrook's business leased them Toppinghoe Hall with 100a for 99 years. They had 170a with a mixture of soil types from brick earth to clay.

Seabrook selected rootstocks suitable for each soil types. It also gave him early crops and he adjusted planting distances. Steam ploughs were replaced by horse-drawn foot ploughs although they had some limitations amongst the orchards and nurseries. He designed a new fruit-farm plough which was off-set. A horse-drawn sledge carried the prunings away and he invented a two-man operated hand pump. Fruit farmers were conscious of the need to spray their crops in the 1920s. Seabrook's spraying equipment advanced stage-by-stage. A 2.5 hp engine mounted on a four-wheeled horse-drawn trolley operated by two men was followed by a mains system, a 5 hp pump and two/four men aiming diluted chemical at the trees. He could achieve an output of seven acres a day. In 1934 the automatic, one-man operated sprayer came onto the scene. The first Cutler grading and sizing machine to be installed anywhere in Great Britain was erected at Chantry Farm and a larger packing shed was built at Little Leighs Hall with a Cutler grader. "At that time it was the largest apple packing shed in Europe".[16] In the 1920s the first Model T Ford lorry was purchased and quickly followed by the first Fordson tractor. Orchard work improved. Spraying could be done by one man who did double the work of 14 men and two horses.

Seabrook recognised the benefits of bees to pollinate the crops and introduced bee houses with 10/15 hives in each. Grafting wax was manufactured at Chantry to his own formula although demand faded when labour costs and materials escalated. The building that produced the wax was burnt down in the 1960s and not rebuilt.

"Boreham was the main tree-raising centre. Every year hundreds of thousands of trees and bushes were lifted, packed, graded and despatched to all parts of the country and abroad...New wooden boxes improved marketing presentation".[17]

Seabrooks stock gained an international reputation and as Tiptree became synonymous with jam, 'Seabrooks Black' was the premier blackcurrant variety and was being grown in back gardens to the end of the century – even if the owners are not aware of its name or pedigree.

The cordon system was replaced by the dwarf pyramid system which gave a boost to Seabrook's output. The new planting system required 1,600 apple and pear trees per acre. Blackcurrants were ordered in ten thousand bush lots. Raspberries and gooseberries in the same sort of quantities. To illustrate the complex programme of breeding stocks, large numbers of cherries, plums, peaches, apricots, nectarines, redcurrants, figs, grapes, quinces, blackberries and loganberries were all required in four different shapes – and at three different ages. In the first 15 years after the war there were significant improvements in planting and management techniques. Seabrooks were always in the forefront of every new development. "Everything was fine in the fruit industry until inflation reared its ugly head, and joining the EEC created more problems".[16] Cheap fruit trees and the dumping of French Golden Delicious onto the British market forced a sharp decline.

Seabrooks reduced the scale of its operations but continued to provide, albeit smaller, stocks of premier quality plants. It was another feather in the cap of Essex farming.

When membership of the European Community was debated in the pre-1973 period many farmers were apprehensive but none more so than fruit growers who saw their markets vanishing like a mirage. The worries proved to be justified. In April 1973, only four months after Britain's entry the government announced a grant of up to £200pa to fruit growers if they would grubb up their orchards. Peter Holden, Penland Trust Orchards at Ardleigh commented,

> "it will give a profit margin sufficient to enable a grower to put in a completely different type of crop. There are many people who will find it much more attractive to give up top fruit now and this will help the industry if the poorer orchards, which put low quality fruit on the market are eliminated".[17]

The following year Giles Tuker one of the doyens of the Essex fruit industry with orchards at Danbury pointed out that the actual payment for grubbing out, "being computed from a combination of numbers of trees to the acre and girth widths etc. it has amounted to about £140 per acre".[18] At that time the orchards of Essex covered 7,744a of which 6,666 were apples, half Cox's with Worcesters following in popularity. There were 665a of pears.

The orchards were already declining and from a peak of over 13,000a in 1954 had plummeted to half that area by 1974. The advent of Britain's entry into Europe, and the encouragement of grubbing-out grants took 1,200a away in one year. In succeeding years there were progressive reductions until there were only 2,699a left in 1996, a pale shadow of the importance of orchards at the peak of their popularity.

This run-down was systematic, but not without its problems. "The tragedy of apple growers arrived in 1979, and around north east Essex hundreds of acres of orchards have been grubbed-up during the last winter as distraught apple growers went out of business...Essex farmers suddenly hit a disastrously bad patch".[19] Fruit farmers lost up to £200 an acre in 1979. It was a situation that could not continue.

'Fruit Focus '80' a national fruit conference was held at Writtle College of Agriculture in 1980 and at the time decorated lorries toured the streets of Colchester as a practical way of publicising apple growers' plight. The '*Womens Farming Union* (hereafter WFU)' was founded in 1979 in Kent and an Essex branch by Earls Colne fruit farmer's wife, Faith Tippett, in 1980. The WFU initially was totally top fruit orientated. After some success it gradually undertook activity with other sectors of farm produce. It provided a link between producer and consumer not then dealt with by the NFU, grew into an all-embracing organisation with subsequent Chairman of the Essex branch being held by women from all sectors of farming. In 1995 another wave of grubbing-out took place and by this time the grant was £1,700 per acre to take out apple orchards under 21 years old and to reduce English apple growing by 40%. "Local farmers have been forced to toe the line".[20] It was costing £4,000 to plant an acre. The uprooted trees lay in profusion in the orchards where they had previously provided a blaze of colour, a haven for bees and birds, an income for the farmer, a contribution to the food larder and rural employment. The war had been over for half a century and the days of shortages were in the history books. But fruit growers with these orchards were faced with a dilemma; "you can't grow cereals and collect the area aid paid under the CAP, because you weren't

83 1948 Southend. Essex Commercial Horticultural Show.

growing them in 1991. You can't grow sugar beet without a contract, or potatoes without a quota. Various supported crops such as rape are ineligible".[20]

Fruit growing was an innovation created by yeomen farmers. In the '30s and after the Second World War attracted ex-servicemen, mainly officers, a tide that increased when ex-colonial tea planters and rubber growers were forced to leave the countries where some had been born. The Australian merchant who told Arthur Wilkin at Tiptree that his jam would sell better if it had the name 'Britannia' on the label was now as much a part of history as the multicoloured orchards which were a distinctive feature of both the aesthetic, and commercial landscape of the county for nearly a century.

Market Gardening

Market gardening had a long history in Essex, but it was confined to the area adjacent to London. The perishable nature of the produce and the lack of rapid transportation precluded any expansion of that area. "The earliest market gardens were established on the rich alluvial soil abutting the Thames...They established themselves mainly around East Ham, West Ham, Ilford, Plaistow and Barking, all of which are within three to six miles of Spitalfields Market. This was apparently soon after the beginning of the eighteenth century".[1] The railways changed that constriction. It had spread to an area around Colchester by 1901 when Rider Haggard noticed that the companies were offering special facilities; "for instance enabling an Ardleigh farmer to supply private customers with produce in special 20lb containers. Market gardening was expanding not only in South Essex but, on a smaller scale, near Chelmsford, Tiptree and Colchester".[2] There were three centres of market garden production. The Rainham and Barking area within easy distance of London, the Ardleigh/Lawford area near Colchester and the Lea Valley mainly in the Essex parishes of Roydon, Nazeing and Waltham Abbey with Cheshunt, Enfield and Hoddesdon in Hertfordshire. This was the largest concentration of glass houses in Europe.

The Hertfordshire production in 1930 was estimated at £4m a year. "Half the total agricultural produce of the entire county".[3] The importance to Essex would not have been such a great proportion, due to the more diverse farming production, and the greater size of the county.

There was a grey area in the segregation of market garden crops. Some such as peas, turnips and swedes, broad and runner beans and cabbages were all grown by substantial farmers. Dr. Collins separates these by what he calls "specialised forced crops"[4] and he includes onions, brussels, early greens, radishes, carrots, celery, runner beans, asparagus and 'first earlies'. In 1877 the official returns recorded 4,184a growing market garden crops. There was an additional 410a 'nursery grounds'. The distinction between special-ised edible crops and non-edible products such as flowers is contained under the label 'market gardeners'. Soft fruit growers would probably come under this definition but top fruit orchard owners preferred to be known as 'growers'. A farmer with a substantial acreage of green crops for human consumption was a 'vegetable grower'. All of these being embraced as Horticulturists. There was a further complication insomuch that some mature orchards were planted with soft fruit, such as blackcurrants, between the rows of apple trees. Thus the same field was both an orchard, and an area of soft fruit production.

The intensive nature precludes any acreage comparison with general arable farming. It would be reasonable to calculate that one acre of glass could produce the same annual turnover as 750a of wheat. This is a generalised observation but it well illustrates the wide gulf between horticulturists and farmers.

Before the First World War there was a considerable expansion in market gardening and fruit growing.

"This period saw the great development of the glass-house cultivation in districts like Worthing, Swanley Junction and above all, the Lea Valley. Fifty years ago the tomato was as great a rarity in England as an Avacado pear is today, a few were imported, a few were grown in private conservatories".[5]

The area devoted to these crops was 25,400a in 1936, 24,111a in 1939, 14,350a in 1990 and 12,700a in 1996 a picture of a decline graph although by 1990 6,352a of peas were being harvested dry for freezing. The days when patient housewives spent many hours shelling peas had gone. There was some expansion of garden centres trade, mainly ornamental shrubs, before 1939 which became more popular from the 1970s. The production of flowers was not strictly a farming operation. The area of glass was partially occupied with these plants, but equally might be utilised for crops of an edible nature at other times of the year. A crop of radishes at Berwick Ponds Rainham, could be produced, out of doors in 20 days. Within a glass house many different, fast growing crops were produced in a year.

osition of market gardeners in 1929 revealed that there were 35% in the a, 22% in the extreme south of the county, 27% in the central block rentwood, Ingatestone and 9% in the metropolitan area, Ilford, Romford. 14% were spread across the county but with only a few on the clay soil in the north. The accompanying table shows the contribution of Essex nurserymen to the national output.

One of the most successful pioneers was the Gunary family who, in 1949, were farming about 750a, some owned and some rented from the Essex County Council. There was 290a at Tendring and two other farms at Stapleford Abbotts. The firm also had its own stand in Covent Garden market. The principle vegetables were brassicaes which formed the basis of a production which extended throughout the year. They averaged three crops from every acre every two years. "This may sound ambitious but is quite practicable, especially if one remembers that we grow many crops that mature in less than six months".[6] The Gunary family also had dairy cows on their farms at Stapleford Abbotts which provided supplies of muck for the vegetable crops although at Tendring there was only a small herd of six sows and about 20 bullocks yarded each winter. "It is therefore necessary for us to buy plenty of organic manures as well as the many varieties of compound and straight fertilisers which we use"[6]

The Lea Valley

In 1967 Lea Valley was producing 51% of UK cucumbers and in 1970 42,968a in Essex was devoted to vegetable and fruit crops. It was in the area devoted to glass houses, and plastic covered buildings or glass substitutes that Essex excelled. In 1973 there was nearly 409a with other concentrations in West Sussex and Lancashire. For many years the Essex area was the largest but Humberside saw an expansion of its glass house industry and in 1986 had a higher glass area than Essex. By 1996 the Essex area was 422.4a which was below its peak between 1980-94 – but still more than in1973.

There were glass houses in the Lea Valley in 1900. As urban development reduced the Hertfordshire side of the valley, engulfing places such as Tottenham there was expansion at Waltham Abbey and Nazeing in the same process which pushed Thameside vegetable growing area further away from the centre of London. As houses replaced nurseries the train services improved and it was possible to supply fresh vegetables on a daily basis from further away. The Thameside development relied upon considerable supplies of manure from London. The Lea, with its glass houses did not require the same quantities. The First World War brought prosperity. Demand for food was a government priority and the glass house area increased and, including both sides of the River Lea, there was 1,100a in 1939. In the Second World War there was not only a shortage of food, but also of fuel and the government priority concentrated upon producing nutritious tomatoes. There were strict penalties for non-compliance.

As regulations were relaxed there was more expansion and the peak of 1,200a was reached in the early 1950s. The combined glass house area of the two counties in 1973 was under 650a, and this included houses which were not in the Lea Valley. In the 1960s the Lea Valley Regional Park Authority was created and considerable areas were designated for recreational purposes. The Valley had always suffered from atmospheric pollution, particularly when coal was the predominant fuel. The clean-up and the abolition of London 'smog' helped to enhance the available sunlight for the crops. Fog had also been a problem in the lower reaches of the Valley but as these were the first to succumb to urbanisation and as the centre of the industry moved up the Valley it proved to be an advantage. The universal availability of piped water reduced reliance on local wells.

The glass houses were in need of continual maintenance, even rebuilding. Most nurserymen followed a policy of routine replacement. In the decade 1983–93 an investment of £22.5m was spent replacing 55% of the total glasshouse area. The older houses were timber framed but the Venio model incorporated individual squares of glass up to one meter wide. The glazing bars were reduced to a minimum, the wooden frames were replaced by lighter, more durable metal and storm proofing was achieved by iron and steel cords incorporated as stays. Interior support members were reduced and two inch diameter steel pipes for heating, as opposed to the four/six inch pipes previously required, the new houses enabled more plants to be grown.

Cucumbers were the mainstay of the Lea, and production was increased by over 25% in the new metal houses. The maintenance was lower and computer-controlled automation was installed. The traditional methods were almost universally replaced, cucumber production from the 1980s was achieved in rockwool, a molten rock spun at high speed to form a woven slab. Seeds were planted in these rockwool blocks and when the plant reached 15in. the block and the plant was placed on a slab in the glasshouse. Plant nutrition could be injected with a high degree of accuracy reflecting the needs of the crop.

Marketing was achieved by selling at Covent Garden. As the supermarket wave became predominant in the shopping pattern of British housewives the Lea Valley growers faced another challenge. The multiple chains required first class produce, every cucumber and every tomato identical to its neighbour. The Lea Valley men formed a growers co-operative and later locally based marketing organisations pre-packed it for distribution to the supermarket chains. By 1993 75% of the salad produce was marketed by this method.

"The early '70s were to deal local growers two swingeing commercial blows; the accession of the UK to the Common Market, and the so-called 'energy crisis' (with its devastating inflation)."[7] In the debate about membership of the EC it was the fruit growers and the market gardeners who faced the greatest challenge. The Dutch had always been traditional arch-competitors and their imports to the UK spiralled as pre-accession obstacles were dismantled. The energy crisis raised the cost of heating oil by 400% in one year. The '70s were also a time of spiralling inflation "but market returns for horticultural produce at best remained static".[7]

It was a time of contraction for the Lea Valley. By 1980 the glasshouse area was only one third of where it had been at its zenith. The cucumber acreage decreased but sweet peppers and bedding pot plants became more commonplace.

The Lea Valley owed much of its expansion to Italian settlers. "Sizeable Italian communities developed in the area, especially in Waltham Cross and Rye Park. The Italian government set up a Vice Consulate in Cheshunt and Italian masses were held in local Roman Catholic Churches. By 1978 British born growers were in a minority in the Lea Valley; 50% were Italian and 9% from other countries".[8]

The 'sea of glass' was a landmark first used for navigational purposes by German bombers in the Second World War and the fragile glass was prone to shattering even when explosions took place some distance away.

Why did the Lea Valley become such an important centre of glasshouse production? Localisation often arose by chance, or the enthusiasm of a small number of growers.

"Once established, it tends to persist given favourable conditions, by virtue of reputation, market connections and the development of a specialised labour force and ancillary industries. Such advantages may enable production to continue even when the circumstances originally stimulating its development no longer apply... the Lea Valley retains the largest acreage of glasshouses in the country 'despite all economic logic'".[9]

ESSEX PRODUCTION AS A PERCENTAGE OF ENGLAND 1970			
Vegetables	5%	Blackcurrant	6%
Beans French & Runner	8%	Strawberries	5%
Beetroot	4%	Carnations	9%
Cabbages Spring & Winter	13%	Cucumbers (Lea Valley)	41%
Onions	10%	Roses	24%
Peas (Green)	14%	Tomatoes	19%
Apples (Desert)	13%	Fruit Trees	11%

Other Nursery 4%

Source: MAFF. Examination of the Horticultural Industry.

CHAPTER 19

The Importance of Cows

Dairy farming had a long history in Essex although the farmers were not 'improvers' until, the 20th century, and there was no native breed. When Kent farmers were using their marshes for fattening cattle Essex farmers concentrated on milk production. In the Great Wen, including such Essex towns as Romford, Ilford and Colchester there was a pattern of town dairies where the animals were treated as a machine to produce milk. In every village the milk supply was produced within the parish. Essex farmers were known as 'graziers', and were prepared to buy cows either in-calf or half grown heifers rather than rear their own. This led to the county herd being composed of a multitude of cross-breeds.

Cheese making was common in the 19th century. The railways opened up the London market to farms 50 miles away. The last Essex cheese was made at Steeple Bumpstead in 1900 and, was delivered by road. Salt butter was also produced in the county but an inventory in Stuart times suggested that there were few large milking herds. Less than 2% had more than 20 cows and the ratio of dairy to beef was 3 milch cows to every beef beast. These came from the unwanted replacements and bull calves. In the 17th century Essex acquired a reputation for veal. Thomas Fuller declared that the Essex calves were; "the fattest, finest and fairest veal in England".

The importance of dairy farming in Essex is surprising. The dry climate was never conducive to lush pastures and the Midland counties and Wales could always surpass the drier Eastern counties for the production of beef animals which could be driven along the drovers routes to the centres of consumption.

The Tilbury marshes played a large part in this trade providing rich grazings for the beasts to recover the meat lost during their journeys. The animals were finished-off before being driven to Smithfield market. The stimulation for milk increased as the population spiralled. West Ham which housed over 25% of the one million population of the county and with East Ham, Barking, Ilford, Leytonstone, and Walthamstow had a market of 600,000 people. This compared to the 38,000 in Colchester and 12,600 in Chelmsford and illustrates the extensive demand which existed. It produced a concentration of dairy cows within those connubations or in a ring of farms surrounding them.

An example of a town dairy was the herd of 30 cows milked by Eddie Billington in Ilford. His grandfather had milked cows in Stratford. Milking continued in Ilford until 1963. The customers collected the fresh, sometimes warm milk in their own jugs, or metal cans. There were a lot of Jewish customers who wanted the milk 'straight from the cow'. This meant literally what it said and the milkman held the can between his knees and filled it from the cow. There was an extra charge for this service. These town cow-houses had no land attached to them. The animals were fed on brewer's grains which were collected from Taylor Walker's Brewery. They ate roots and waste from the vegetable market in Ilford. They also had some hay. Local market gardeners willingly collected the resulting manure for their crops. It was a flying herd with a variety of breeds. Eddie

***84** 1934 Romford. Palmer's milk float. 5d. a quart delivered. Produced on the premises.*

Billington's father had a milk shop in Walthamstow and expanded up to seven/eight rounds in the Romford area.

There were problems of over supply in the lush summer months followed by a shortage in the winter. Cheese and butter making were by-products of liquid milk sales. In the 1880s a condensed milk factory was built at Colchester for the surplus milk and this factory accepted milk by rail from Ipswich as well as its own hinterland.

When the first agricultural statistics were correlated in 1866 it was recorded that there were 16,559 cows in the county, but these early figures are notoriously inaccurate and both heifers and cows in calf, but not being milked, were included. When these were separated in the 1907 census it showed that cows in milk accounted for 75%. 25% were heifers, in calf but not yet in milk. Using this assumption there would have been 26,727 milking cows in the county in 1900. By whatever standards of inaccuracy might be applied to the 19th century returns an upward pattern had developed. This appeared to accelerate as the depression deepened in the 1880s when farmers turned to dairying as an alternative.

There was an upturn in the prospects of farming after 1900 and in 1902 the Eastern Counties Dairy Farmers Society at their AGM at Chelmsford noted from the Annual Report; "that it was satisfactory to be able to chronicle an upward tendency of the price of milk".[1] There were nearly 2,000 more cows in 1914. But there was a discernible trend for the cow population to decrease in wartime. In the First World War the number declined by 3,404 but by 1939 there were 8,000 more cows than in 1914. By 1945 there was a decrease of nearly 1,400. Essex farmers turned to dairying in depressed times, and reduced their herds when conditions improved.

In 1913 there were 5,295 farmers with holdings over 20a. If the average size herd at that time was (conjecturally) 10 cows it follows that 58% or 3,075 farmers kept a herd of cows. In terms of area and with the supposition that the total requirements of the herd could be met from a ratio of five acres per milking cow, then 33% of the county was devoted to dairy farming. The 42% of farmers without cows were often those with an off-hand farm which did not have a cowshed. There were a few, like Archie Matthews at Falconers Hall, who farmed without livestock, and many market garden growers, although they needed to import muck from London to sustain their crops. On the large arable farm by-products such as barley straw, wheat straw, sugar beet tops and 'stubba' (red clover stalks after the seed had been threshed) was fed. There were advantages in an integrated farm that could supplement part of its feeding from waste products.

In 1931 Offin and Rumsey's michaelmas sales included a herd of 20 milch cows, a Red Poll and a Shorthorn bull, a total of 84 head of home-weaned cattle for Captain S.W. Wingfield at Fobbing Farm, Vange. At Steward's Elm, Great Stambridge, Messrs. Belton Bros. had a herd of 11 milch cows and heifers and a Dutch bull. Mr.C.W. Hawkins, Hall Farm, Mucking, had a herd of 55 cows and heifers, some down-calving with a pedigree Aberdeen-Angus bull. S.J. Squier was anxious to give up milking at Great Malgraves Horndon-on-the-Hill where he had 35 cows, two bulls and a herd of 93 Shorthorn cattle. Two years later the same auctioneers were advertising 26 cows with two Shorthorn bulls

85 1946 Hylands Park Chelmsford. Pushing the lesson home about milk production at the Essex Show.

for H.R. Phelps at Loftmans, Canewdon. Mr.C. Wright had eight cows and only 11 head of cattle at Gore Ox Horndon-on-the-Hill and G.A. Thorpe and Sons gave up milking and sold 43 cows and heifers at Sheepcotes, Hockley.

In pre-1939 days there was a bull on every farm and the average sized herd has been calculated on the assumption that the number of bulls is equivalent to the number of herds. Judging by the 3,556 bulls recorded in 1942 it is a reasonable assumption that there were this number of dairy farmers. A very few might have had two bulls, but conversely a small producer with only five cows might take them to his neighbour's bull. It is assumed that these twin factors would counterbalance each other. On this basis the average herd, was 10 cows before 1914, went up to 20 in the '20s and remained constant until the 1950s, rose to 31 by 1957 with the more universal acceptance of machine milking, although there were hand milked small herds up to 1960, when the average herd reached 36 cows. The next 20 years saw a progressive rise to 101 in 1980. Thereafter it remained remarkably static for the remainder of the century.

H.T. Smith (Farms) Ltd. at Bury Farm, Felsted, had a Friesian herd of 120 in 1973, and planned to increase this to 150 with a prototype rotary milking parlour that could milk 90 cows an hour with only one man. In 1974 John Hawkes of Cowland Stebbing, had a herd of 170 cows which had all been descended from seven heifers which his father had bought in Chelmsford market in 1920, for a total of £175. The bulls had all come from Essex herds; Lord Rayleigh at Terling, J.S. Blyth at Ardleigh and Walton-on-the-Naze, Peter Dixon-Smith at Braintree. Hawkes' herd was sold in 1975 to Fountain Farming who built the most expensive cow shed in Europe at Boreham which could accommodate 400 cows and was the largest clear span timber farm building in the UK at the time.

The trend towards large scale dairying was described by Ralph Sadler in 1976;

"A number of farms are now stock-free, but milk remains the major livestock product. Gone are the churns and small Shorthorn herds, to be replaced by the tanker, the herringbones and the rotaries, and by herds of from 100-300 accredited British Friesians".[2]

Cow keeping methods changed rapidly. In 1966 Strutt & Parker (Farms) Ltd. erected a new cowshed for 240 cows. They were milked in a herringbone parlour, lay in cubicles and were fed mechanically from Tower Silos. It was an investment of £230 per cow. Nine years later Fountain Farming's dairy unit at Boreham cost £582 per cow. Strutt & Parker (Farms) Ltd. at Terling, Lavenham and Beaumont were milking over 1,100 cows by 1945, in separate herds. Twenty years later the number of cows had increased by 9% but the income from milk sales had increased by over 80%.[3]

The story of the Strutt family of Terling is synonymous with the story of British agriculture, it was a dominating factor, and in particular in the story of dairy farming in the county. Sir William Gavin has related how they brought dairy farming on a mass scale to Essex.[4] Primrose McConnell said in 1891; "it is doubtful if, of recent years, dairying pays better than other forms of farming";[5] and in 1907 the comment was made; "dairy farming is the only kind that is really profitable, and yet Essex is far more suited climatically for wheat-growing, being sunny and dry in summer, too dry for the best pasture".[6] Yet Hon. Edward Strutt recognised before the turn of the century that dairy farming a lifeline, but it was also antiquated. He set out to re-organise the whole system

86 1953 Burnham. Wilfred Newman's attested friesians which won three cups and was adjudged the best herd in the Eastern Counties 1951-2. Watson Steele's Ayrshire herd at Gosfield had a string of gold cup successes in the 60's and Peter Padfields Holstein's from Hayleys Manor, Epping won the Bocm/Silcock National Herds Competition five times, and a long list of other achievements.

of cow-keeping. He applied his ideas of feeding and management, an innovative emphasis upon autumn calving to milk production through the winter months. He considered that hay was too expensive, and that it could be bought in from other farmers thus allowing the strong mid-Essex fertile land to grow cash crops. His son, Gerald, had an unerring eye for stockmanship, with a reputation of being the best judge of cows in England. A pioneer of the Friesian Society he had the benefit of his father's milk recording which was introduced in 1896 long before the Essex Milk Recording Society was formed in 1914, and was then the largest in England with over 7,000 cows being recorded on a daily or weekly basis.

Douglas Smith, Wickham Hall, Wickham Bishops, wrote in 1926 that;

"it is surprising how soon an intelligent cowman gets keen on milk recording...I was shown a paper with the records of three high yielding cows out of a small herd of 30, and these three cows were giving between them just under 20 gallons of milk a day...there are plenty of herds of 10 cows   giving no more and the extra milk obtained is worth much more than the extra cost incurred. Once a recorder, always a recorder".[7]

Realising that the retailer was making more money than the farmer, Strutt founded 'Lord Rayleigh's Dairies' in 1900. It was sold to the Express Dairy Co. in 1929 but retail dairies were opened at Clacton-on-Sea in 1933 and Walton-on-Naze in 1935. There were others at Cambridge and Felixstowe.

Gerald Strutt's crowning achievement was the purchase of a young Friesian bull in 1929, Marthus, who became the most famous bull in the history of British Friesians. The prize-winning records of his progeny was endless. When Marthus died in 1936 his head was mounted on the farm buildings at Taylor's Farm, Terling, and he was buried in an upright position.

The importance of the bull and the genetic line had not been previously recognised and up to 1948 the number of bulls on Essex farms corresponded to the number of herds. From a peak of over 3,500 in 1942/3 the number of bulls had declined to 815 in 1960 although the number of cows had not fallen to such a large extent. The acceptance of artificial insemination enabled small dairy farmers to forego the expense of keeping a bull themselves and achieve advantages in upgrading the milking potential from carefully selected semen.

The Essex AI Centre was established at Writtle, close to the Institute in 1948. Two years later a sub-centre was opened at Lexden and the service extended to the Suffolk border. The Writtle centre was built to house 18 bulls but by 1979 it had outgrown the demand. The bull stud was withdrawn and the animals absorbed into other centres throughout the country. The Lexden office was closed and after amalgamation with Writtle the service moved to new facilities at Boreham.

In 1900 the Shorthorn, bred from the Holderness was the most common cow in the county. The Scottish farmers introduced Ayrshires. There was a multitude of other breeds but the majority of the animals which passed through the markets were of indeterminable ancestry. This gradually changed. In 1967 of the inseminations carried out by the Writtle Cattle Breeding Centre 67.5% were Friesians, 3.5% Ayrshires, 5.7% Jerseys and the remainder in a variety of breeds. At that time beef breeds accounted for 19.4% of all inseminations but the traditional Aberdeen-Angus and Herefords were being overtaken by the newly imported 'exotic' breeds from Europe. The milk from the Friesian was not high in butter fat. It was often scathingly dismissed as 'white coloured water'. To maintain required levels many herds had a Guernsey or Jersey cow to counterbalance the insipid character of the Friesian. Later in the century when the demand for skimmed milk and yoghurt expanded the quality of the Friesian was more suited to the demands.

Before the Milk Marketing Board was established to give stability to the milk market in 1933, Essex farmers, particularly those at the London end of the county, were fortunate that they could obtain contracts with London retailers for 1s.0d. (5p) per gallon in summer and about 1s.5d. (7p) in winter. Farmers in the West Country were sometimes forced to accept less than 6d. (2.5p) per gallon.

Farmers made strenuous attempts to popularise milk drinking. In 1931 200 Essex schools were operating Milk Clubs and at Friars School, Chelmsford, over 60% of the children were enrolled and drank milk at 10.30 every morning. "They then have a lesson at which they are seated for a quarter of an hour, then comes the play interval. By this arrangement the children do not take any violent exercise immediately after drinking the milk".[8]

The introduction of milking machines would have been regarded with scepticism by the cowmen of 1900. In 1936 Charles Draper, Hill Farm and Claybury Hall, Woodford, bought his third Alfa-Laval milking plant. It was a four-unit Combine-Recorder and was installed in his off-farm at Epping. Strutt & Parker installed one of the first milking machines at Landermere Farm, Beaumont in 1926.

The importance of dairying declined sharply in the second half of the century. The county herd dropped from 41,619 cows in 1950 to 8,323 in 1996, a reduction of 33,296 cows. Milking had been the salvation of Essex farmers in bad times, and was sufficiently widespread to have small herds in every village. The only farmers without them were those with a large arable acreage. Cows were a part of the scenery. At their peak probably over 65% of Essex farmers kept some. By 1956 the MMB had 1,230 registered milk producers in Essex. This dropped by nearly 50% within 10 years, another 50% in the next decade to 1976 and a similar reduction in the following 10 years. By 1994 there were only 101 milk producers. The decline in cow numbers was less constant. As producers relinquished dairying there was an expansion in herd sizes. The area of land required for cows decreased and between 1965/9 dropped from 1.68 acres per cow to 1.3. Electric fencing, a more scientific approach to nitrogen applications and rotational grazing contributed to more economical land usage.

Essex was a high milk producer. In 1966 the output of 27m gallons was higher than Suffolk (25m) and Kent (24m). Essex farmers produced more milk with fewer cows than Kent. The superiority of the Friesian as a milk producer was responsible for the enhanced output. When, in 1971 Essex herds had been decreasing by over 50 per year, a 21% drop in the number of cows was matched by a 13% drop in milk production.

87 1966 Terling. 240 cows. Living-in with cubicles and mechanical feeding.

There were two factors which contributed to the general decline. The introduction of the EEC Dairy Herds Conversion Scheme in 1973, and the Quota system which was imposed in 1984. Half the overall decrease in the Essex herd occurred before either of these inducements had been imposed. There was an overall drop of 16,526 before and 16,777 after. The conclusion from these figures suggests that farmers did not need encouragement to sell their cows.

There was a growing trend to specialisation. The costs of installing new milking parlours rose sharply – and arable farming was more promising. The effect of the Dairy Herds Conversion Scheme did not have the impact of Quotas. The first was a voluntary scheme which offered an inducement for farmers to abandon milk production but they were obliged to keep beef cattle. The quota system was obligatory and until the legal tangle of quota transference was resolved it sent shock waves through the industry. In the 1980s a total of 8,800 cows left Essex farms which was almost twice as many as in the previous decade. The impact of BSE in the 1990s had a defined effect but in the first six years 1990/6 the drop was 3,377. Clearly farmers had come to terms with the new priorities.

The Conversion Scheme had excluded herds of under 11 cows but there were more applicants from the larger herds where the problem of capital investment became more important. On many farms the sale of the dairy herd was prompted when the last cowman retired. Fewer of the younger workers wanted to be shackled to a seven-day week, and did not have the love or understanding of the animals which their predecessors had in abundance. There was a 50% rise in the number of beef cattle. The immediate result of accepting a payment to relinquish milk production, and the embarrassment of the milk-lake that was affecting the EEC politics. When quotas arrived in 1984 the value of cows dropped. In March an animal in milk fetched £600 but by May it was £460. Halstead farmer and NFU president, Sir Richard Butler described the situation; "the detailed regulations for milk quotas have been a bitter pill to swallow. They have been forced upon us".[9]

The 20th century produced many changes in the methods of cow-keeping, in its feeding, in an enhanced healthiness after the battle against tuberculosis was mastered in the 1930s although the county did not become an Eradication Area until 1959, the compulsory clean-up of Brucellosis in 1974, the innovation of milk recording when farmers had their results published monthly in the Essex Farmers Journal, the abolition of churns and the introduction of bulk collection, the complete dessimation of the Shorthorn in favour of the Friesian, which was a strange, ungainly animal in 1900 and the unparalleled number of prizes which Lord Rayleigh's and Strutt & Parker's herds achieved. The Scottish farmers had brought their Ayrshires into the county and had convinced many indigenous farmers that, drudgery it might be, but milking cows was more profitable than growing wheat. The Scots gave up milking as readily as local farmers although, with notable exceptions they continued to specialise in arable crops.

Cows played an important part in the economy of the county until 1980. They were an integral part of many livestock/arable systems. Despite the apparent contradiction of trying to grow grass in one of the driest counties in England. Fountain Farming built their cow palace at Boreham in a dry year and tried to move their cows to other locations where there was more rainfall. The reputation of Essex Friesians and the breeding which came from the progeny of Marthus was second to none. But at the end of the century the importance of dairy farming had seriously declined.

British breeds, of which the Friesian had now become a dual purpose animal and a British breed, were insular. From the 1970s a transformation took place, spearheaded by the Charolais from France and followed by a considerable number of new breeds.

At Great Totham Col. C.C. Lancaster MP established the first Essex herd of Charolais at Home Farm. Four heifers were bought in France in 1967 with a second importation the following year. They became famous as the 'De Crepigny' herd the prefix derived from the Estate at Langford Grove, Maldon. The herd was supervised by David Allerton head of the Farm Management Department, Strutt & Parker, and later by Guy and Gill Lyster. Guy Lyster was a renowned cattle judge but the herd was dispersed in 1987.

Peter Padfield, Hayleys Manor Epping, imported Canadian Hostein strains in 1972. He introduced "Hayleys Hutches", one of the biggest advances in improving calf health and lowering mortality. He was milking 190 cows in 1999.

In 1984 a jumbo jet landed at Stansted Airport with the first cargo of 63 bulls from Canada. Amongst the Holstein cattle was a two year old Canadian Belted Galloway. In the same year the Murray Grey made its debut at the Essex Show. First imported from Australia 11 years earlier they were a breed that dated from 1905. Rowley Eccleston, Grange Farm, Tendring, and David Black, Great Bentley, formed the nucleus of a Murray Grey herd in 1973. Their herd was the only one in East Anglia.

The Rare Breeds Survival Trust was active in preserving ancient breeds that were in danger of extinction. Simon Gilbey, Chief's Farm, Great Bardfield, had 29 Longhorn cattle, whose origins were linked with the original wild cattle that roamed Britain and were identified as an independent breed in the 16th century becoming dominant in the 1730s when their cheese potential as well as their meat was popular. By 1850 they had virtually disappeared.

PRINCIPLE LIVESTOCK CHANGES					
Year	Horses	Cows in Milk	Other Cattle	Sheep	Pigs
1900	30,804	35,766	54,611	295.051	88,743
1996	Nil	8,323	36,564	76,083	111,923
Change %	(100%)	(77%)	(33%)	(74%)	+26%

1996	Cows in Milk	Total Cattle	Sheep	Pigs
Essex	12,763	44,887	76,083	111,923
Suffolk	16,374	57,609	69,904	653,679
Kent	21,641	73,235	520,337	32,773
Norfolk	30,426	107,096	142,987	699,044

CHAPTER 20

Beef and Sheep in a Dry County

Beef production played a minor, although not insignificant part, in the agricultural economy of the county. Bullocks were never regarded as a cash crop, unless is was during the euphoria of 'baby beef' as at Stowmarket in the 1960s, which was a short-lived phenomena. Young gave numerous descriptions of bullock feeding methods; fattening by summer grazing on the marshes, or the rich valley meadows such as at Dedham. They were reared by suckler cows, were kept to graze off parks and the greatest reputation gained by Essex farmers was for the succulent veal. They preferred to sell younger animals rather than the three year process of producing the 12/18cwt animal.

Those that were kept to maturity, put on meat during the summer season and very little during the winter. The profit was negligible. Mr. Hanbury at Holfield Grange, Coggeshall produced a meagre profit of 25p from his animals; "leaving on these beasts only the dung...in regard to profit he has no doubt of it, for the dung has a value which no manure to be got in this country comes near to".[1]

Until balanced fertiliser ('bag-muck') became economical, and commonplace from the 1950s most farmers regarded the resulting muck as essential for their crops. Where they had a combination of unploughable, riverside meadows or marshes, the bullocks were able to feed themselves cheaply for half the year. As dairy farmers gave up cows they replaced them with bullocks, either stores which they might summer graze and sell, or winter yard. When the Dairy Herds Conversion Scheme was introduced in 1973 it was specifically directed that if a farmer agreed to go out of milk production, he must maintain his stocking rate and not convert to arable. Sheep were discounted at a ratio of 6.6 to each cow. As a result of this scheme the returns of 'other cattle' in 1974 rose by 10,860. The number of sheep went down.

The size of the Essex beef herd is unclear from MAFF returns. All that can be achieved is to monitor the trends. The previous chapter outlined the numbers of cows in milk. In 1938 it was revealed that whilst 40,000 cows were in milk an additional 1,034 beef cows were milk producers. There was a differentiation between those of a dairy, or a beef breed. Also between those that were producing milk for sale, and those cows that are being used for suckling calves. The 1938 returns show that out of 110,528 total cattle, just under 19,000 (20%) were beef cattle.

Herefords and Aberdeen-Angus were the archetypal beef animals with the former being larger. The Longhorn which had been the predominant British breed was replaced by the Shorthorn. It was after mid-century before Friesian bull calves became recognised as beef animals. The Ayrshire was too skinny. Jersey and Guernsey bull calves were never in this category. It was the importation of European breeds; the Charolais followed by the Simmental, Limousin, Gelbvieh, Chianina and many others.

In 1958 there was optimism of a prosperous future for beef.

"I can say with confidence that almost the only thing that can fulfil all the qualifications today is the production of beef cattle...beef is undoubtedly

88 *1934 Epping Market took over the town. Predominance of Longhorn Cattle.*

something that is entering a new era in this country.

There are two very good reasons. The first is the scarcity of meat in the methods of rearing and fattening bullocks".[2]

Beef management had undergone a radical change. It had previously taken three years to produce a 12 cwt beast. Suddenly it was possible to produce a 9 cwt bullock in 14 months. The demand, as with pigs, was for leaner meat and the smaller, barley fed meat was more succulent. Bullock keeping changed from being an operation designed to produce muck, to a profit making concern.

Suckling calves became popular at this time and there were several herds of cows on the Essex marshes with their calves. They had been imported from the North of England and Scotland and were rugged breeds that could out-winter. The cows calved in the field and reared their offspring through the summer. When they were nine months old they were brought in, fed on a nutritional diet and were quickly killed. "Like everything else in farming it has changed, and in this case there seems to be scope for it to continue to thrive and expand in the coming years".[2]

Major problems hit Essex beef producers in the second half of the century. The recurrent outbreaks of Foot and Mouth Disease, the aversion to beef eating from the

89 1945 Terling. Land Army worker cutting linseed cake at Taylors Farm. Machine made at Heybridge by Bentall & Co.

effects of Mad Cow Disease, and, traumatically, Brightlingsea was in the forefront of the protests against the export of live animals.

In 1958 well over 1,000 pigs, sheep and bullocks were slaughtered at Robert Lennox's Wick Farm, Layer-de-la-Haye as part of the stringent regulations to control Foot and Mouth Disease. Peggy Greer of Layer-de-la-Haye wrote; "the animals were collected from at least eight different farms at great distances from one another. The fear of contact was very remote. These animals should have been isolated for the infection period and not slaughtered. It has created a waive of protest and disgust".[3] In 1967 another outbreak occurred and cattle were again slaughtered, farmers meetings were cancelled, salesmen were advised not to travel around farms, the public was advised not to travel between infected, and non-infected areas, markets were closed and a siege mentality developed. Roderick MacRae, divisional veterinary officer for Essex found himself with only two senior colleagues to man his HQ. The remaining vets had been drafted to western and northern black spots in the UK. The Essex County Standard commented; "there is almost the atmosphere of a wartime operations centre in Mr.MacRae's office in the Government buildings at Beeches Road, Chelmsford. Telephones seldom stop ringing. Official messages and instructions pour in".[4] The outbreaks of Foot and Mouth Disease stopped after Argentinian beef was only imported off the bone. The public perception of beef as a traditional British fare, and the growing popularity of beef burgers did not materially affect the demand.

Concern greeted the first hints of Bovine Spongiform Encephalopathy (BSE) which had overtones of an ancient animal disease known as the 'staggers', for which farmers blamed an excess of lush spring grass and kept the animals in a yard until they recovered. The scare started in 1986 and reached greater proportions in 1997. In 1990 it was stated that; "beef is an important enterprise on many local farms. The Christmas fat-stock shows in the local markets bear witness to the high quality of locally produced beef. Many are reared from calves from Wales and the north of England".[5]

But in 1996 those intrepid farmers who had continued in beef production suffered severely. In one week in late March 1996 not a single beef beast was sold in Chelmsford or Colchester markets. 35% was knocked off the value and farmers desperately kept them back, hoping for a recovery in the trade. Thereafter beef prices were never up to former levels and it became impossible to make a profit from them.

The "Battle of Brightlingsea" lasted throughout 1995 when, the town, with its single approach road was blockaded by protestors against live animal exports. The focus of media attention showed angry scenes as thousands of protestors from many miles away converged with placards. Cattle lorries were assisted with their legitimte occupation by the Essex police, and the end bill was over £2 million. The prime mover in this trade was Roger Mills, a Suffolk exporter.

It was finally the strength of sterling which made the business uneconomic. Veal calves were too expensive for continental buyers and the trade dried up. It had been an unfortunate episode in the history of Essex farming. A Layer-de-la-Haye farm was picketed and there were other disruptions. The numbers of beef cattle in the county, which had been over 55,000 in 1900 were under 12,000 in 1996.

SHEEP

The visible evidence of the prosperity of the woollen industry was remembered by the rich churches of Saffron Walden and Coggeshall, as well as a proliferation of Wool Halls. The wool market at Horndon-on-the-Hill was another monument to the flourishing wool trade. The reputation of Essex clothiers was extensive, and regarded as one of the best in England. It was a manufacturing industry with a large volume of the output being shipped from Tilbury and Harwich to the continent, Spain and Portugal being particular destinations. Wool manufacture was carried out in many locations over the county although the fame of Colchester's 'Bays and Says', and the quality of Coggeshall's products was well known. "For centuries, the woolen manufacture remained by far the most important industry in the county, other than agriculture".[6]

The historical importance of this industry would suggest that sheep were an integral part of Essex farming systems. This would not appear to be the case and the raw materials for the woollen industry were often purchased in Lincolnshire and other counties. Transport was usually by sea around the coasts.

90 1930s. Will Goodchild's sheep on Wallasea Island.

Sheep were, never-the-less, as indigenous to Essex fields as swine and oxen. The coastal marshland was never afforested and was the home for most of the 46,000 sheep which were surveyed in the Domesday Book (1086). Why were so many sheep kept at that early date? "...these marshy flats had no recognised existence in 1086...but they were the home of the sheep. And even as the cow was then valued not only for its milk, but its flesh, so was the sheep expected to supply not only mutton and wool, but, above all, milk. The production of cheese from sheep's milk was a recognised Essex industry".[7]

In the 12th century whilst pigs and poultry were cotttage industries it was sheep-farming, and the price of wool which made them the chief source of profit. In the 15th century there was an "increasing abandonment of animal husbandry for sheep-farming [which] brought about a less demand for labour".[8]

There were three sources of income from sheep; the milk for cheese making, the annual crop of wool, and the meat. When sheep were no longer milked but suckled by their lambs it was these that provided an alternative source of income – with considerably less labour than the disliked job of making cheese. "The progressive and factory-farming men of Essex also had another profitable sideline which they supplied to the rich tables of London. This was the production of fat lambs for Christmas".[9]

In analysing the importance of sheep on the Essex farm it must be observed that the annual MAFF returns were recorded in March 1866. On 25th June until the 20th century, on 4 June, thereafter. This had its repercussions on the sheep count. There were two systems. The early spring lambs or those born in September for the Christmas trade. In June some of the first of the spring lambs, would already have left the farm, whilst the others were unborn. It would seem reasonable to suggest that the figures given, with reluctance by farmers until 1926 when the Return was made compulsory, would indicate a return below the numbers at other times of the year.

With these provisos the peak of sheep in Essex was in 1870. The ewes were not separately listed until 1893 when they accounted for 36% of the total sheep population of the county. Using this formula for the 1870 Return it would appear that there were 146,824 ewes, which at a ratio of three per acre, plus the lambs, gives a land usage of approximately 50,000a, nearly 25% of the grassland. They grazed off many acres of turnips during the winter months. In 1900 sheep were still an important part of the agricultural economy. Although there were 110,925 less than in 1870. The increase of 15,000 cows using the equivalent of 6.6 sheep per cow [10] would appear to be in direct proportion, a substitution of sheep by cows. This was not so pronounced in the marshland areas but on upland farms sheep were considered an expensive alternative to arable crops.

Sheep remained the predominant animal in such places as Foulness, Canvey Island and on the Dengie peninsula. In depressed times farmers increased their flocks. In both world wars there was a marked decline but a noticeable upsurge again during the 1920s/30s. The numbers continued to fall until 1922 when the full impact of lower wheat prices persuaded farmers to increase their flocks. By 1939 the numbers had increased to only 6,867 less than there had been in 1914.

The drop during the Second World War was more pronounced. The downward trend continued and in 1950 there were only 38,261 sheep left from a population of 165,485 in

91 1950s Great Bromley. Champion breeder Herbert Hayward, shepherd Sam Hurst, traditional lambing fold.

1939. The number of ewes dropped from just under 76,000 in 1939 to under 15,000 in 1950. In the second 50 years sheep profitability followed an erratic path, but an acquired taste for lamb by French customers, gave an added boost to sheep farming.

The lowest level of the century was recorded in 1976 when there were 40,487 in the county and only 18,622 ewes. Since Britain had entered the Common Market 9,000 sheep had disappeared from Essex farms. They never reached the level or the importance that a flock had acquired from the middle ages onwards, certainly in Victorian times, and it was the impact of two world wars which reduced the importance of sheep in this county.

Breeds

The native Essex marsh sheep had descended through many centuries and were similar to the Romney and Thanet breeds. They had a dense heavy fleece, and a high resistance to liver fluke and foot rot. There were attempts to improve the native stock and in the 19th century Charles Western, Felix Hall, Kelvedon, imported some Spanish Merinos. Exports were banned from Spain and the Essex importation was 'disguised' as a present from the Spanish aristocracy to King George III. He gave some to Squire Western who, with his friends, formed a Society to promote the breed, and remove the bad points. The Merinos were accustomed to mountainous country and found the moist climate and rich pastures too indigestible. They were not meat carriers and their conformation resembled a miniature dairy cow. The Southdown was the most popular at the time and Western tried crossing them. Despite improvements the Anglo-Merino was not a success.

In the early part of the 20th century the main entries at the Essex Show were Suffolks, Southdowns, and Hampshire Downs. Eventually it was the Suffolk breed which became the most popular, although at the 1948 County Show there were only 872 entries which was exactly the same number as goats. The only three Essex flocks which were exhibited in 1948 were; Hill and Johnston, Pattiswick Hall, George Goodchild, Great Yeldham Hall and Herbert Hayward, Badley Hall, Great Bromley. There were other flocks in the Tendring Hundred including those of Stanley Webb, Abbotts Hall, Mistley and John Jiggens, Bradfield Lodge, who were both neighbours of Hayward, both pedigreee Suffolk breeders, both judged at shows throughout the country and won many prizes themselves. At the 1950 Tendring Show there were also Suffolk sheep entered by Mrs. M.R. Mitchell, Elmstead, J.S. Blyth, Walton-on-Naze, Charlie Pirie, Great Bromley, Charles Gooch, Elmstead and William Strang, Manningtree.

It was Herbert Hayward's flock which became a standard bearer for the excellence of Suffolk sheep. Before the Second World War he was sending rams to Canada, all with the prefix 'Badley', and soon after Churchill extolled the nation, Hayward named his prize ram 'Badley Defiance'. Later, in 1944 it was 'Badley Victory' which was exported to Canada. The flock had been started in 1903 by John Hayward and was a livestock enterprise that was integrated with arable farming on the 600a, most heavy clay, with about 100a of lighter land where the sheep were wintered. On his 600a there was only 90a of permanent grass.   In 1952 Foot-and-Mouth Disease hit the flock "and the work of nearly 50 years of breeding went in one night with the slaughter of 483 sheep, including a ram that had been sold for export to Canada. That was a terrible blow".[11] Hayward rebuilt his flock as he bought descendants from his original stock which were to be found unaffected by F and M Disease. He restored the flock of Suffolks and went on to top the prize lists at the Essex and Royal Shows.

226

Essex became famous for the sheep which bore the name of the neighbouring county and in Alberta there were descendants of Goodchild rams, which were named 'Yeldham blood'. There were many strains of sheep in North America which came from the progeny of the top Essex sheep farmers.

The Suffolk was one of the first of the Southdown-based breeds, animals that were "so despised in the field and so popular upon the table of the connoisseur of well-flavoured mutton".[12] They were not called Suffolks until 1859 and in 1867 they were condemned at the Royal Show at Bury St. Edmunds for their long legs, short ribs, thin necks, bare backs and naked heads. By the turn of the century many of these unfortunate characteristics had been bred out of them.

AVERAGE DECADAL SHEEP FLOCK			
1900–09	244,464	1950–59	56,146
1910–19	179,933	1960–69	96,660
1920–29	127,641	1970–79	47,770
1930–39	176,179	1980–89	68,800
1940–49	83,547	1990–96	87,100

SHEEP				
YEAR	ESSEX	SUFFOLK	KENT	NORFOLK
1965	86,820	80,208	696,776	80,070
1970	54,220	49,896	562,129	62,896
1975	48,065	54,667	591,789	98,100
1980	52,918	46,655	616,807	99,994
1985	69,039	46,414	627,546	117,398
1990	87,464	70,736	636,712	176,730
1995	79,323	77,569	550,468	153,530
1996	76,083	69,904	520,337	142,987

CHAPTER 21

The "Essex" Pig

Pigs and poultry were the only farm animals which increased during the century. Cows, cattle, sheep, and of course horses, all declined. Pigs and poultry disappeared indoors. Prior to the 19th century, and to some extent still evident in 1900, these animals were regarded as scavengers. Young said that; "hogs are too frequently conceived to be a trifling and unimportant part of the stock of a farm"[1]

Pigs, hogs or swine probably had the greatest antiquity as farm animals, although they were revered for hunting in the earliest days. If equally divided amongst every farmer in the county in 1866 there was less than two sows per farm. It was not an equal distribution, although every farm had a couple of fattening pigs which existed on kitchen scraps and were killed for the benefit of the farmhouse, the sows were more probably grouped into farms and regarded more professionally. Young talks of Thomas Pittman, Barking who had 35 sows, five boars and 600 pigs at any one time which he had reared himself. Being close to London was a greater incentive than at the other end of the county. There were some notable breeders in the early 19th century, but with these exceptions the largest percentage of the 11,078 sows recorded in 1900 were on small farms in individual sties.

The sentiments of earlier comments were echoed in 1936 when Viscount Astor and Seebohm Rowntree commented "until the recent artificial expansion, pig production was a subsidiary branch of British agriculture. In our opinion it should remain a by-product of farming. It should not be encouraged to become a major live-stock industry almost solely dependent on imported foods".[2] Yet it was in 1936 that the Essex pig population reached a new peak of 132,400.

In the period before 1914 the number of pigs remained reasonably static. Numbers did not decline significantly until 1917 and in the following year the lowest number to date (54,418), was recorded. This remained the lowest point until 1947 when there were 10,000 fewer. It was in the inter-war period that pig farming acquired greater importance. In 1930 an estimate of farm production suggested that over 11% of income came from pork, almost as important as barley and second only to dairy products which, at that time, were producing 49.5% of output.

Pigs had now become an important sector of Essex farmers economy and were treated more professionally, although sows had their litters in mobile pig sheds, and were encouraged to root the soil with their powerful snouts. In winter this produced a quagmire! In summer the animals grazed the grass, as a century earlier pigs had often been fattened by turning them onto clover. This new emphasis which regarded pigs as an important contributor to farm income, and no longer a scavenger, resulted in an increase between the wars of 81,347 (149.5%). The competition from Danish farmers had been a cause of considerable concern during the 1930s but with the wartime blockade this was removed.

Keeping pigs was discouraged by feedstuff rationing, and the six years of the Second

92 1946. The Essex breed was enjoying a boom. They were prolific and excellent mothers.

World War resulted in a reversal of the pre-war trend. There was a drop of 75,736 pigs. There was a reduction in 1946 of the basic rationing allowance for pigs and poultry which brought it below the wartime level.

The second half of the century proved a traumatic time for pig farmers. They were hit by successive waves of bad prices, a new disease, Swine Vesicular Disease caused disruption of markets, cancellation of pig classes at the summer Shows, and a roller-coaster economic return which emphasised the dictum that pigs were either 'muck or money'. During the 50 years pig numbers rose steadily and reached a peak in 1973 with 286,789 on Essex farms. It proved to be the peak of the post war trend. From 1980-96 pig numbers dropped by 112,919, or 50% in 16 years. Despite these falls the number of pigs being kept was more than double the numbers pre-1950. Pig farming had become intensive and specialised. Sow herds of 10 were average in the early years of the century but herds of 250-500 sows were not unusual in the latter years.

The Essex Pig

Amongst the many breeds in the British Isles the 'Essex' achieved a degree of popularity in the 20th century, but long before the end they had disappeared. It was a Saddleback with white shoulders and four white feet. A rotund conformation they had no future when the long backed Landrace began to provide the lean bacon that the public was demanding. The Essex was a good mother and in the early post war years they were crossed with a

229

Large White which produced a speckled light blue and white pig which was robust, put on liveweight rapidly and produced, in the 1950s, the sort of bacon that was liked by the factories at Dummow, Ipswich, Elmswell and Calne in Wiltshire, which was the destination of a considerable number when pig production was under strict government control.

"The ultimate origin of the breed is, of course, utterly obscure...but there appears to be little doubt that it's antiquity is as long as that of almost any other breed".[3] It was Lord Western of Felix Hall, Kelvedon who imported a male and female Neapolitan which he discovered between the Bay of Naples and the Bay of Salerno. Western crossed them with the old native Essex leaving the Saddleback markings which were so distinctive. They were now called 'the Improved Essex breed'. Western died but Fisher Hobbs, who had been his steward and moved to Boxted Lodge, was responsible for the breeding and evolution which produced the only farm animal to carry the county prefix.

The Essex Pig Herd Book Society was formed on 2 August 1918. It was incorporated under the Companies Act in 1920 when the definition was recognised as a Saddleback pig with a white saddle over the shoulder, fore legs and white hind feet and tip of the tail. The inspiration for the Society came from R.M. Wilson who was Principal of the East Anglian Institute of Agriculture (1912–23). He discovered the white shouldered pig in many villages where they had been bred for generations.

> "Except in a few herds, breeding had been carried on in rather a haphazard
> fashion, and it appeared that the formation of a Society, and the establishing of a
> Herd Book, were absolutely necessary to enable the breed to take its legitimate
> place among the pure breeds. A position which its performance has so fully
> justified".[4]

The Society elected Hon. Edward Strutt as its first president. Ralph Matthews, Newarks, Good Easter was the first chairman. George Baynes, Broxted Hall, Dunmow, was one of the committee. Charles Cousins, Cressing Lodge, whose herd became famous was another.

Such was the success and expansion of the breed that there were talks of an amalgamation with The National Pig Breeders Association, but the Essex Society preferred its independence. It was during the depressed '30s that the number of pigs in the county almost doubled. We do not know the ratio of breeds but pedigree Essex pigs were well established with important herds founded by A.J. Cousins, Cressing, W.Ritchie, Margaret Roding, F.J. Bosworth, Willingdale, Tinney and Hitchcock, Rickling and H.S. Ashton and Mrs. F. Hilda both at Ingatestone. By this time the Essex pig had spread its fame and was well known in Lincolnshire where it was more popular than the native Lincolnshire Curly Coat pig.

By 1945 Essex pigs were being bred in Scotland, Wales and the West Country. The 1946 Herd Book (Vol.28) listed 5,690 females and 1,004 boars.

Shows and sales took place at Chelmsford, York, Edinburgh, Norwich, Cambridge, Crewe, Doncaster and Gateshead in the 1940s/50s. The Essex was at the pinnacle of its popularity. Four litter sisters from Cousins Cressing herd realised 700 guineas. At Richie's Margaret Roding sale a boar 'Roding David 6th', made 300 guineas and was sold to Tinney & Hitchcock. A record 500 guineas was paid for F.Carter's Bradwell boar. Robert Browning, Gt.Tey, was awarded the first prize at the Smithfield Show for the best

93 1950s Clavering. Hunter Rowe and some of his pedigree sows.

entry of four bacon pigs of any breed other than Large White. It seemed that nothing could stop the expansion of the Essex. In 1966 George Lewis, Sible Hedingham and John Cousins, Cressing, jointly exported Essex pigs to Italy. But the writing was on the wall.

Whilst pig farmers liked the Essex, its carcass was becoming out of tune with the demands of the market. "We were told...that coloured pigs were not wanted, in time the only place we would be able to see them was in a zoo".[5] The Landrace pig had already been imported by Bernard Partridge, Weeley and they were taking over the British bacon industry. The Essex Pig Society amalgamated with the Wessex Saddleback Breed and became integrated under the joint name of 'British Saddlebacks'. The Essex prefix disappeared and at the 1977 Royal Show there were no Essex pigs. It was a short-lived history of the 20th century that lasted only just over 40 years.

The Dunmow Flitch Bacon Factory

Before the First World War farmers realised that they must become involved with the marketing of their produce. The founding of the Dunmow Flitch Bacon Factory in 1908 was an example.

The Dunmow Flitch Trials, a test of marital harmony with a flitch of bacon, presented annually to a happily married couple, was revived in 1855 and had been the subject of a novel. Dunmow and bacon were synonymous. On 29 April 1908 Hon. Edward Strutt, who was always involved in the initiation of strides to the benefit of Essex farmers, presided at a meeting in the Town Hall, Dunmow. It was an attempt to popularise the British, and in particular the Essex product against the considerable imports of Danish bacon which was under-cutting local farmers market prices. The Germans had

231

94 *1950s Essex bacon at the Essex Show*

imposed high tariffs on Danish pigs in the 19th century. The Danes, ever enterprising in finding new outlets, sold their bacon in the UK under the label 'Yorkshire'. In 1907 18mt of bacon and ham came into Britain.

William Hasler called a meeting at his house, The Croft, in the centre of Dunmow. Eighteen farmers, with a collective 20,000a between them supported this project and after the Town Hall meeting a sum of £20,000 was suggested as the launching capital. The Board was made up of William Hasler, Joseph Smith, William Dannatt and J.B. Frankham. The City welcomed this initiative as a scheme of investment. The capital was slow in forthcoming but by September the Daily Express reported that an advertisement stimulated interest. That month over £21,000 was raised and two and a half acres was bought beside the railway station.

A year later the first 50 pigs were killed and by December 1909 an average of 200 pigs per week were being processed. Silver and bronze medals for pale, dried bacon were won by the factory in 1911. In 1914 an average of 263 per week were killed. It was a successful enterprise which helped to regain some of the market which the Danish farmers had taken. This was a continuing concern of pig farmers, except in wartime, throughout the century. Only when Essex farmers adopted Swedish Landrace pigs could they compete.

Dunmow Flitch continued as a farmers co-operative until 1922, when it was taken over by C & T Harris (Calne) Ltd., Wiltshire bacon curers since 1770. Forty years later it became part of the Fatstock and Meat Corporation, the largest meat group in Europe.

By 1974, with up-to-date machinery 1500 were being killed a week The hourly slaughter rate was 138 pigs. 90% of the carcasses were turned into bacon.

Gone were the days when 'monkey boys' climbed the chimneys to hang the flitches up to smoke. Matured oak sawdust gradually smouldered below, and although this antiquated method was traditional and disappeared with the passage of time, the principals in the modern Dunmow factory remained the same. The smoke was blown by pressurised air, the moisture content carefully gauged and the whole process subject to stringent hygiene rules. The factory closed in and the prominent site in Dunmow is now a bingo hall. Another piece of Essex farming history disappeared, but is not forgotten.

AVERAGE DECADAL PIG HERD			
1900–09	94,700	1950–59	174,000
1910–19	73,600	1960–69	215,500
1920–29	93,200	1970–79	266,500
1930–39	114,000	1980–89	186,500
1940–49	68,000	1990–96	128,500
1900–49	88,700	1950–96	194,200

CHAPTER 22

Chickens – From Scavengers to Big Business

Arthur Young's comprehensive survey of Essex covered every aspect of cropping and livestock. Rabbits; "a subject I know not much of myself" gets four lines. Pigeons get six lines; "universal depredators upon corn-fields". Fish get five lines and he lamented that they were a neglected source of farm income. Bees on the other hand warranted one and a half pages which he described as; "extremely profitable for farmers and cottagers" But chickens are dismissed in five lines; "by no means an object of sufficient importance to excite the particular attention of our larger and more spririted farmers".[1] Poultry were the scavengers of the farmyard, they laid their eggs in secretive places where the farmer's wife searched for them. Those that escaped arrived later as a brood of chicks scratching amongst the tail corn and rubbish of the farmyard. Foxes kept the numbers of chickens down and when an old rooster could be caught the meat was a special treat. Chickens had no place as commercial farm animals.

This changed in the 20th century. Eggs and poultry meat, particularly at Christmas time, became an important way of cashing wheat. During the first half of the century not only did specialised poultry farms arrive with 1/2/3 springing up in every village, but later the mass production of broilers elevated poultry from the most expensive meat on the table. As prices fell chicken meat became cheaper than beef, lamb and pork.

Chicken farmers, were looked down upon. It was not real farming, and a chicken was not a real farm animal. The traditional Michaelmas goose was part of the fare. The Christmas turkey similarly and Norfolk turkeys, with tarred feet, were driven through the Essex roads on the way to London. They often rested, as did other fattening animals around the Tilbury area.

The disregard for poultry prompted MAFF to exclude them from the annual census until 1926. The Returns had attempted to include chickens, ducks and turkeys earlier but the entries were quickly removed, poultry as a farm industry did not warrant its inclusion. In 1884 there were just over a quarter of a million chickens in the county, 60,000 ducks, 13,000 turkeys and nearly as many geese. These figures were undoubtedly highly inaccurate. In 1913 another attempt put the chicken population at nearly three quarters of a million, ducks had declined to 45,000, turkeys had gone up to 18,000 and the number of geese had halved. These figures must also be treated with reservation, and excluded poultry kept in back yards. Poultry farms escaped the enumeration if they were less than one acre in extent.

Farmhouse tables groaned under the weight of chicken meat, and in the towns the well-off could afford this delicacy which ranked in the same league as game birds – not farm animals. Lord Ernle wrote; "Even down to the end of the century poultry keeping still halted between the methods of the fancier and of the farmer who had a mongrel flock picking about his stack yard".[2]

It was after the First World War that they became a 'proper' farm animal although until after the end of the Second World War the majority of chickens were the prerogative of the farmer's wife, sometimes housed in rough straw built shelters. Hobby farmers indulged in pucka chicken sheds. But a movement was gathering pace and the consumption of eggs was increasing. Lancashire had been one of the centres of poultry keeping in England and some of the settlers from that county brought their enthusiasm and expertise to Essex. It was a business which few arable farmers understood.

In 1890 there were only two breeders listed in Kelly's Directory. In 1902 there were six of which three were ladies; Mrs. Rachel Bailey and Mrs. Alice Gowlett both at Great Canfield and Mrs. T.C. Darby at Pleshey.

Expansion was prompted by the downturn in cereal prices after 1921. By 1929 there were 10 breeders in Essex, six manufacturers of poultry equipment based at Wickford (two) Billericay, Thundersley, Romford and Elmstead. There were two poultry house builders, at Stanway and Heybridge and 224 poultry farmers. Poultry keeping was being taken seriously but it was restricted to three main parts of England. A small area in the south, the northern industrial area of Lancashire and Durham, and the three eastern counties Essex, Suffolk and Norfolk. The Essex area; "suffered particularly from the difficulties which mixed arable farming has encountered, so that farmers paid more serious attention to building up the poultry flock, which previously was rather scoffed at as 'the wife's affair'".[3] Between 1924/34 the number of fowls in the county doubled and MAFF suggested that there could be a shortfall of about 33% which were kept on allotments and private gardens. The contribution which poultry and egg production made to the agri-economy rose from 3 % to 10 % in the decade up to 1934.

An early Essex pioneer was R.J. Girling, Larges Farm, Great Holland who started a poultry enterprise in 1927 "with little more than a shoe string to back it".[4] On a windswept Essex farm on the east coast and on difficult clay Girling wrote in 1946;

> "farmers were quick to realise that here was a way to turn their cereals into hard cash. Their returns per acre rose, and they had into the bargain, an added source from which to maintain soil fertility. Essex has been the home of some of the pioneers of the hatchery business. Few people can have imagined that from such small beginnings a great specialist industry would grow".[5]

A.M. and H. Rankin Ltd., Stambridge Mills, Rochford, advertised a range of formulated feeds for poultry. A layers mash and a growers mash. Apart from the inclusion of two by-products of wheat; bran and middlings, with a small part of 'Sussex ground oats' the mixes also contained imported maize meal. The scale of poultry farming advertisements in 1931/2 give an indication of the seriousness which poultry farming had become associated.

In 1931 S.J.K. Collins gave up his Colne Valley Poultry Farm at Earls Colne and Balls & Balls sold 4,500 pure bred and first cross pullets, 3,300 well-grown birds hatched in 1931 and 1,200 birds hatched the previous year. There were 13 sectional laying houses, 11 sectional brooder houses, 58 slatted floor houses on wheels, 135 night Arks, eight Gloucester Incubators and 20 Blue Flame Hovers. The following year A. McCombie, Felsted sold up his entire flock of 3,000 Rhode Island Reds. His cockerels were described as "hardy and in vigorous condition". There was an ancillary list of equipment for poultry keeping.

Not only had intensive egg production arrived on the Essex scene but there was a

95 *1909 Beauchamp Roding. Isaac Mead looks at the egg collection of the day.*

boost to rural employment. Danny Rowe, Sudan Turkey Farm, Bulmer, estimated that "in those days 1,000 lay hens might employ one or two people".[6] The most common method of poultry keeping in the 1930s was on grass where pens were moved daily, or free-range hens were moved into a series of wire netting paddocks whilst the vacant ones re-grew the grass, aided by the poultry droppings.

Poultry keeping in the 1920/30s was orientated towards egg production. The number of hens in the county rose by 352% between 1921-39. Average eggs per bird was estimated at 72 in 1908. It was 120 in the early 1920s and pre-war average was 149. Better breeding management and specialisation had transformed the humble hen from the farmyard scavenger into the cash machine. As this new 'industry' expanded there was an urgent need to give guidance to budding poultry farmers. "The amateur or beginner must undergo a lengthy training; a year at a recognised Poultry Institution, and a year or two on poultry farms run on sound commercial lines, is the safe and sensible way to begin".[7] The East Anglian Institute of Agriculture set up the first County Egg Laying Trials in 1928 on Glebe land attached to Widford Parish Church. The following year a Review suggested that a poultry station was required which could accommodate 500 birds, would need 10 acres and a resident manager with a two year course. In 1931 a site was found at Beehive Lane, Galleywood, and an Instructional Station was opened by the Poultry Commissioner of the M of A., P.A. Francis who painted a rosy picture of the prospects for expanding egg production in Essex. "The County of Essex has made good progress since the number of adult hens in the county showed an increase last year [1930] as compared with 1913 of some 110%, whilst the estimated value of the eggs produced in the county was £376,000 as compared with £92,000 in 1913".[8]

The Station was an experimental farm and a teaching unit. Poultry farmers sent their birds and the results were published. The Galleywood Station remained active until the new campus was built. The war intervened and a 25a Poultry Station was established in 1947. The objectives were wide. It set out to give students hands-on experience in poultry keeping as an extension of theoretical work. The new poultry station set out to provide an advisory service for household poultry keepers and to carry out experiments, research and recording. The emphasis was towards egg production but a surprising development was about to be launched when an americanism called a 'broiler' arrived on the British scene. The Writtle Poultry Station closed in 1966 but from the early 1980s, the college syllabus was widened to include turkeys.

Before the war egg production was highly profitable. A comparison of the period 1930/9, and the decade after 1945, using the average prices show that pre-war eggs were 2s. 6d. (12½p) dozen. Wheat, the main constituent averaged £6.64p. Wages averaged 32s.0d. (£1.60p). In the second period eggs averaged 5s.0d. (25p) dozen which was double the pre-war value of them but other costs had gone up disproportionally. The average price of wheat in the second period was £23.38 over 350% increase. Wages averaged an increase of 260%. Whilst the two major cost inputs, labour and food had gone up by over 300% the value of eggs had increased by 100%. There was less profitability in the immediate post-war period, only mitigated by the larger size of flocks. The average egg production per hen declined during the war years, due to a lower nutritional standard of food, and did not recover the pre-war average of 149 eggs until 1953. Battery birds were later laying 300 eggs pa.

The expansion of poultry and its respectability spawned a new supply industry. Many Essex firms founded in the 1930s acquired international reputations. Hall-Mark Hatcheries, Wickford, became one of the largest producers of day-old chicks. They manufactured poultry houses and equipment. A specialised feed industry was centred by Nitrovit at Witham which provided a high energy formulation designed to promote rapid growth.

Chalk at Sandon, Holmans at Boreham, Bonnett, Common Farm, Ramsden Heath, Doubleday at Stanway, Ernst at Weeley, Sterling at Avsol Park, Felsted and Luckin at Parsonage Farm, High Easter, were all suppliers of chicks.

David McMaster, Mount Bures, produced outdoor brooders and fowl houses which became nationally known. May & Butcher at Heybridge. The Cobb Breeding Company with its major hatchery plant at Rayne, later part of the Anglian Food Group, produced over 50% of the UK supply of broiler breeding stock at London Road, Braintree. They exported to Eastern Europe, the Middle East and Africa. The Rayne hatchery was bought by Facenda Chicken Ltd., an integrated broiler company from Brackley, Northants. The receivers were called in to AFG in 1975. Cobb were also involved with sheep breeding and produced the Cobb 101 Ram and other sheep from its hybrid developments.

Kelly's Turkeys was launched in 1965 by Derek Kelly at Springate Farm, Danbury. A new breed of white feathered turkeys was produced that exceeded the growth of known breeds at the time. "If a human being put on weight as fast as a turkey, a baby would reach 16 stone in 18 months and turkeys are only exceeded in growth by trout".[9] Kellys eggs for hatching were supplied by Essex farmers. "They are mostly large-scale cereal farmers with a turkey business as part of their farming operations".[9] Eggs for hatching were sent to the Falkland Islands. Turkeys like chickens had lost their rarity.

Broiler production in Essex started in the 1950s. Farmers rearing cockerels for the Christmas trade discovered that they could sell them after three months and make a handsome profit, filling their sheds again – and collecting two crops in the same period. The quick turnover, mass production, and massive numbers of young birds exploded into the broiler industry. John Ogier, Rough Hill Farm, East Hanningfield, was the first chairman of the British Broiler Growers Association. He had one Nissen hut with 1,000 birds and another three houses had 5,000 each. The profit, after 11 weeks was 1s.0d. (5p) per bird. "If you think in terms of broilers you think in terms of thousands".[10]

Ten years later Jonathan Nott, Hunts Hall, Pebmarsh, had built a poultry unit which covered a third of an acre and held 15,000 birds being reared for egg production in 20

96 1949 Mersea Island. Laying hens kept in a yard at Bocking Hall. Farmer Allan Gray.

weeks, the operation was run by one part-time stockman. The birds were fed from an overhead bulk store which 'piped' the meal into a mobile trolley and filled the hoppers. Nott farmed 500a and the enterprises were mostly cereals with sugar beet. His father, Major Jack Nott, Spoons Hall, Pebmarsh, had run a pedigree herd of Jerseys and had a poultry hatchery for new laying stock. Anfood, Colchester, a subsidiary of the Pertwee Group, produced large quantities of food for this burgeoning industry. When 'broilers' were first segregated in the MAFF returns in 1960, there were 867,353 in Essex, a county total only exceeded by Norfolk. Expansion was rapid but the official figures were probably lower than the actual numbers. It was a quasi farming business that could be operated on a very small area. Broiler houses with little surrounding land sprung up in odd corners such as the back garden of the Donkey and Buskins at Layer-de-la-Haye. These escaped the enumerater. The official count recorded 1.3m in 1965 and 2.2m in 1974 before a downturn affected the industry. In one year 200,000 broilers disappeared from the Essex scene. Another 100,000 went in 1976 before a slow recovery to just over 2m which was sustained until 1981. In 1983 the Essex total reached its peak, at just under 2.4m. There was a rapid loss of over 1m birds by 1984 as another bout of trouble hit the industry. The numbers remained around 1.5m for the remainder of the '80s, climbed to 2.2m for most of the '90s and settled back at 1.5m in 1995. A drop of over half a million birds from the previous year.

There were 25,000 turkeys in the pre-war period, remained constant until 1953 when feedstuffs rationing was abolished, rose to nearly 42,000 and within four years had risen to nearly 84,000. The 100,000 mark was reached in 1959/60 and almost doubled in 1961. The '60s were the profitable time for turkeys. A great change had come over the style of turkey rearing. Their popularity as farm animals was mitigated by their temperamental qualities not least their propensity to die in heavy rainfall. The big change was to keep them under large umbrella buildings, wire netting sides gave them ample fresh air.

Turkeys were also farm scavengers. Cecil Harvey, Kellers, Elmstead, cashed a poor trade in cabbages by turning his turkeys onto them. "They have turned to good account a crop of cabbages...the heavy dressing of manure which they leave behind at Christmas is cashed in the following year with a crop of early potatoes". Harvey had a flock of 2,700, Mammoth Bronze which were crossed with Broad Breasted blood to improve the breast shape. They were part of the farming system being bred on the farm, reared under square pyramid hovers, moved into arks which were set out on a one-year ley after the hay had been cut. A ryegrass and trefoil mixture gave the turkeys continuous grazing. The expansion of the turkey flock was the result of moving turkeys from the fields, and into farm buildings. It was the peak of turkey production in Essex. The numbers declined by 75% in the 1970s and continued to remain at a lower level towards the end of the century.

Ducks, usually white, were to be seen swimming on every farm pond in the pre-war days. There were only a few specialised duck farms. The farmstead flock maintained a consistent level by natural breeding. The figures suggest that there were nearly twice as many ducks as turkeys pre-1939 and that they reached a peak of over 61,000 in 1948. By 1975 there were only 3,000 but by 1990 there were 20,000 and double that figure in 1995.

Geese were not kept commercially after the war. There were nearly 20,000 in 1948 but as mass production expanded poultry meat the popularity of the goose declined. By 1960 there was only 25% of the numbers on Essex farms in 1948. They never quite became extinct and during the last 30 years of the century there were roughly 2,500 the county.

CHAPTER 23

From Windmills to Mergers

There were 140 windmills in Essex in 1880, 49 in 1908, 24 in 1917 and after mid-century the Essex County Council took over four, to preserve them as museums. Aythorp Roding, a postmill and one of the largest in the country in 1941. The only tower-mill, at Stock was purchased in 1945 and the sails replaced in 1956. Mountnessing was transferred from the parish council in 1956. Finchingfield, in a semi-derelict condition, from the parish council in 1957. There were others which survived, including Tiptree without its sails. The Victoria County History enumerated 225 mills[1] and Kelly's directory in 1902 listed 200 millers – 32 less than a decade earlier.

Windmills were mainly on the high inland parishes around Dunmow, Stebbing, Thaxted, Saffron Walden and Chesterford with some in the south at Hornchurch and Rayleigh as well as Peldon situated only a few feet above sea level. Every river and tributary in the county had a succession of mills along its course and there were a small number of tidal mills at such places as Walton-on-the-Naze, Dovercourt, Thorrington, St Osyth, Clacton all in the Tendring Hundred and Battlesbridge, Rochford, West Ham and Barking. The majority of the village mills existed to grind the parochial produce, which was converted into bread by the village baker.

Kelly's 200 millers in 1902, if equally spread, would have provided a mill in every other parish. This was not the case "12 windmills were worked regularly within the limits of the Borough of Colchester, but of these only one remains in 1906".[2] Larger mills using steel rollers replaced the mill-stones which had been imported from Germany and France, mainly through the ports of Colchester and Harwich. At the dawn of the century there were mills at Chelmer, Chelmsford, East Mills at Colchester. Townfield Mills at Chelmsford was established by T.D. Ridley & Sons Ltd. Along the Thames, near London a galaxy of milling complexes arose which could receive their inputs by water. This rationalisation of the flour milling capacity of the county was a revolutionary concept. Never-the-less the village millers were still a considerable force to be observed. The agricultural depression in the late 19th century had been partly responsible. Wilson Marriage and Miss C. Fell Smith said;

> "wheat growing in England has diminished extraordinarily, and in no county so much as in Essex. The importation of foreign wheat renders it essential to erect mills near the ports of grain entry in order to avoid cost of land- carriage. Two very extensive mills have recently been erected at the Docks on the Essex side of the Thames".[3]

Wind and water had already been threatened by 1890 when there were 97 steam-powered mills against 202 operated by natural elements. By 1929 the 200 millers of 1902 had been reduced to 78. The numbers powered by wind had dropped from 126 to only 111. New sources such as oil six mills, gas two and electricity one. In 1890 29% of mills had dual energisers and in 1929 less than 1%. Flour was being moved in lorries. The bran and

97 1910 Hornchurch wind mill and a typical pantiled barn and cart lodge. A gantry from the mill house on the right.

middlings were returned to farmers for animal feeding, the staple diet of pigs supplemented by kitchen scraps and rotting fruit, and the gruel was steeped in water overnight to prevent constipation, but did little to fatten them.

The rise of agricultural merchants offered a two-way trade, buying the farmers' grain and selling compound feeding stuffs and fertiliser. They came into prominence in the 1920s. Long established companies such as the two branches of the Marriage family at Chelmsford and Colchester, Gould at Loughton, Brooks at Mistley, Cramphorn at Chelmsford, Hasler at Dunmow, Matthews at Great Sampford and Battlesbridge, Rankin at Stambridge were amongst those who expanded.

There were others who concentrated upon producing quality seed such as Folkards at Copford, Cooper-Taber, Witham, Kings at Coggeshall, Church at Bures, who specialised in Essex red clover and mangold seed, whilst new companies arose such as Richardson & Preece. Formed in 1918 when Richardson devolved himself of a threshing tackle contracting business whilst Preece followed behind and bought the corn. They decided to become partners and formed a grain merchanting company. The founders of the original companies all came from farming stock.

The only family to have adopted a reverse policy was the Strutts of Terling who had been prominent millers along the Chelmer in the 18th century,

Towards the end of the 20th century all the merchanting families had lost control of their businesses, their names had disappeared under corporate umbrellas although some of the original premises were still occupied. The only name to have survived, Cramphorn, diversified out of agricultural marketing, severing its involvement with the Hythe at

241

Colchester in 1966 and concentrated upon garden centres and gardening equipment. The famous names from the '20s–'60s all disappeared.

The role of the corn merchant, once the mainstay of farming and the main cash source for arable farmers was changing to such a degree that the Essex County Standard asked "do we need merchants at all?"[4] Farmers, in the last 20 years of the century discovered that they were in the export business. Prices were influenced by the value of sterling, which caused considerable devaluation of price levels in 1997/8 when sterling was strong. Farmers were exporters and dispatching corn from the farm was dependent upon storms in the North Sea. Merchants could no longer be accountable for delays in grain movement.

In the last 40 years of the century a maelstrom of activity accompanied a complex webb of flotations, amalgamations and mergers, acquisitions, identity changes; all in the name of rationalisation! Merchants had always been aware that a defaulting farmer could cause them financial embarrassment, but few farmers were declared bankrupt in this period. It was the failure of four agricultural merchants which caused many farmers severe financial problems.

The '20s/'30s was a disastrous period for farmers but it was a period of expansion for merchants. "At the same period, about 1929, the bank began to take us a little more seriously and for the first time four figure amounts in the red were allowed on our bank statement".[5]

Although farming was in the doldrums both pigs and poultry had moved from their role, 'as the wife's affair', to a commercial enterprise that could make a significant contribution. Said Norman Pertwee, "provision of compounds for Pigs and Poultry had become a rather more stable occupation...our enlarged trade enabled us to buy barge loads of Maize in particular...a Tattersall Screw food mixer was purchased. This ton mixer did yeoman service for some 30 years".[5]

Farms were rapidly losing their self sufficiency, and their isolationism. It was the first step in the transformation of farming from a peasant, into a business operation. Eleanor Roper suggested another reason why merchants expanded at this period.

"Those millers and maltsters whose premises were situated inland, or were inconveniently placed, or far from a well-metalled road, railway or port, then had difficulty in obtaining supplies of grain with which to carry on their businesses. Some met this situation by diversifying their trade and have become agricultural merchants supplying a range of goods including farm seeds".[6]

The traditional self-sufficiency of the farm was fast disappearing. The grain was mixed with other lots and redistributed to small poultry farms who proved to be good customers.

After the war as agrochemicals became widespread the merchanting companies appointed specialists and new companies appeared which were solely devoted to selling chemicals, with all the advisory, field-walking, which this required. Key and Pell, a Lincolnshire firm which started trading in 1962, expanded into Essex in 1973. Profarma a chemical retailing company from Wisbech and owned by chemical giant Ciba-Geigy with a depot at Bures, was sold to Boots Farm Sales Ltd. in the same year. In 1973 Boots sold their Crookes Veterinary Company to Anglian Food Group Ltd., Braintree who had previously been involved in many diverse enterprises ranging from a hybrid pig company Europig Ltd. producing pigs to accommodate the european palate and a company at

Poole developing oysters. Anglian was also involved through the Kimber group of companies with the development of 'Cobb' strains of both sheep and chickens.

The flurry of take-over activity started in Essex in 1972, and within a decade had wiped away many of the household-names. There were many factors that led towards the amalgamation of the middle ranking Essex companies. There had already been a considerable amount of rationalisation. There were 22 less corn and flour merchants in 1902, than a decade earlier 39 less millers but with 193 in the county there was one in every other rural village. There were 65 maltsters, 79 brewers but only 30 seed merchants. Between 1902-29 there was a further reduction of 34 corn merchants, down to 69. The number of maltsters dropped by 52, from 65 to 13. The brewing industry saw a decline of 53, from 79 to 26 but it was the millers, particularly the small 1/2 parish mills which declined by the largest amount, a drop of 115, from 193 to 78. The number of seed merchants, specialising in corn and small seeds for farmers did not materially change but there was a considerable increase in the numbers of general merchants, who stocked a range of requirements, including seed, for farmers. Of these 11 had their roots in the corn and milling trade. Two grew from being maltsters, although one of them, Cramphorn, had been involved in several branches previously. None of the brewers converted into general merchandising. The roots were in the grain trade, and most of the companies had been originally founded by Essex yeoman farmers.

In 1947 there were 51 corn merchants in the county. Twenty years later 23 of these had succumbed to changing times, although in the same period 16 new firms came into

98 1925 Maldon. Pneumatic tyres were used for road deliveries.

existence. James Matthews operated from Harold Wood, Romford, W. Brooks and Sons at Mistley were maltsters, Robert Hasler running a company known as Hasler and Claphan at Dunmow and the two branches of the Marriage family with E. Marriage & Son running East Mills, Colchester and branches at Southend-on-sea and Burnham whilst W. & H. Marriage & Sons Ltd. had Chelmer Mill, Broomfield, Moulsham, Bishop Hall and Croxton's, in total three windmills and five watermills stretching along the Chelmer. Pertwees had started in 1899 with a small business in Colchester to supply seed and animal food for Frank Pertwee's own farm. Goulds at Loughton and Hasler at Dummow were in the minor league when compared to either Marriages of Cramphorns. Charles Archer at Colchester had five shops operating as corn and flour outlets which were taken over by Matthews in 1921.

Cramphorns were the most widespread company in 1900, operating Bulford Mill, Cressing, head offices in Brentwood and Chelmsford and eight branches which by the Second World War had expanded to over 40, and had 70 shops when they pulled out of agricultural and farming operations in 1963.

The oldest of these companies was W & H Marriage & Sons Ltd. whose business was founded in 1826 with E. Marriage & Sons at Colchester in 1840. Hasler started business in 1863 and Matthews in 1895. They were all the product of Victorian industrialisation and commercialisation.

Essex with its meandering rivers; Stour, Colne, Blackwater, Pant, Chelmer and many tributaries spawned mills almost every mile along these waterways. "At one time or another most of the water-mills between Chelmsford and Maldon were in 'Strutt' possession".[7]

Bernard Lewis wrote in 1994;

> "In the middle of the last century there were about 10,000 flour mills in the country but with the coming of steam power the mills got larger. It is a sombre thought that today there are some 88 flour mills, 82% of which are in the hands of the national companies – R.H.M., A.B.F. and Dalgety. Sadly the days of the family flour mill are nearly over".[8]

Rankin operated Stambridge Steam Roller flour mills and Garratt the Rayleigh Roller Mills at Maldon. Hitchcock at Wormingford and Bures. Imposing Corn Exchanges were built at Braintree, Saffron Walden, Colchester, Chelmsford where the buyers came to acquire supplies to keep their businesses running.

Free Rodwell at Mistley, Daniell's at Castle Brewery, Colchester and West Bergholt, Ridley with Townfield Steam Mills, Chelmsford and Hartford End Brewery at Felsted, the Writtle Brewery Co., Greene King at St Peter's Street, Colchester, Ind. Coope at Romford, Seabrooke at Romford and Southend, Nicholl at East Hill Brewery, Colchester, Epping Brewery Co., Randall at Dunmow, Cooke at Halstead, Day at Castle Brewery, Saffron Waldon and many others were direct buyers who purchased the best malting barley. Only two, Brooks and Cramphorn developed into full-blown agricultural merchants.

W. & H. Marriage & Sons Ltd.

The Marriage family were Huguenot refugees who came to Essex around 1640. They settled at Stebbing. Nearly 200 years later, in 1824, William Marriage of Broomfield died leaving twin sons William and Henry, 17 years old. Their uncles, Joseph was a miller at Bishops Hall Mill, John at Broomfield and their cousin John at Moulsham.

The Chelmsford Marriages invested in farmland. They accumulated an estate of 2,110a. Henry Marriage noted in his "Agricultural Activities of W.H.Marriage & Sons" the progress of farming in the early days of the century. They grew eight acres of sugar beet in 1926, few potatoes before the First World War, but more later, they were founder members of the Essex Pig Society with a herd at Chignal and another at Good Easter. Two flocks of sheep, a herd of pigs. "These pigs ran with the fattening bullocks and were supposed to live and thrive on the food the bullocks wasted!" A herd of cows at Chobbings contracted anthrax and were destroyed, never to be replaced. They had their own set of threshing tackle and their own steam engine. Firstly a Burrell and later a Wallis and Stevens replaced in 1934 by a Marshall; "said to be one of the fastest on the road ever to be built". They never owned their own steam ploughing tackle but until 1956 employed Keelings. "We believe we were the last in Essex, if not in England, to steam plough by contract". The farming operation was large enough to run their own stallion, they had up to two blacksmiths and a wheelwright. Timber for the wagon repairs was felled from their farms, taken to the saw yards at Chelmsford and brought back the same day to be kept and used as required.

W & H Marriage & Sons remained independent, concentrating on pet and ostrich food.

E. Marriage & Son Ltd.
Edward Marriage bought East Mill, Colchester in 1840. When the railway was extended it did not pass close enough for a siding to be built and when consignments were dispatched they had to be taken by horse and cart.

In 1905 Marriages purchased part of Felixstowe Docks. Marriage's flour had a national wholesale reputation, they also had a considerable retail trade, and part of the East Mill complex contained the Siege House. Edward Marriage's grandson, Wilson Marriage Impey, was the last descendant to be involved with the company and became a Director of R.H.M. after the merger in 1962.

Brooks of Mistley
It was here that the Norman family founded their business. William Brooks went to work for Edward Norman and when he died the business passed to Brooks. William Brooks' great great grandson, John, wrote about his family; "I do not know when the family arrived in Essex but they were farming in the Tendring Hundred in the 18th century. I know that they farmed Golden Ferry Farm, Bradfield and Spinnels Farm, Wix, and other farms in the area".[9]

Edward Norman acquired an estate of nearly 2,000a. Both Golden Ferry Farm and Spinnels Farm were included in the sale of the estate in 1948. The company became known as 'Brooks (Mistley) Ltd.' in 1927. Sales of land had provided capital to finance the extension of the firm's seed cleaning plant. In 1939 a new seed granary had just been completed.

With their own herd of pedigree Red Poll cows Brooks took many prizes, and they also developed a reputation for their cow cubes and 'M' calf gruel boasting; "note the silky skin of the calves"[10].

99 *1900 Writtle Brewery. Wooden casks in evidence.*

Brooks were principally known for the malt which they produced. Situated at Mistley they were in an ideal position to purchase the high grade malting barley for which the Tendring Hundred was famous.

In 1940 incendiary bombs hit the building and it was burnt out. A new mill was completed in 1953 and was one of the first in England to make cubes. The achievements of Brooks were considerable. They produced the first commercial crops of a new barley Plumage Archer in 1905 exporting some of the seed to Chile. A long forgotten predecessor of Plumage Archer was Chevaliar "grown in 1830 and received at our maltings in January 1831. That variety was raised by Rev. Dr. Chevaliar from a single ear in 1819 and remained popular for some 100 years".[9] There was a string of championships at the Royal Toronto Winter Fair. Andrew Davidson's wheat took the world championship. Barley grown by Mary, Lady Delamere, Six Mile Bottom, took the world championship for barley. They took the rye championship twice, there were successes for peas, rape and red clover seed.

Brooks, like many others, faced a dilemma; to borrow massive amounts and increase the capital commitment, or to amalgamate. Brooks became part of RHM Agriculture in 1962. It was the start of the closures which followed these mergers. The small-time (comparatively) mills and maltings dotted around the countryside were swallowed into centralized, and more modern complexes.

In 1969 Brooks was amalgamated, with Vitovis Ltd. of Bungay. Three years later, in 1972, it was merged with Alfred Savill & Co. Ltd. Mellis, Near Diss and became Brooks Saville Ltd. the HQ remained at Mistley. Hasler covered West Essex and Herts. Brooks had a wider coverage of East Anglia and the facilities of a mill at Earsham on the Norfolk/Suffolk border. RHM sold off the prize winning herd of Red Poll cattle.

In 1976 RHM completed another re-organisation. They had bought a large feed mill at Bury St. Edmunds from J. Bibby & Sons Ltd. and closed down three mills, including Mistley. The Essex County Standard lamented; "no longer will grain from the Tendring Hundred be taken into the Mistley Mill, made into animal feeding stuffs, and then sent back to many local farms near where it was grown".[11] The last member of the Brooks famiy to be involved with the business at Mistley was Lt.Col. C. Attfield Brooks. Alan Nicholls followed Col. Brooks. His father had been chairman of Hasler and his cousin, Francis of Kings, Coggeshall.

There were other names that recurred through more than one generation; Bolton, Sarson, Neville. By the 1990s they had become the property of Trent Wharfage. A scheme was advanced to convert the maltings into houses and Prince Charles took an active interest, one of only seven pilot projects in the country.

Brooks and Mistley were synonymous. A stone plaque on the wall stated "these eight maltings were built by Edward Norman, 1806-1828". The name disappeared in 1983 following the take-over of RHM Agriculture by Dalgety-Spillers.

Hasler's of Dunmow

When yeoman farmer Robert Hasler, Throws Farm, Dunmow built a windmill in 1863, he little realised that his farm would acquire an international reputation.

He became an Alderman of the County Council and a JP. In 1900 there was a Brooks, Marriage and Hasler on the County Council. It was the era when successful men returned some of their experience into public duties. Robert Hasler was an eminent leader in the county's affairs. He was closely involved with the foundation of the Dunmow Flitch

100 *1908 Ongar. Matthews traction engine for delivering cattle food. Solid wheels and a solid tree!*

Bacon Factory. He tried to promote sugar beet in 1911, long before it became a popular crop and eventually the Felsted sugar beet factory was built on his son, William's, fields at Felsted.

Father Robert and his son William bred a variety of wheat known as 'Hasler's 37'. It had a short life and was never popular in its county of origin although grown in the Midlands. William founded the Essex Seed Growers Association in 1933 and allowed trial plots of grasses and clovers at Throws. They also developed a variety of winter beans, "Throws (M/S)". In 1900 Hasler found an amalgamation with G.F. Clapham who owned the Great Dunmow windmill, created a partnership; Hasler & Clapham. In 1912 a new mill was built in Dunmow. The company became incorporated in 1917.

The Essex Herbage Seed Association was the successor of the original group "and it is believed that this was the first such body to cause the Government to be aware of the need for and to start certification schemes for herbage seeds in this country".[11]

Hasler's expanded rapidly and by 1930 they had five branches in addition to the head office at Dunmow; Ingatestone, Braintree, Rayne, Felsted and Saffron Walden, with the addition of an up-to-date mill and facilities for 350 ton barges at Maldon. Cock Green Mill, Felsted, was bought from the executors of C.J. Whiting in 1955. They had also opened a branch at Cavendish, Suffolk, and Braughing, Herts.

The jewel in Hasler's crown remained the Experimental Crop Husbandry Braugying Farm, Throws 475a with an annual rainfall of 22.3 in., comprising heavy Calcareous boulder clay with about 60 acres of loam. At 250 ft. about sea level it was situated in one of the high spots of Essex, on the central upland plateau and being heavy clay the trials had considerable relevance to Essex farmers.

They set out to test, evaluate and develop varieties of cereals, field beans, grasses, clovers, roots and the forefront of crops such as grain maize. There was a flock of pedigree Clun Forest Ewes but the summer Open Days, which in 1974 attracted more than 1,000 farmers, had 2,000 control grown plots. They also grew 20,000 plants of spring beans in peat pots at another centre at Cockfield, Suffolk. Throws continued as a major development and evaluation centre under the ownership of RHM and subsequently Dalgety.

One hundred years after its foundation in 1963 Hasler's faced the problem that had arisen with many other 'middle-ranking' companies. They needed more capital to remain independent. The Hasler family owned two-thirds of the shares "and there were no Haslers likely to follow Alan to keep this money in the firm" wrote Eleanor Roper.[12] RHM had taken over Brooks in January 1962, and in December Hasler became part of the group.

For 21 years until 1983 RHM dominated the East Anglian farming merchanting scene. There were more mergers and acquisitions MD Alan Nicholls said in 1977 "I know there are some farmers in our trading area who do not like to see so many changes taking place in the companies which serve them".[13] but other amalgamations were taking place.

Into Spillers

As feed formulations became more scientific a number of companies were created, mainly along Thameside, which produced specialised ingredients. Seemeel, a protein concentrate derived from fish meal, was produced by British Feeding Meals Co. Ltd. at

101 1980s Hythe Port Colchester. The motor vessel 'Tarquence' loading a cargo of wheat for French buyer J. Soufflet at Pertwee's new Haven Quay silos.

Stratford. Union Oil and Cake Mills, later adding British to make BOCM, launched a national milk-yield competition in 1926 and promoted their balanced dairy nuts. Their mills were at Silvertown and in 1937 advertised the example of P.H. Sparrow, Wick Farm, Steeple, Southminster whose cow 'Sutton Hall Beryl' had exceeded the 3,000 gallon mark of milk for the second time. Mrs. J.T. Wigan, Danbury, achieved first place in the Essex County Annual Milk Recording Herd Competitions. The herd had been fed on Spillers Dairy Cubes. Olympia Oil and Cake Co. Ltd. appointed East Essex Farmers Ltd., Southminster as their sole agent for Essex.

Spillers had five agents. Goulds Ltd. covered Ongar, Loughton and Saffron Walden, Cole & Lecquire at Grays, C.E. Young at Braintree, Frank Pertwee & Sons at Colchester and Richardson & Preece at Witham. Cramphorn bcame a Spillers distributor in 1936. There were some such as E. Metson & Sons. Stisted and Blackwater Mills, Braintree who boasted that their famous pig meal had been produced on the same formula since 1910. Hasler bacame agents for Blue Cross Pig Meals. Only the larger companies such as Marriages and Brooks had the facilities to produce their own balanced rations. Cramphorn produced their own as well as Spillers foods. Rankin at Stambridge produced a range of dairy cubes and pig meals.

Two companies which had their origins in the 1920s Newman & Clark at Halstead and Richardson & Preece at Witham, merged in 1971, with the guidance of Len Ratcliff to form Newgrain. Goulds of Loughton and Moreton Mill near Ongar also joined this group. In 1974 Spillers acquired the merchanting and port facilities at Colchester from Newgrain to create Spillers-Newgrain. Spillers had been founded by Joel Spiller in 1830. In total 19 local companies became amalgamated under this new banner. They reached from Devon to Lancashire but the main trial centre was at Ongar where 2,500 individual plots were annually sown and the agronomic characteristics recorded. In 1979 Dalgety launched a hostile offer for Spillers with a £70m bid. Three historic Essex companies came under the wing of Dalgety, a company with antipodean origins but which had Australian born MP for Maldon, Brian Harrison, and senior partner of Strutt & Parker, Mark Strutt, both prominent Essex men on its Board.

Goulds had originated in 1863. George Gould 'gent', lived at Trappe Hill House. Early in the century they acquired Albion Granaries, Loughton having founded a retail milk business, advertising in 1929; "the only safe milk graded and certified".[14] They were also involved in removals and warehousing and included a range of agricultural interests; corn, forage, dog and poultry foods, household flour and cereals, seeds, bulbs and garden sundries. By 1929 they had established outlets at Buckhurst Hill, Woodford Green, Harlow and Saffron Walden. They also came into possession of the Moreton Mill at Ongar which became their HQ.

Newman & Clark had a mill at Halstead and depots at Great Yeldham and White Colne. The amalgamation of these three companies gave them a coverage of the central and north western part of the county.

Some that Disappeared

In 1863 G.H. Barnard was listed as a Coal Merchant, London Road, Saffron Walden. Thomas Barnard was a 'Corn Factor' in Market Place. In 1902 the firm had become Barnard Bros. with a head office at Newport and depots at Audley End, Elsenham and Littlebury. They were by this time 'Seed Merchants'. Barnard Cross were still in business in 1937.

Supplying farmers with steam coal when this was the major source of fuel for steam engines was a major purchase, before oil supplanted it. Amongst the coal supplying merchants were malsters and brewers Free Rodwell and Brooks. Clapham at Dunmow who merged with Hasler, Rankin at Stambridge, Seabrooke at Grays, Clover's at Dedham, Archer at St Osyth and Colchester, later bought out by Matthews.

Myhill & Sons. Ltd. with granaries and wharves at Goldstreet, Saffron Walden and at Linton, Cambs., supplied a wide range of poultry foods, agricultural seeds and seed corn. They were also coal merchants.

One of the few Scots settlers to diversify was R.H. Currie, Moulsham Lodge, Chelmsford, who supplied Scotch seed potatoes advertising in 1925 "ex-docks in London, ex-barge at your nearest wharf on the Essex coast or delivered by motor lorry to your farm"[15]. Currie's told farmers "experiments and experience show that the average crops obtained from seed potatoes direct from Scotland are at least two tons per acre more than those from once-grown seed potatoes" and in 1953 they were promoting Irish seed potatoes and fertilisers.

CHAPTER 24

Merchants Who Came and Went

Twenty-one year old James Matthews with no farming connections moved to Harold Wood, Romford, in 1895 to create his own corn and seed business. With no local knowledge, and limited capital, he set out to find customers and soon discovered that there was a two-way business opportunity.

He sold farmers feeding stuffs, which he collected from the docks in the metropolitan area, and took back loads of hay and straw which was dispatched to the equine demand in London. In 1904 he built his first mill finding that his small shop was inadequate for the burgeoning trade. A new warehouse followed in 1910 and production of Matthews seeds began. In 1912 he bought premises at Ongar. This interest resulted being appointed an official private seed testing station under the Seeds Act 1920. In 1933 he erected one of the most up-to-date mills at Battlesbridge. At this time he was buying one new wagon, and another pair of heavy horses every year.

Like Brooks, Hasler and Cramphorns he had his own fleet of 50 lorries by 1935. Before the war in 1939 Matthews had created a network or branches all over Essex, he discovered that there was a lucrative business selling pet food and garden seeds to householders. The business developed into a chain of retail shops which obtained their own brand supplies from Battlesbridge and Wickham Mills. He also had a coal depot at St Botolphs Station, Colchester. After the war, with the development and purity of cereal seeds more important Matthews set up their own seed production company and seed cleaning machinery at the Hythe. In 1967 they labelled their seed 'Essex Crown' chosen as a result of so many customers saying that the name of Essex was generally accepted as representing the best in cereal growing".[1]

Competition from the national producers of pet foods put the pressure onto the smaller companies and in 1964 they closed down a number of branches and concentrated upon the Battlesbridge livestock foods, and the Hythe seed operation. They became part of BOCM, who already had an evaluation farm at Hobbs Cross, Epping with a herd of cows to monitor and record. In 1969 BOCM decided to re-locate Matthews from Harold Wood and they moved into premises at Little Maplestead. It was during the '60s that many companies found that the safety net of a powerful parent company was a route for survival. Independence was lost and reconstruction inevitable.

During the post-war period whilst farming was more secure it was merchants who faced stiff competition from both national companies and the requirements of vast capital injections. National millers set out to capture the merchanting and retail trade. It resulted in the loss of identity of many companies. The large multiple grocers, later called supermarkets, went direct to farmers with contracts for the supply of products. It was an innovation into the structure of marketing which the small independent millers, maltsters and brewers had previously occupied.

Cramphorn had corn and flour businesses at Brentwood, Stratford and Chelmsford in 1890. In 1902 they had eight branches, in 1931, 23 and in 1953 a network of 45 throughout the eastern counties. The retail side went ahead three times as fast as their farming operations. They had 70 shops in 1963 and 90a of associated nurseries. The main business was to meet the increasing demands for packet seeds, roses and garden plants.

Cramphorn operated Cuton Mill at Springfield and had granaries at Brentwood, Chelmsford and Halstead. They were strongest in the west of the county with shops at Dagenham, Grays, Ilford, Laindon, Rainham, Shoeburyness, Tilbury, Romford and many others. When the agricultural side was paramount, they had supplied the poultry foods for the egg-laying trials when the Royal Agricultural Show visited Ipswich in July 1934. They decided to pull out of farming and In 1963 they sold the agricultural side to Newman & Clark Ltd., Halstead. Included were the maltings at the Hythe owned by Associated British Maltsters.

Pertwees of Colchester

Frank Pertwee founded his company in 1899 and although many companies barely survived their founder, this was not the case with the Pertwee family. Frank's son, Norman, took control of the business soon after the war. Although his father remained chairman, under Norman's guidance Pertwees diversified never missing a chance to hit the headlines with ideas as 'Operation Airdrill' when, in the wet autumn of 1960, they tried to spread seed corn from the air. It was not entirely successful. They introduced fork-

102 About 1912. Before the days of lorries, merchants collected grain and delivered seed by single axle wagons. This one was dressed for a show.

lift trucks to the seed trade, an innovation in 1954. By 1967 Norman Pertwee had seven subsidiary companies.

When the most trenchantly established companies were falling into the hands of the national conglomerates, Pertwees remained staunchly independent but realised they could not live by grain alone. Norman's energetic personality encouraged him to spread out in many directions. Having formed Anfood to produce blended poultry food he established his own egg packing station and formed Main Line Eggs Ltd. in 1964 at Marks Tey. "Here we would be the seller of food and the buyer of eggs, and it probably would have been a brilliant payoff if we had a little more luck with timing and circum-stances".[2] Not content Pertwees had bought three separate sites at Langham airfield and built units to house 15,000 chickens. Rearing pullets was contracted out at Pebmarsh. The chickens became heavy consumers of the products of Anfood.

He bought a chalk pit at Claydon near Ipswich and developed machinery to spread the chalk on fields. And a merchant company at Clopton named Farm Production Sales. An association with Stimpson at Reepham, Norfolk developed into a fertiliser blending operation and they launched mini-bags to transport their products. He exported poppy seed to the USA and Canada but turned down the idea of going into an arable farming venture, although his son, Christopher, later became a partner in a Suffolk farming company.

Frank Pertwee had founded the Wivenhoe Sand & Gravel Co. which he sold in 1958. Realising that chemicals were to become a much more important part of husbandry techniques Norman launched into 'European Helicopters', "a natural extension of our crop protection activities".[2] They sprayed raspberries in Scotland and potatoes in Essex. Bad luck often dogged his efforts and the year after this venture had been launched there was a dry season (1959) and potatoes were not attacked by blight. To fill the gap he sent his helicopters to spray the rice for Fidel Castro in Cuba. The contract was held up and Pertwee later wrote; "as the purpose of my journey had been to sell the helicopters, it can only be recorded as a failure."[3]

In 1978 Pertwees took over Twyman's of Feversham, a chemical distribution. He founded 'Colchester Grain Storage Ltd.' whereby shareholder farmers were able to put their grain into centralised, but individual silos, at the Hythe. The intake dressing etc and monitoring was operated by Pertwee's and the grain, when eventually sold, passed through Pertwee's hands again.

Norman's efforts were directed towards closing the gap between the farmers' fields and the market place. His interest in air-work was a latent ambition to be a pilot. At the age of 66 years he obtained his flying licence. Ruaton Garden Co. had been founded by the Jansma family at Clacton-on-Sea and specialised in growing tomatoes. Pertwee took over the company. The valuable site was sold and a new one was bought. They produced plants for national shopping chains, such as Marks & Spencer, and also extended their range with an interest in the Caribbean.

The writing was on the wall, and consolidation and concentration was the task of his son Christopher. "Shortly following my retirement from executive life, we had decided that our field of operations was too broad".[4] Valley Farm Eggs Ltd. was sold to Dalgety, the Langham poultry units to Meadowlay, the Marks Tey egg station became a printing unit, the transport company was amalgamated with the Pertwee fleet.

In 1980 the group employed 300 people. In 1985 there were 200 and in 1988 the

103 *1974 Coggeshall. Fork lift trucks were taking over from workers' backs.*

closure of grain operations marked the end of a trading history which had lasted for 89 years. The extensive premises along the waterfront at the Hythe were vacated. An amalgamation with a Kent chemical company, Wilmott, and the building of an office at Langham signalled the formation of Wilmott-Pertwee.

As the leaders of the agricultural companies had performed public duties on the Essex County Council, so their sons directed the national trade associations which had arisen. Attfield Brooks, Len Ratcliff, Norman and later Christoper Pertwee were all presidents of the National Seed Association (UKASTA). Christopher became High Sheriff of Essex and Master of the Worshipful Company of Farmers in 1998.

Competitors

Norfolk company Gregory & Hampson launched onto the Essex scene in 1972 when they opened a grain office at Station Road, Manningtree. A year later Kenneth Wilson, the Leeds based grain company, backed by Bunge, at that time the largest private company in the world, with K-W being the largest grain merchants in the UK, bought Gregory & Hampson. K-W had been formed in 1910 and went public on the death of its founder in 1946. They merged with Bunge in 1962 and were not known in East Anglia. They closed down the operation 11 years later.

Dalgety launched a sales foray in 1974 and attracted Maurice Rix from Haslers to spearhead this extension. After taking over the other companies Dalgety was the major force in the county and subject to a management buy-out in 1998.

New companies were being formed. Great Horkesley farmer's son, John Page, formed his own grain merchanting firm at Colchester in 1969. He had previously been a trader with Ridgeons. He formed an association and became Page-Wills, before becoming part of the Soufflet group with a trading office at Bury St. Edmunds. Traders now operated without warehouses or lorries. They were a new breed of middle men who matched the farmers' goods to the most appropriate outlet. Mark Lawrence had been MD at Richardson & Preece, but left when the merger with Newgrain took place. M.L.G., as it became known was taken over by Hugh Baird & Sons in 1994.

Baird's, a Scottish company formed in 1823, built a malting plant at Witham in 1961 and became part of the Conagra group in 1962, hived off to Tate & Lyle in 1975 and rejoined the Canada Malting Co., part of Conagra Malt in 1989. The true parentage of nearly all the companies dealing in the agricultural world was obscure and diverse with frequent changes.

Frank Folkard who farmed at Copford had a successful seed business at Marks Tey, adjacent to the railway, and with five sons, of which one was the long serving secretary of Colchester Farmers Union, but into the next generation there were only two heirs. One was a fruit farmer, and it was bachelor Peter Folkard who decided to close down the business when the Stanway bypass section of the A12 was upgraded into a motorway. It ran right through his warehouse!

In the '70s farming looked set for a burst of prosperity following the UK entry into the EEC, but it was Ashdown-Rawlinson which later became a disaster for many farmers.

Launched in April 1972 it was a partnership between Ron Ashdown, previously a trader with Newgrain at Halstead and Peter Rawlinson who had a milling company at Alderford Mill, Sible Hedingham founded by his father in 1926. The new company had a share capital of £100,000. In the first year of trading they grossed a turnover of £6m. Expansion to Chilton airfield near Sudbury where they spent £40,000 improving the old wartime hangars, and installed drying and storage capacity for 14,000 tons of grain. The Essex County Standard said "Ronald Ashdown has built up one of the largest grain businesses in recent years".[5] Within three years Ron Ashdown resigned and Rawlinson in conjunction with William Weir founded Chilton Grain. Ashdown created a new company, bearing his own name. It expanded rapidly as harvests increased and there were considerable export opportunities. For some years Ashdown was the largest grain buyer in the county. In 1990 there was a spectacular bankruptcy which lost £10m. It resulted in a jail sentence for Ashdown and Kings Grain and Pulses, Coggeshall, which had been set up as an independent division of Kings was forced into voluntary liquidation, as were several other companies in Suffolk. Farmers too lost many thousands of pounds.

Colin South, who had been grain manager for Kenneth Wilson at Manningtree formed his own business, Dennick-South at Brightlingsea in 1985 and closed it down five years later. Merchants found that they had to form links with each other in order to fill the 5,000 ton grain shipments that were going out of Ipswich. But more closures occurred. Clovers, who at one time had a string of mills on the River Stour, with their HQ at the historic Dedham Mill, closed due to the problems of obtaining the right quality wheat they required under new EEC rules. It was the end of a long tradition. But others were intrepid.

Tucks of Burston built a new mill at Earls Colne in 1982, lauded as the most modern animal feed mill in Britain. It was erected on a coal siding by a disused station. A capacity

104 1980s Coggeshall. Dr.Bland demonstrating arable break crops on Kings Farm.

to produce 1,500 tons of bulk animal feeds every week. Tucks had been founded by William Tuck in 1922 but had an Essex connection when they took over Pertwee Anfood just before the new mill was built. It was symbolic of the critical attitude that local residents objected. It was labelled as; "a blemish on the rural view across the river to the picturesque cluster of houses and ancient church which are Colne Engaine".[6]

In 1975 John D'Angibau bought Unwins, a company at Birdbrook which had specialised in clover and kale seed. It had a long history. George Unwin was farming Old House, Stambourne, before 1863. They also had a mill and moved to Baythorne Hall. In 1902 Daniel Unwin was a miller at Brockles and Moat Farms. George Ernest J.P. moved to Baythorne Hall and it was here that the family seed growing tradition continued. D'Angibau took over the company and in 1995 it became part of International Corn. Members of the Unwin family continued to farm in this corner of Essex. Hitchcocks were a company which specialised in producting pet foods and a small amount of animal feeds. A mill at Bures and one at Fingringhoe which they bought from E. Marriage & Sons Ltd. in 1933. It was sold to Clark & Butcher Ltd., Soham in 1989.

In 1989 Pauls of Ipswich, a subsidiary of Harrisons & Crosfield plc bought Edward Baker Ltd. of Great Cornard near Sudbury. Bakers had taken over Green Brothers (Maldon) Ltd. in 1943. Greens was an amalgamation of two historic Essex millers.

Hoe Mills, Woodham Walter, was owned by a successful stoneground miller Samuel Garrett. Garrett was inspired by the new steel rollers and in order to install them he built a new mill at Maldon. It commenced production in 1896. Early in the 20th century he took into partnership Mr. Pemberton "and it was said to be an unholy alliance". This was reputed to be the cause of Garrett's bankruptcy which occurred two weeks before the First

World War broke out on 4th August 1914. "It would have been saved...the next day all flour mills came under Government control and stayed so until 1919".[7] The Maldon mill lay empty for two years.

William Green, a pig farmer in the Dedham valley had built a flour mill to feed his own pigs with the offal. His success encouraged him to buy another mill at Raydon, Hadleigh, (Suffolk). When this mill was burnt down in 1916 he bought, for £2,000 Garrett's old Maldon mill. When William Green died in 1921 the Maldon mill became a partnership and in 1924 they operated what had become known as the Rayleigh Flour Mills, Maldon, and the 'Gold Belt Roller Mills' at Brantham, Manningtree. They also had a flock of pedigree Suffolk sheep. Most merchants at that time had a farm where they produced seed, did experiments, or utilised waste products from their mills to feed their animals cheaply. In 1943 Green Brothers was sold to Edward Baker for £36,000. This was the company which Paul's purchased in 1989. The imposing Sudbury mill had been closed by Green in 1967 and became the 'Mill Hotel'. Clover's Dedham mill later became flats.

As merchants looked over the hedge and pondered whether they should become farmers, so farmers looked at the merchants and were tempted to cream-off some of the profits of the middle-man. Farmer controlled co-operatives, were common in France and other European countries. From the '70s onwards farmers were continually encouraged

105 1951 Mistley. 9 tons per lorry, 7 lorries = 63 tons of animal feeds ready for farm delivery. Sack barrow on top for unloading. Workers carried them on their backs into the farm store shed. Poultry feed, particularly when broilers became popular, was big business. Nitrovit built a new plant at Witham to cope with demand

to improve their marketing. At its best a strong co-operative force could help to stabilise the markets, and, with insider knowledge, make sure that the margins of the merchants were kept within proportions. It was not the intention to usurp the merchants but to provide an alternative. There were four such forays in Essex; West Essex Farmers operated along the Hertfordshire/Cambridgeshire border country, SHRIM in central Essex around Chelmsford, Dengie Crop Dryers in the Dengie Hundred and surrounding areas, Eastern Counties Farmers, with its HQ at Ipswich was strongest in the east of the county. They were all farmer owned.

The initial thrust of W.E.F. and SHRIM was in buying the requisites which farmers required. "Everything we sell is at the wholesale rate, and everything we buy comes at the retail rate. Never-the-less the rumours of 50% discounts on wire netting and batteries are sufficient, even if untrue, to encourage farmers to give the buying groups a try".[8]

They all, later developed an arm to market cereals. The premise dictated that if enough farmers offered their grain jointly, as a 5,000 ton lot, they would be able to influence the market. This philosophy did not successfully transpire. End-users did not want such 'bumps' but required a steady flow of grain throughout the year. The individual merchanting sector was too strong, and bulk grain lorries widened the catchment area to the main exporting ports such as Tilbury and Ipswich. Grain was moved from many miles away, with less trouble than shorter distances had previously been.

Dengie Crop Dryers was the brainchild of 12 farmers in the Dengie Peninsular who combined to build a co-operative plant with the objective of turning lucerne into pellets for animal feed. They agreed upon a site at Asheldham and contracted to grow a minimum acreage to keep the plant supplied. It was a success. They had 600 cows between them and the inability of rye grass and clover mixtures to give a satisfactory yield on this exposed part of the Essex coast persuaded them that lucerne, with its vitamin rich, high protein, quality would be an alternative. The original cost was £67,000 and it was an act of faith. Twenty years later they had added a cereal marketing and purchasing division.

East Essex Farmers Ltd. was formed and a grain plant was built. It remained controlled by its farmer founders but by 1988 the 12 had grown to 27 members. The assets had grown to £500,000. They were exporting their dried lucerne, known as alfalfa, to North America and it was being used in the UK for cattle, horses, goats, sheep, deer, rabbits and zoo animals. They aimed for new export markets in Scandinavia and the Middle East.

The grain store had a capacity of 16,000 tons with an oil seed rape addition when rape became a prominent crop. They had a niche market with the lucerne, and the grain marketing operation became more important. In 1989 the various divisions, all co-operative in nature, were transferred into a private limited company, Dengie Crops Ltd. and the first year revealed a turnover of over £12m with net assets valued at £1.7m. A great advance for the 12 founders 23 years earlier and their investment of under £6,000 each. They were not restricted to dealing on a 'members-only' basis but actively purchased grain and other crops in competition with the major grain buyers. Essex Growers Trading Association Ltd. at Hockley mainly supplied fruit growers with a wide range of requisites.

SHRIM, coined from the five villages where the founders farmed; Stock, Hanningfield, Rettendon, Ingatestone and Margaretting, originated in 1960 as a buying group. Seven years later the Cereals Pool concept was created. It continued to be fully

258

farmer controlled under the original chairmanship of John Lyster but they soon needed a full-time secretary with an office and Reg Masters guided the Group through its founding years.

Based at Billericay it followed a pattern that was led by Suffolk farmer, Stephen Horvat who founded a similar organisation called Framlingham Farmers. The NFU were, at that time, taking tentative steps, at the behest of their members, into commercial sidelines such as N.F.U. Seeds Ltd. Witham. Farmer controlled groups, on a smaller scale were being created in many villages.

Within 10 years SHRIM had formed a cereals committee and in their first year they achieved a premium of 67p per ton above the average market prices for their members. In 1967 they topped the market by £2.50p per ton. Unlike Dengie the grain remained on the farm but there was a system of advanced payments for those who wished to achieve enhanced values by selling later in the cereal year. It was run as a non-profit making enterprise.

Harlow Agricultural Merchants (HAM) was founded in 1980 when Tim Parker, a Colne Engaine ex-Colonel and poultry farmer's son, left Newgrain and decided to set up a semi-farmer owned and controlled business to cover the North-West of the county, which was untouched by co-operative ventures apart from the incursion of SAMCO which operated in Hertfordshire and Cambridgeshire. The concept of HAM was to issue a share capital of £200,000 of which 50% was subscribed by farmers and the remainder by the principals and staff. Nearly 20 years later the farmers involvement had reduced to 40%. Parker became chairman of the company and Ian Low its chief executive. They were based at Little Hallingbury and supplied farmers with seed, fertiliser, agrochemicals as well as buying grain.

Eastern Counties Farmers' Co-operative Association was the oldest co-operative venture and was formed on 17th May 1904. It was, despite its ambitious title an Ipswich, and primarily Suffolk, business. In 1908 Essex farmers had rebuffed an approach to amalgamate but as the years passed ECF gained members from Essex. In 1953 they had corn offices at Pondfield Pastures, Dunmow and North Hill, Colchester. Owned by its farmer members ECF operated on a system of trading bonuses, returning profits as discounts.

Farmers could become members by the purchase of a minimal number of shares. In the '60s ECF expanded throughout the Eastern Counties, achieving a presence to service the requirements of its 9,000 farmer shareholders. The value of the trading bonuses give an indication of the tight margins which the merchanting trade was experiencing.

Half percent on fertiliser purchases and the same on grain, seeds and livestock. 2 % on other purchases. These rates were varied from time to time and the shareholders received a normal interest payment from their stake holding. The terms were generally not attractive enough for farmers to give ECF all their business. It struggled to achieve the full loyalty of its members.

To obtain membership a farmer was required to buy £25 worth of shares and by leaving his annual trading bonuses with the company there was a target of £1 for every acre farmed, and a maximum holding of £1,000 to prevent any dominant stakes arising.

ECF was a democracy. By 1970 it covered six counties and had a pyramidical structure of control. There were 18 branches throughout its area, 10 district committees with 109 farmer members sitting on them, and every meeting was attended by top

106 1950 Royal Albert Docks. Red Clover seed being loaded for Canada.

management from Ipswich. There was a central management committee of 23 men and with such a structure it tried to satisfy the smallest whims. When a small number of farmers suggested that they found Welsh calves better performers than Scottish ones, ECF set out to achieve member satisfaction by organising, what turned out to be a very small and loss making operation.

In 1974 ECF purchased the St Edmunds Bacon Factory Ltd., situated at Elmswell and formed by local farmers in 1911 it had been, like the Dunmow Flitch Bacon Co., purely involved in the slaughter of pigs and the curing of bacon. Elmswell had developed its own brand, 'Farm Kitchen', of pork based pies and sausages. The company was running at a loss when ECF, at the instigation of some of its pig producing members, took over this business. Three years later they had turned a deficit of £300,000 into a profit of similar size. The staff had been cut from 500 to 300 but an injection of £1.5m was required to upgrade the factory to the new EEC standards.

ECF had an insatiable need to retain capital for new ventures. A new state-of-the-art mill was opened at Ware, continual upgrading took place at Ipswich, a seed cleaning operation was established at Rougham, Suffolk and they broadened their operations in a way, and to a degree, that no other agricultural merchant had attempted. They became involved in fuel distribution, the only grain merchant to do so, and a role normally reserved for specialist distributors. There was a pulse marketing division, they bought and sold grain, sold fertiliser, milled and blended livestock feeds, supplied livestock and operated the Elmswell Bacon Factory. It was a wide ranging business.

It was also far removed from the original seven men and their idealistic ethics in 1904. Such was inflation in the '70s that the turnover of £13.4m in 1970 had risen to over £91m a decade later and £135m by 1985. Unfortunately the profits had not risen by the same degree. At the end of the decade Halstead farmer and NFU president Sir Richard Butler told the AGM "the amount of trade available to co-ops in the six eastern counties is about £750m. This is shared between 107 co-ops, at least 70 of them probably being in competition with each other".[9]

On top of their already wide portfolio ECF decided to foray into the machinery world. They opened depots throughout their trading area, but could not acquire the agencies of the leading tractor makes. Great Leighs was the focus of ECF operations in Essex and a machinery depot was opened opposite the Essex Showground. They created cereal syndicates, of which four groups were established in Essex; Great Leighs, Mid-Essex, Colne and Three Rivers which were later combined under the chairmanship of Tony Bosworth, Willingdale Spain and became known as the 'Rodings Syndicate'. They were in competition with other grain groups, such as Dengie, SHRIM also farmer controlled.

A good profit in 1980 was followed by a poor one in 1981. There were no trading bonuses for members, the staff had received £170,000 in 1979 and got nothing. There was no payment on the issued share capital. A revival in fortunes the following two years was followed by a decline. ECF had invested heavily and had an overdraft of £10m. In 1985 the Great Leighs machinery branch was closed. Turnover started to decline but another £1m was spent on the Ipswich mill. For the remainder of the decade it was a tenuous survival. They launched an appeal for farmers to inject more capital to keep the company solvent but in 1994 went into voluntary liquidation. Many of its farmer customers who had delivered grain lost heavily. The dream of its founders had been shattered. It had a purpose, but no sense of direction.

Conclusions

During the century many long established names vanished. Others achieved prominence but also succumbed as times changed. Conglomerates intruded into the family scene and important village millers were but a distant memory, many legends being lost completely.

Owen Parry Ltd with its Oil mills at Colchester producers of the 'Harry' brand of linseed and cotton cake, decorticated ground nut cakes, was sold to Unilever, who sold the site at the Hythe to Pertwee's, who vacated it and applied for development rights. Parry's name was forgotton. Harrison, Barber & Co. at Stow Maries boasted that they had been formed in 1894 and in 1924, "had the largest horse slaughtering business in the world".[10] Henry Whitmore operated the Victoria Flour Mills at Romford and was established in 1858. C.J. Taylor, Billericay, was a corn and seed merchant. C.B. & A. Sworder, Epping, in a similar business but included selling coal. There were many others whose names went into the history books.

Most of the earlier firms had their roots, and their ancestors on Essex farms. The impetus was often a desire to vertically integrate their farming with that of milling or animal feed production. It was a natural process. After mid-century the breed of chairman and managers of the merchanting companies did not, in general, have this farming background. W. & H. Marriage & Sons at Chelmsford survived independently by scaling down and concentrating upon supplying pet foods. Church of Bures, founded by an Essex farmer, William Church, in 1902 went into the fourth generation at Bures and their 1998 catalogue listed three varieties of beans, seven of peas, nine clovers and grasses, eight root crops, six miscellaneous odd crops, and two game cover crops. In 1900 game birds were the prerogative of the landed classes. The birds nested and fed as scavengers. The idea of planting special mixtures would have been anathema 100 years ago.

Companies which superficially appeared to have survived, such as Kings at Coggeshall had become part of a corporate umbrella. The name remained but the ownership and control had gone. Others which came and went include Pinkerton Grain at Tilbury, Bolton & Tanner at Boreham, Abbotts at Chignall St James, C.G. Pulford & Son at Stebbing, C. Simpson & Son, Dunmow and Aythorpe Roding, Chas Farnham Forage Merchants at Brentwood, Thames Valley Seeds at Asheldham.

EDME (English Diastatic Malt Company) closed down its malt syrup business in 1999 after 115 years. They continued to produce flour and cereal flakes. EDME's tall chimney was a landmark at Mistley, and they had been a good buyer of locally grown barley.

It was an ever changing scene.

CHAPTER 25

The Machinery People

The blacksmith did not naturally translate into the new breed of farm implement makers. The decline of the horse was accompanied by the rise of the motor car. Some smiths turned into garages, although there was still a trade until after mid-century. Farmers had their own variations on proprietary implements and the local blacksmith was called in to effect these modifications. Such items as harrow teeth were a speciality, and plough design was changed to suit local conditions. Anything more complicated was left to the larger foundries.

The decline in the number of blacksmiths and farriers from 522 in 1890 to 298 in 1929 was caused by the expansion of cars and lorries, and not the decline in farmer customers. Side-by-side with this development was the rise in agricultural implement manufacturers. There had been 19 in 1851 but the years of depression reduced them to 17 in 1890 but there were 22 in 1902 and only 11 in 1929. Some manufacturers had now become 'agricultural engineers' and adding these two categories together the advance of mechanisation is more clearly shown. 1890 (24), 1902 (30), 1929 (39). There were some such as Ernest Doe, Ulting, who was listed as a blacksmith, later a motor engineer, but also made farm implements.

The companies which achieved prominence did not spring from the smithy trade. Hunt was a millwright, Whitlock a forage merchant and Doe was the son of a miller from Terling Mill. The remainder were farmers turned inventors who saw more future in making machinery, than in farming. This line of descent was in contrast to the corn merchants of the 20th century who, predominantly had a history in the same business. Of the 22 listed firms in 1902 [1] only eight achieved any degree of fame. Some of the others were only, in reality, extended blacksmiths.

There were others such as Taylors who came from the north of England to build Abberton Reservoir and Joseph, when it was completed, opened a blacksmiths shop to serve local needs and later into the construction of steel framed buildings during the boom period of modernisation after 1960. They eventually went into liquidation. Seven companies had their roots in the 19th century and one, Bentalls of Maldon was founded in 1795. The products of these early manufacturers became superseded and they were, eventually, faced with closure.

The most prominent firm in Essex which supplied farming requisites in the first part of the century was J. Brittain Pash. They boasted that they had "the largest stock of agricultural machinery, dairy goods, and spare parts in Essex".[2] Pash was the sole agent for Massey-Harris. They claimed to have introduced Reaping Machines to Essex in 1866, Sheaf Binders in 1892 and tractors in 1915.

The business was founded in Joseph Brittain Pash's workshop on his farm at Galleywood in 1866 and by 1900 was supplying a range of goods mainly in the Chelmsford area. They opened a depot at Hill St., Saffron Walden in 1934, and their chief salesman was Norman Joscelyne who went to the markets at Romford, Rochford and

107 1910 Kelvedon. Threshelfords Farm. Darby Digger contracted by W. Moss (in front).

Stanford-le-Hope every week. Joscelyne was appointed mechanisation officer under the EWAEC during the Second World War. H.E. Williams & Co. covered the same range for Colchester and North Essex.

J.B.P. made very little themselves with the exception of angle-iron stakes which were common in pre-war days. They had a staff to erect fences and were prepared to travel up to 100 miles. In 1934 they were also manufacturing water carts which, with the dry conditions in Essex found a ready market. In 1932 they became agents for a new potato planting machine. The first was sold to A.M. & H. Rankin Ltd., Stambridge Steam Mills, Rochford. They had promoted tractors with working demonstrations 17 years earlier and they laid on a planting demonstration at Rickstones Farm, Rivenhall, for Messrs. E.C. Wells & Son.

In 1941 they were agents for 120 manufacturers and when Lord Nuffield launched his tractor J.B.P. became the agents for Essex. In 1952 the TVO model cost £425 but a diesel engine cost £625 10s. By this time, although the name remained prominent, the company had been incorporated with builders merchants Brown & Son Ltd., which gave them the advantage of a depot at Hawkins Road, Hythe, Colchester. They became agents for the new David Brown 900 but as competition became stronger, and the Nuffield was never a truly successful seller to Essex farmers, the agricultural interests were displaced as Brown expanded its activities in building materials. A name that had been predominant in farming circles had gone and Joseph Brittain Pash almost forgotten.

Bentall's of Maldon

Bentall's, as implement makers, came into existence in 1795. The 'Goldhanger' plough was the corner stone of the company's prosperity. At the turn of the century Bentalls was an established company with an impressive record.

In the First World War they became one of the first engineering companies to employ women in their workshop. In 1914 they were employing 6/700 workers and the factory covered 14a. The output of farm machinery showed growth every year. This was halted by the war and production was switched to shell cases. After the war an association of engineering firms was created under the name; 'Agricultural and General Engineers Ltd.' (A.G.E.). Bentall & Co. was merged into the consortium. Initially AGE prospered but with the slump which followed, the consortium found itself in difficulties. Edward Bentall, the largest individual shareholder lost the money which might have put Bentalls on its feet again. This bankruptcy lost Bentalls the confidence of their customers.

In 1933 he began the task of reviving the family fortunes. "Year by year the position showed an improvement, the whole of the Company's debts were finally paid, the borrowed capital was repaid, and by the end of 1938 the annual accounts showed a small profit. Bentalls was on its feet again".[3]

The Halifax bomber was equipped with tail-fins, bomb-floors which were made at Maldon. During wartime Bentalls doubled their output. In 1946 it was re-organised as a public company, and continued to produce large numbers of chaff and root cutters, their tractor tandem disc harrows had sold for £34 in 1935 and the tractor plough for £14.35p. William Bentall's 'goldhangar' had sold for £3.60 in 1845 – with a 7s.0d. (35p) discount for prompt cash! Pre-war they built tractor mowers, the 5ft. cut having a price of £41. The same mower made for horses cost £31.

In 1949 Bentalls took over Tamkin Bros. & Co. Ltd. Chelmsford and the Beehive Lane Works was closed. Their wide range of machinery was transferred to Heybridge. Tamkin was famous for its iron tractor wheels which were a single circular plate with unique curved lugs bolted on each side. They also produced a one-man operated two-row sugar beet lifter, and had the Tamkin-Rafo hay sweep, Tamkin-Bird road bands, Tamkin-Darby combined mole drainer pipe and cable layer. It was a handsome purchase for Bentalls and widened the range of their production. Tamkin's name was too famous to be abolished.

In the post-war years they developed the Bentall Mechanical Muck-Spreader. By 1949 the works at Maldon was overstretched. A new foundry was built and in 1955 Lt.Cdr. Kemp wrote "they were pioneers, resting their faith in a belief that the age-old methods of farming were changing. With this vision they saw the advent of mechanisation on the farm, with their skill they led the way with their mechanical inventions".[3]

Six years after this was written the company was taken over by the Acrow Group, famous for their scafolding. William de Vigier, a refugee who escaped from Europe in 1936 named his company after his solicitor, Arthur Crow. Acrow bought its first works at Saffron Walden in 1940. They turned out bomb trolleys, parts for tanks, and form work for Mulberry Harbour. The new Coronation Works was opened on a 45a site in 1956.

The acquisition by Acrow marked the end of Bentalls traditional products. The future lay in highly specialised markets and it was the post-harvest problems of storage and grain dryers that looked the most promising. In 1974 a giant complex covering 150,000sq.ft. and costing £2m was opened. The new image was the promotion of the 'Bentall Feedcentre', 4% of the production from Maldon was exported.

Simplex of Cambridge had been formed in 1936 and with Alfa Laval occupied the

108 1933 Rainham. Spraying potatoes for S. Gunary and Sons. The early sprayer was pulled by a horse!

leading reputation for milking machines. Acrow acquired Simplex and changed the name to Bentall Simplex. They introduced innovative industrial bulk storage, slurry conservation and horticultural equipment. Bentall Simplex elevators and conveyers were matched with their seed cleaning machines, an advisory service, and the circular grain bins which Simplex had been developing. The Simplex idea had been for free-standing storage bins. The old name was retained and they became known as 'Goldhanger' bins. The 18th century plough had become a modern grain silo.

William de Vigier, decided that the future, which had once looked rosy, was saturated. The Heybridge factory was closed. The large building was used partly as an Intervention Store after the 1984 harvest and it later became occupied as offices. In 1998 the electronics giant Industrial Control Service occupied many of the sites that had seen the rise of Edward Bentall's dream. His name lived on. The new industrial units were known as the Bentall's Centre. A hospice was established and the school opposite, which had been endowed by the Bentall family in the 19th century became a Training and Enterprise Centre.

Earls Colne and Great Yeldham

Reuben Hunt was employing 300 men at Earls Colne in 1900. It was the days of paternalistic Victorian industrialists who, following the lead of the aristocracy, provided 'everything from the cradle to the grave'. The factory dominated the village which had suffered from the decline of the cloth industry and later straw plaiting. As Hunts grew there was a ready-made labour force. He built over 100 terraced houses from a foundation in 1825.

Hunts were famous for their cast iron rolls. They also manufactured pulleys and sharpening for industry and, like Bentalls, they relied upon the export market. British engineering products had a world wide reputation at this time, but "Hunt was in the middle ranking of a league of firms based in the Eastern Counties that came to dominate the agricultural engineering industry during the nineteenth century".[4]

The association with Ransomes was cemented when, due to changing demands of their product range, a lack of innovative ideas and an inability to continue without a considerable injection of new capital, Ransomes took over Hunts. They continued to produce heavy iron castings for their rolls and a range of other less well known products. In 1988 the business was closed and the village of Earls Colne was bereft of its patrician founding factory.

Whitlocks at Great Yeldham emanated from Walter Whitlock, Poole Farm, who was also a forage merchant. He was a successful farmer with land in eight Essex villages and when he retired in 1919 he had over 1,000a.

The forage business was a successful one and there were over 70 workers employed in 1914. It was through this diversified, but ancillary trade that Whitlock became interested in machinery. When he discovered that spare parts were difficult to obtain he sent one son to an engineer in Scotland and another to Hunt's at Earls Colne. It was these two sons, Thomas and Herbert, who started the agricultural engineering business.

They became agents for some of the most prominent machinery manufacturers, did

109 1920s/30s. Fordson tractors were the most common on Essex farms.

repairs, and supplied spare parts "in what was then described as an isolated part of the country".[5] In 1924 Whitlock Bros. had developed a carpentry division with the emphasis upon pig feeders, poultry houses, shepherds' huts and a range of similar equipment. In 1953 they continued to make wooden cattle cribs, calf mangers and hay racks.

They diversified into the Whitlock Dinkum Digger and were the first UK company to make a tractor-mounted excavator loader. Whitlocks' diggers were ahead of their times and the integrated pivotal Dumpers were the forerunner of the Volvo and others which were used extensively for earth moving. Under Carleton Whitlock, chairman from 1941, the company flourished but after his death in 1966 the dominance of the Whitlock family had gone. Their designs had not been developed and they lacked the capital to expand in the way in which Joe Bamford (JCB) had expanded from making iron hay-rakes and other farm machinery at Uttoxeter.

The company became part of the London & Midland Industrials Group in 1967. They were absorbed into the Powell Duffryn Group in 1972 and integrated with Hy-Mac, the producers of cranes and earth moving equipment.

The prominent Yeldham site, almost opposite the 1,000 year old 'Yeldham Oak' was occupied as a depot for an aggregates and machinery company, part of it became used as an International Tractor and Combine branch but the name disappeared from the village.

Darby's in Trouble

In 1900 the Darby Walking Digger had a national reputation. Thomas Darby of Pleshey Lodge had invented his digger in 1877. "As the sheds clanged to the sound of the hammer on rivet, the revolutionary shape of the first walking broadsider took shape".[6] In 1900 the rotating forks replaced discs and it became known as the 'Revolving Screw Action Digger' and the operation was moved to Stilemans Works, Wickford. Times were hard. Darby's son Sidney, recalled in 1947 "Round about 1907 it was very hard work trying to sell farm machinery owing to price cutting by dealers and the extended credit required by farmers and I have known new American Horse Rakes difficult to sell at five guineas; Mowers at ten guineas and Binders as low as £24".[7] He described his father's efforts in difficult circumstances. He grew linseed at Pleshey Lodge and fed it to his horses. They became too fat, although they had glossy coats. The straw of the linseed was soaked in ditches and Darby made a machine for scrutching it. "We obtained good results with very nice bales of fibre but foreign competition beat us and we had to give up".[7] Darby overcame the problems of flexible power drive but Paxman Colchester works produced a competitive digger which proved to be more popular. An engine was produced known as the Darby Maskell. J.W. Maskell of Tillingham had invented the 'Maskell Motor Cultivator'. It was a combined motorised cultivator which was powered by a four cylinder 25hp engine. Primarily designed for orchard and market garden work it cost £400 in 1919 but by this time was being made at Stamford Lincolnshire.

One of the last Darby diggers to be constructed was viewed by King George V at the Royal Show at Bristol in 1913. "Darby and his sons were never to achieve the success which they so richly deserved. In the end Darby, through the Pedestrian Digger Co. and the Syndicate lost in excess of £100,000, an enormous sum even now".[8]

Sydney Darby took over the Stileman's works and became a machinery agent advertising Maxwell cars in 1924, the deluxe model costing £330. In 1928 he had developed a good trade in second hand farm machinery and become an agent for Fordson & International Junior Tractors. He also advertised "travelling motor workshops at your immediate service".[9] Seven years later, Sydney had perfected the Darby 'All-Weather' wheels to fit tractors and combat a problem to which the early spade-lugs were prone. He appointed R.J. Hawkes, Bell Yard, Chelmsford, as his agent. The following year he opened a branch depot at 29 Railway Arches, Chelmsford.

Darby continued to expand and in 1943 was agent and stockist for the International, Massey-Harris, David Brown and Fordson Tractors. In 1952 he had added a Leyland diesel generator to his range and at the Orsett Show in 1953 he exhibited a British built crawler tractor. The International B-TD6, and was still operating from Wickford.

19th Century Roots

Manufacturing farm implements in Essex had a long history. "Apparently, the industry is of greater relative importance with us than in most other counties".[10] A clutch of companies had been formed at various times in the middle of the 19th century onwards. Some of them were still surviving in 1900. T.W. Wedlake & Co. produced implements at their Hornchurch Iron Works. Maldon Iron Works came into production in the 1860/70s. At the Essex Show in 1931 they displayed a sugar beet hoe (horsedrawn), a hay rake, stacking elevator and a hay sweep, pulled by two horses with an operator sitting on an iron seat and a steering wheel. In 1937 they had evolved the 'Maldon' low-loading tip carts, ploughs, and a set of tractor-drawn rolls with a width of 24ft. Post-war the 'Maldon' carts and trailers had pneumatic tyres, the 'Maldon' drag harrows had a fitting for a tractor to lift them clear of the ground and a range of tractor hoes.

William Joseph Suckling started his business about 1900 at Steeple Bumpstead and in 1929 it had become Suckling & Baxter. After the war John Suckling, invented the Bray Centaur. It was a conversion of a Ford six cylinder engine and Bray four-wheel drive designed to have a plough mounted fore and aft. It was (in principle) the forerunner of the Triple-D and the later pivotal monsters.

Wm. Cottis & Sons Ltd., Archimedean Iron Works, Epping, invented the 'Cottis' patent expanding horse hoe. In 1890 they were producing a hand-pushed lawn mower and claimed that their implements; "are now in use in the Four Quarters of the Globe"[11] and also claimed the first patent on the horse-drawn hay sweeps in 1924. Cottis produced a wide-range of barn machinery and a 'Thistle plough'. Others were Burgess at Brentwood, Dendy at Hornchurch, Joslins of Colchester and Barnard & Lake at Rayne.

In 1863 the Rayne foundry was operated by Goss & Peeme and was listed as agricultural machine makers and iron founders. In 1890 Barnard & Lake had taken over and had achieved some eminence in this field. "Rayne ploughs, root graters, Royal Prize Thatch making machine, prize steerage horse hoes".[11] In 1929 Blyth & Pawsey Ltd. were producing agricultural implements at Rayne and also had an iron foundry at Saffron Walden. Blyth & Pawsey became Massey-Harris agents at Saffron Walden, but in 1929 Barnard & Sons at Rayne had become motor engineers. C.S. Blyth had taken over the Rayne foundry in 1906 and carried on the range of implements which Barnard & Lake had been producing. Pawsey joined him later.

Charles Julias was an implement agent at Dunmow. He produced farm wagons with steel frames and by the end of the war had become agents for International Harvester Co.

Christy Bros. & Co. Ltd., Chelmsford, advertised in 1924 that they could supply;

110 1960s. Birch Gate House Farm. Early M-F 780 combine. Traditional Essex farm buildings could not accommodate the new monsters of the fields.

"everything electrical for the farm and house". They introduced the 'Essex Major' in 1942. A compact, electrically driven, grinding mill that was ideal for small livestock farmers to mill their own home-grown grain, beans etc. This mill was used extensively in the 1950s. It had a capacity of half a ton of ground wheat per hour. It was eventually displaced by higher output machines. The company had become Christy & Norris Ltd.

W.J. Morray Engineering Braintree produced packing and weighing machinery introducing, in 1976 the Walthambury range which included a weigher/bagger which could automatically handle 300 bags per hour – all neatly stiched-up. They had a smaller weigher with an Avery scale which could pack vegetables. Lockwood at Chelmsford produced graders for potatoes and apples,

Sandon Engineering Works became agents of the world's first high density self-propelled baler. It was the Welsh-made Jones 'Invicta'. There were also stationary models. Sandon were also agents for Marshall, and Oliver tractors and the 'Davison' Proudlock potato planter in 1948.

The sticky Essex clay was instrumental in the design of at least three implements. In 1913 the Crawley Agrimotor was produced. The Crawley family were farmers at Hadstock in the 19th century. In 1929 they were described as; "Crawley Brothers, Enginners".[12] In 1929 E. Crawley was at Hall Farm and A.H. Crawley at The Yews, and was noted as the principal landowner in the parish. The Agrimotor, a 30hp petrol/paraffin engine was an integrated machine with a plough. It was produced from 1913–24 and cost £500. In 1978 Michael Moore, Wellingditch, Stow Maries, invented a mole-plough with a double beam, doubling the output of mole-draining and could be pulled by four-wheel drive tractors. The split beam had the effect of spreading the weight.

John Salmon was taking 50 man-hours to lift an acre of sugar beet, "a sorry lot for a farm worker in winter weather."[13] With Salmon's harvester an acre of roots could be harvested in 3 man-hours. It was a 'first' in its conception and John Salmon had the business acumen to launch his own company and build a factory at Martels, Dunmow to produce them.

The Salmons had been Dunmow farmers for many years. John Salmon was born in 1908. At the age of 16 he had to run the 50a family farm. This was at the outset of the depression and Salmon developed a mole-draining business which had become well known before 1939. In 1941 he bought Martels, a 200a farm. He was frustrated at the heavy labour requirement for lifting sugar beet.

He designed his own harvester and launched it on Christmas Eve 1946. Six months later he had bought and sold six. Eight years later the income from the factory, by now 25,000 sq.ft., equalled that of the farm and contract work. He was soon producing 700 machines a year, winning silver medals at the Royal Show. There was a continual demand for a machine which could do the work of 12 men.

Named appropriately after the year of its introduction, the '55' sold 100 machines in 1955, over 200 in 1956, 360 in 1957 and 430 in 1958. In just over three years the output had more than quadrupled. The 'Salmon' became world renowned.

John Salmon died in 1971, aged 64 years. Three years later John Salmon Engineering Co. Ltd. was sold to the Irish Sugar Co. The Salmon beet harvester became known as an Armer-Salmon but the intention was to close down the Dunmow factory and transfer production to Eire. The contract drainage business continued to expand with the company changing its name to John Salmon Land Drainage Ltd. and employing up to 70 men at peak times in the late '70s before its sale to Hugh Pearl in 1984. The company continued as John Salmon Farms Ltd.

After the war the draining of fields became big business. Hugh Pearl of Ongar, another Essex farmer founded his own company specialising in land drainage and four Essex farmers, Robert Brice, Rivenhall., Donald and David Rees of Braxted and Edward Watson who had been manager of Fisons Fieldwork at Feering before they ceased drainage work, founded Anglian Land Drainage.

Ernest Doe & Sons Ltd

Ernest Doe & Sons was one of the few companies to survive the whole of the century. Marriages at Chelmsford was another. Cramphorn diversified out of farming but the number of survivors was small. In the corn merchanting trade, the companies, if they survived, were amalgamated and the family names forgotten. In the machinery world the companies which succumbed usually went into liquidation. Ernest Doe's greatest claim to the history of the 20th century was its innovative 'Triple D' tractor.

The antecedents of The Doe family were rooted in the milling trade and farming but in 1893 Ernest went to work for a blacksmith, George Wood, at Ulting. When Wood retired Ernest bought the business and it remained on the same site throughout the 20th century. The bend on the road was named 'Doe's Corner'. Pre-war Doe's were selling seven different tractors. Fordson was the most popular because it was good value but Case and Allis Chalmers also sold in great numbers. The first hint of creating sales areas came with the war when it was suggested that Essex should be divided into sections. "To counter this, the company decided to open branches and legend has it that Ernest Charles Doe bought three in one Saturday morning".[14]

In the post-war period when machinery, was being invented rapidly, Doe started to manufacture his own. He concentrated upon conversions. The light-weight Allis Model B was adapted for low clearance, and a high clearance machine was suggested by Seabrooks for orchard work. They built a Wild Oat and Weed Seed Collector onto a Fordson Major. At the request of a customer a green crop harvester in conjunction with R.G. Tayler manager for Strutt & Parker Farms Ltd. was based on the Massey-Harris 726 combine. These harvesters were known as the Tayler-Doe and won a silver medal at the Royal Show in 1952.

Doe's were still selling tractors but also 150 MH combines a year. In 1956 exclusivity became the by-word for the tractor companies and Doe's dispensed with their wide range to concentrate upon Ford. It was with this single minded agency that the Triple D was born. It was a request, and considerable design help by George Pryor, Navestock, who wanted a heavy hp machine that had the pulling power of a crawler, but more versatility. Pryor had started to build one in his own workshop which resulted in two Fordson Major tractors joined together. It had its drawbacks but Doe recognised the potential and obtained manufacturing rights from Pryor.

The Triple D was modified and improved. The front wheels were removed, hydraulic controls operated by the driver on the rear tractor made the 19ft., ungainly machine into a power puller. It was surprisingly manoeverable and initially named 'Doe's Dual Power', but only six were built before the Triple D had usurped it. An opportunity to prove itself appeared. The 1958 harvest left Essex fields in a waterlogged condition. The first Triple D fulfilled all the expectations. It travelled when crawlers were bogged down.

Further modifications were installed and in 1960 the Triple D won a silver medal at the Royal Show. "Put to test on Lord Rayleigh's Farms near Chelmsford in August 1961 with a six-furrow plough, the tractor ploughed over thirty acres in twelve hours, an average of 2.5a an hour".[15] Its success was undiminished. 290 Dual and Triple Ds were made between 1958–64. It was demonstrated around the world and in the USA was known as the 'Double-T'. One of Doe's originals was exhibited at the Moscow Show and three were sold to the USSR. It was later known as the Doe 130 to reflect the increased hp.

In 1965 it cost £2,975. The 130 was superseded by the Doe 150 in 1968. The price was then £4,200 but only a small number were made. "Doe's tandem tractor had nearly reached the end of the line".[16] Large purpose built tractors, less cumbersome were giving farmers the big tractor which they required. Doe produced a complete range of equipment to use with his tractor. In 1961 they designed their first reversible plough, but only 20 were built. A later model was more successful.

It was the unreliability of Ransomes parts which persuaded Doe to become involved in the importation of Lemken ploughs. Doe had taken over the premises of Thomas Moy in Hythe Hill Colchester. Ford dealer Willetts went into liquidation in 1946. Doe tried to take over the Fordson franchise. This was not acceptable to the Ford Motor Company unless he gave up selling other makes. He refused to do this and the Hythe Hill premises became the home of Colchester Tractors Ltd. formed in 1947 as sole Fordson dealers. Another company, Colchester Tillage was formed to import Lemken ploughs, cultivation equipment and Tico cranes. They also started crane conversions. In 1993 most of the tillage business was sold to Lemken UK and Colchester Tractors Ltd. became stockists and Ford dealers. Colchester Tractors existed from 1947 to 1993.

In 1948 there were seven Fordson distributors in the county; Doe's at Ulting, Colchester Tractors, Cleales at Saffron Walden, Hensmans at Brentwood, Donald Denoon at Chelmsford, Reynolds at Dagenham, W. Harold Perry at Westcliffe and Whalley at Bishop's Stortford, Mann Egerton at Ipswich also sold Fordsons to Essex farmers. Dealers competed with each other. Part of the key was the ability to dispose of the second-hand machines that were being taken-in. Doe's developed a lively export market and reliable tractors, some only one year old, were exported via Harwich and Felixstowe.

Ferguson had developed a popular tractor and a tie-up with Massey-Harris in Canada, to whom they were eventually linked as Massey-Ferguson. Doe's concentrated upon Ransomes Viking and Allis-Chalmers Gleaner and the German Claas of which reputedly the first silver post war models were made from salvaged metal from redundant war equipment. They sold Claas combines until Ford was taken was taken over by New Holland when they got back into the big time combine business

111 1961. Essex Show. Doe's Triple 'D'.

From Ulting they developed seven other branches around Essex with one in Kent. In the 1990s cut-back by farmers when tractor sales slumped Doe's could fall back on the extensive garden equipment and horticultural aids which they had developed. The engineering side of the business, after the unfortunate demise of Whitlocks, had blossomed.

The quiet village of Ulting nestling beside the placid waters of the Chelmer was unknown to most of England. Doe's was not and when, in 1961, the Doe Show was launched. It became a mecca for farmers from all over the British Isles. "He personally knew of one man who had come from Aberdeen and two from Yorkshire, while there were several farmers from Lincolnshire and the Midlands".[17] At the 7th Show in 1967 they had 180 machines on display and a range of equipment working in an adjoining field. In 1976 it was estimated that 12,000 farmers attended the 16th Show. Both the equipment and the prices had changed. In 1976 Roger Freeman wrote, "second hand combines are now quick movers as the price of new is way out of range to all but the very big farmers". [18] This was nearly a quarter of a century before the largest combines had a price of £150,000 on them.

Little Grey Fergies

The many American makes were uncommon in Essex fields. The blue Fordsons dominated the scenery and the only serious competitor was the 20 hp baby Fergies which embodied science as opposed to brute force. The hydraulic linkage system developed by Harry Ferguson pre-war was incorporated into Fordsons which resulted in expensive litigation. Ford lost the case.

In Essex, Eastern Automobiles covered 75% of the county. H.E. Williams & Co. who had been general ironmongers in Colchester before 1890 covered the north eastern corner of the county.

In Essex Peter Bingham-Wallis, John Craske and Hugh Flower three men who had served in the Forces during the war returned to civilian life and decided that selling tractors had a future. As an off-shoot from Eastern Automobiles, and with a capital of £5,000, Eastern Tractors was launched in 1946. The first location was a bombed-out car showroom in Chelmsford. John Craske delivered the tractors to farms by driving them himself – and caught a bus back! The company Ferguson had founded was rescued by Massey Harris. It became M-F and a full range of red painted tractors set out to be a strong competitor to Ford.

Lord Nuffield developed his Nuffield tractor. David Brown, whose main business was gears and gearboxes produced tractors in the Midlands. There were others but Dagenham was the home of the then largest tractor plant outside the USA. Essex was Ford country.

Despite this opposition, Eastern Tractors expanded its depots. Chelmsford, Corringham and Braintree, and in 1966 at Bishop's Stortford. With another at Steeple Bumpstead. Eastern Tractors was broadly farmer-owned and farmer-controlled. The site at Steeple Bumpstead had been provided by agricultural contractor, John Suckling whose pioneering work with the Bray Centaur has been described. In the days before mobile phones it was considered innovative when in 1966 the new Steeple Bumpstead depot operated with the assistance of seven radio-controlled service vans in conjunction with the Braintree branch. In 1969 E-T's were selling 650 tractors and 100 new combines from their four depots (Corringham had been closed). The company from its £5,000 start was then valued at £3.25m.

H.E. Williams changed when Feering farmer Kenneth Ireland decided to give up farming and develop his interests as a storekeeper. By various take-overs it became Colchester's largest department store; Williams and Griffin. The tractor side remained within the company, although it was an independent subsidiary. Harry Gray had been instrumental in promoting Ferguson sales to the extent that he was known locally as 'Mister Fergie'.

In 1969 Eastern Tractors, after two years' discussions, acquired Williams' agricultural, horticultural and machinery interests. At that time Williams had an annual turnover of £400,000. They had acquired premises at Cowdray Avenue which remained with the Ireland family until it was leased to Cramphorn for a garden centre. With this acquisition Eastern Tractors became the largest Massey-Ferguson distributor in the world, excluding concessionaires for complete continents. It's success was a model achievement. The take-over of Williams severed a long link. Kenneth Ireland had purchased one of the first Fergusons made in the late 1930s – number 33. It was used on his seed farms at Kelvedon and Feering.

In 1972 a dock strike affected Claas and New Holland combines. It was only resolved at the last moment but a strike at Scunthorpe by workers at the British Steel factory disrupted supplies and grain barns, needed for harvest were uncompleted when the combines commenced work. Far from the days when agents had out-bid each other to sell tractors. The disruptions caused shortages. Materials and machines were often on a six months waiting list.

Disruption was also caused when workers at M-F Kilmarnock factory went on strike in 1973. Two Directors from Colchester, Harry Gray and John Burfield, staged a headline hitting 'raid' on the factory. Having led a party to Scotland they drove the combines through the lines of pickets to waiting lorries which transported them to a secret destination in Essex before delivery to distraught farmers. In 1973 Perkins workers, who made the engines, went on strike. E.T. diverted combines which were destined for Mexico, and delivered them to farmers who had a harvest to gather. Claas combines from Germany were held up at the docks and deliveries were late.

The 1970s were a time of rapid inflation. In 1975 Harry Gray said, "two years ago a combine cost £7,000, but the same machine has now gone up to £12,000+".[19] The M-F 1200, a pivotal tractor with four identical pneumatic wheels had become a versatile competitor for Doe's Triple D and in 1975 it was costing £9,300. Despite these increases farming was in healthy shape – but Eastern Tractors had 100 back orders. The irregularity of supplies had become a problem.

They tried to expand into unknown areas and lost considerable funds in an abortive Mozambique venture. They were forced into liquidation and the M-F franchise was taken over by car dealer Tom Cowie to become known as Cowies. They opened a depot at Frating after vacating the Cowdray Avenue premises but this was closed in 1986.

Spot Machinery, originally International agents had a depot at Earls Colne aerodrome, and a branch at Weeley eventually took over Whitlock's old premises at Great Yeldham but in 1986 severed the Weeley connection. At the end of the century it was impossible to buy a M-F tractor from an Essex dealer. The nearest was Thurlow Nunn at Bury St Edmunds.

The powerful U.S. John Deere tractors and combines found an Essex base when Tuckwells opened a branch at Ardleigh in 1975. During the last quarter of the century the dark green John Deere tractors became as popular as the red M-Fs had been. It was a far cry, and over half a century since the days of the 'little grey Fergie'.

A Tale of Two Factories

Essex became the home of two of the most important factories producing agricultural machines. Ford at Dagenham and Rotary Hoes at West Horndon.

The tractor plant at Dagenham commenced production in 1933. But in 1964 production was transferred to Basildon, finally ceasing in 1990 when, having been taken over by the New Holland Machinery Co., production was transferred to N.H. Geotech. During its sojurn Ford produced 1.098m tractors at Dagenham and 1.347m at Basildon, a total of 2.446m.

Before Ford produced his first car he had planned to build a tractor. The memory of walking behind his father's plough was the motivation. He built 4m tractors. Seventy thousand tractors were made at Dagenham by 1939 and on four separate years tractor production was greater than commercial vehicles. During the Second World War tractor production was also ahead of cars since very few were made at that time.

Ford tractors were re-assembled at Cork to aid the war effort in 1915. Full scale production continued after the war but Ford was looking for another site. He chose Dagenham and paid £300 per acre for a low-lying piece of marshland abutting the Thames in 1924. Against advice that the site was unsuitable because of its geophysical nature, Ford required a position which had deep water facilities. At that time the L.C.C. had embarked upon a rehousing scheme and there was an abundance of available labour. The first sod was cut with a silver spade on 17 May 1929. The model 'N' was produced from 1929–45. It was the most popular amongst Essex farmers and in 1936 cost £135, with cleats, £140 with spade-lugs and £180 on pneumatic tyres. When production started at Dagenham; Ford was said to have painted his tractors "in a distinctive dark blue and orange livery, reputedly to match the colours of the Essex farm wagons".[20]

Ford bought the Boreham House Estate in the early 1930s, the ancient home of the Tufnell-Tyrell family. During the war part of the estate was requisitioned to build an air base for the USAF. Its role lasted just over one year and post-war Ford decided to use the runways and perimeter tracks as a racing circuit. Believing that co-operative farming had a future he split off the remaining farmland in 1946. Co-Partnership Ltd. became a public company but Ford retained the mansion and 80a. There had previously been a training school at Lake Farm Dagenham. Boreham House became the new training school in 1956. Demonstration workshops, and test-bed facilities for 'secret' new models were tested at Boreham.

It had been purchased by Percival Perry, Henry Ford's aide who lived at Lilystone Hall, Stock. Perry had no children and when he died his substantial fortune was used to create The Perry Foundation.

After a long history Ford decided to sell their tractor patents, the wide range of machines, and their name; to New Holland. They retained the familiar blue livery but by 1997 the name had gone. Due to a merger with the Italian Fiat company the same models were available in maroon. Ford remained the largest company in the county but its days as a tractor maker were over. Henry Ford had walked for the last time across a ploughed field.

112 Electronic sorting and bagging machinery developed by Walthambury, another Essex innovator

The Perry Foundation

The Perry Foundation made a unique and far reaching contribution to the advancement of agriculture. Its activities were largely unsung and unheralded. Not that it sought anonymity – but it maintained a low profile. This did not detract from its success, and effectiveness.

By 1997 it had accumulated investments which exceeded £3.5m, and in that year made grants exceeding £108,000. This was achieved by expending only 10% on administration, an example rarely matched by any charitable organisation in the UK. Research awards to a wide range of agricultural colleges and other bodies, with individual post graduate scholarships provided a wide range of support.

Writtle Agricultural College received assistance to investigate Break Crops in 1979, a Distance Learning system in 1983, a seminar on combinable Break Crops in 1980 and another on alternative Break Crops in 1985. The University of Essex was supported to investigate the role of nitrogen in soil fertility in 1984 and to look at the nitrogen requirements of winter wheat grown in Essex. In 1986 Dengie Crop Driers Ltd. were helped to develop the extraction and use of juice from lucerne and grass The Animal Health Trust looked at New Forest Disease in 1983. These were the grants which were given to Essex. There were many others.

The Foundation was also responsible for establishing the '*Animal Health Trust* (hereafter AHT)' at Lilystone Hall, and where financial support was given from 1954 until the AHT concentrated their activities at Newmarket in 1972, "because it lacked sufficient financial support from other sources".[21] Originally known as the Farm Livestock Research Station with four separate divisions they found themselves the subject of government cut-backs after they had been taken under the wing of the Agricultural Research Council and in 1954, having shared a station with poultry research, the now named AHT was homeless. "In 1954 the problem seemed to be solved when the Boreham Institute offered to underwrite the cost of building laboratories in the gounds of Lilystone Hall, a large country house near Stock in Essex. In addition the Institute would provide £30,000 for the purchase of equipment".[22] The laboratories and offices were officially opened by HRH The Duke of Edinburgh in 1957. The AHT occupied Lilystone rent free and also received an annual grant, but they relied upon voluntary support from farmers. It was not always as forthcoming as they desired. "Farmers are, in fact, gradually rallying to the cause, but the pace is slow and the numbers so far very limited".[23]

In 1930 Henry Ford saw the derelict condition of Essex farming and promptly bought the 2,000a Boreham House Estate. Perry was put in charge of what became known as; 'an agricultural experiment'. Fordson Estates Ltd. owned the property and financed many improvements. Twenty-six cottages were built in 1933/4. The organisation of purchasing and marketing was carried out by an Industrial Co-operative Society known as Danbury Co-operators Ltd. which was created in 1933. Glasshouses were built and tenants were encouraged to concentrate upon fruit and market garden produce. 2,500 bacon pigs pa were also fattened before the 1939 war. The mansion house and the immediate surrounding land was transformed into the Henry Ford Institute of Agricultural Engineering, and supported with funds from America. These dried up in 1943, when money could not be transferred to the UK, and the British Ford Motor Co. took over the responsibility. This arrangement ceased in 1952 and student training was no longer available.

Boreham House was offered to the Essex County Council as a centre for agricultural education but they were developing the new Institute of Agriculture at Writtle which had been completed in 1938. At this time Fordson Estates Ltd. was converted into Co-Partnership Farms. The Ford Motor Co. took over Boreham House for a nominal sum and it became the main training centre for Ford Tractor Operations.

The Trustees of the previous Institute of Agricultural Engineering were enriched with a donation of £20,000 from Lord Perry, from which the Perry Foundation was started. In his obituary The Times said; "His chief interest outside the motor industry was farming...he was responsible for a remarkable experiment in co-operative farming known as the Fordson Farms".[24] With the gift of Lilystone Hall in 1956 the Perry Foundation was able to embark upon its programme for the advancement of agricultural research and science. Objectives which Perry would have considered eminently suitable – and farmer's son Henry Ford would also have approved.

Later chairmen of Ford's were Sir Terence Beckett (Ch.1976–80), Director-General of the CBI and Treasurer Essex University. Sir Leonard Crossland (Ch.1968–72) retired and bought the 800a Abbotts Hall, Great Wigborough where he continued to farm. He was President of the Essex Agricultural Society in 1971.

A Rugged Aussie and an Essex Farmer

When Clifford Howard came to England from Australia in 1938 with his revolutionary

278

rotavator he looked at several possible sites but chose one at West Horndon which had been part of the Thorndon Hall Estate of Lord Petre. It was within seven miles of Tilbury Docks and with the Southend arterial road already constructed, and a railway station at the factory gates.

Howard was the inventor and he found an ideal partner in Capt.E.N. Griffith who farmed at Little Hallingbury. Griffith was the financial man. It was a partnership that was compared to Rolls and Royce. Howard's inventions were based on the rotating premise. He maintained that when a machine built up its revolutions, the impetus would reduce the energy requirement. The rotavator was on this principle with blades which assisted in pushing the tractor forward. It became more sophisticated as developments were incorporated. There were models for the largest tractors, and walk-behind ones for gardens. He produced a popular muck spreader which worked on the same principle with rotating chains flailing the fym sideways out of the machine. There was a wine-press, and the range of products increased.

As with many other companies the more successful they became the more crucial were the decisions – and the likelihood of failure.

Howard's turnover was £6.5m in 1964 and £38.3m in 1973. Exports trebled, profit trebled and they employed nearly 4,000 people. The constricted 31a site at West Horndon outgrew even the UK demand and in 1961 they built a new factory in Norfolk and another in Suffolk in 1968. Government grants for the north-west were attractive and after 36 years they closed the Horndon works and moved to Washington, County Durham. Howards had already expanded into other fields. They had amalgamated with Manns of Saxham, Claas combine importers and the joint company produced the Harvestor silos which had been bought from a US company. Previously trading, and famous as Rotary Hoes Ltd., the founder's name was perpetuated when, in 1974, the company was renamed Howard Machinery Ltd.

CHAPTER 26

1950–2000

The second 50 years were generally prosperous. Improved farm houses, buildings and fields promoted this conclusion. It was not to suggest that it was a smooth or uneventful period of agrarian history. There were several bankruptcies, caused by mismanagement, but others took their farms. The economic climate was optimistic until 1998 when all farm prices slumped. There were numerous political farming demonstrations.

Dutch Elm Disease, Myxmatosis as well as Foot and Mouth Disease, Fowl Pest and Swine Vesicular Disease. The incidence of B.S.E. was a major blow which affected the meat eating habits of the farmers' customers. There were some dramatic climatic events, the East Coast Floods in 1953 and the hurricane in 1987. Drought and wet harvests ravished the crops.

During this period the status and image of farmers changed. In the early post-war years they were seen as food providers. As villages became populated with newcomers and as food was transformed from rationing to surpluses; the role of the farmer deteriorated. In the early part of the period farmers deplored being called businessmen, with its connotations of pin-striped suits, but later they embraced the accolade with fervour. The more business-like they became, the more critical became their detractors. The fringe activities of pressure groups suddenly became relevant. Farmers were attacked as countryside despoilers.

Political power all but vanished. Most were traditionally conservatives, but were often overtly critical. Other powers were stripped away and the Planning Officer became an important man. The final stage of the transition from a rural economy was enacted.

Although farming was prosperous, this was more consistent for arable than livestock. Farmers sought to increase the size of their businesses. The majority of farm sales were completed with the purchase by a neighbour. Downturns speeded up this process as farmers struggled to maintain their incomes by enlarging their farms. They moved from peasants to agri-businessmen. In 1949 there were 185 farms in the county over 500a and only 11 with more than 1,000a. Within 20 years there were 292 over 500a and 46 had more than 1,000a with seven over 2,000. This trend is demonstrated by the 22% drop in the farmed area against the 73% drop in the number of farmers.

The farmed area showed a steady rate of decline and although the Second World War brought land back into cultivation, the requirements of the military authorities mitigated a large part of the increase. The 1953 storm flooded 41,000a but it was reinstated in succeeding years. The introduction of set-aside in 1992 initially removed 81,000a from crops, but not on a permanent basis. The average rate of farmland loss up to 1950 was 1,568a, although it was higher after 1925 than before. From 1950 the rate averaged 1,939a. This was spread unevenly with complete farms swallowed under housing estates. The overall loss during the century was the equivalent of 60 villages.

There were over 7,000 farmers in 1900 and 1,923 in 1996. The difficulty in ascertaining the number of farmers is confused by those who are whole-time and those part-time. The Yellow Pages Directories listed 836 farm addresses although there were some omissions. MAFF recorded the number of holdings but some were amalgamations, whilst others were farmed by the same family but retained individual registration. Despite these anomalies the trend was significant. MAFF returns in 1986 revealed 3,598 holdings with 2,177 'principal' farmers giving an average sized holding of 185.5a, but an average sized farmer of just under 305a. Suffolk and Norfolk were slightly higher but Kent was lower. In 1900 the average farmer had 113a and 336.8a in 1996. Area per farmer trebled. In 1987 Joe Matthews calculated that there were 3,600 farms but only 1,700 of them were "full-time holdings".[1] The trend towards increasing farm sizes, and a diminishing number of farmers was well illustrated in the EFU membership, of 2,814 in 1968 which was 85% of farmers. The total number in the county would have been 3,310.

In the decade 1986/96 there was an annual loss of 25 farmers. Farms got larger and livestock in the fields declined. The UK entry into Europe eventually decimated the dairy herds, minimalised the orchards, hit the Lea Valley growers, all of which had a visual manifestation. Superficially the crops still came to harvest at the same time, autumn ploughing, with its seagull followers remained photogenic. Farmhouses retained their outward appearance and many timber-framed cart sheds and barns remained, although they were of little use to the needs of modern farming. Concrete superseded muddy yards in winter, and the new grain barns were larger than their predecessors. It was an agricultural revolution which promoted more changes in 50 years than in the previous 1,000 years.

Angry Farmers
Pre-war they boarded trains at Southminster and Colchester to march through the streets of London in protest against the tithes. They objected to this payment to the C of E when some were catholics or non-conformists. Prices of farms in the 1930s often concealed arears of tithe payments which had to be made when a property changed hands. The June 1936 demonstrations persuaded Parliament to pass a new act which froze the payments, long since converted from a tenth of the harvest into a fixed sum and the payments were scheduled for extinction. Inflation eroded its impact and in 1977 the cost of collecting the remaining unredeemed tithes was more than the income which they generated. Wrote Ralph Sadler, "Many of the 1936 demonstrators lived to see tithe abolished in October 1977".[2]

In early 1939 farmers again took to the London streets. "By special train, more than 900, the main body, travelled from Ipswich and Colchester. Some carried sheaves of corn, shepherds' crooks and spuds, and a thatcher brought his tools. Many of them had never been to London before". The demonstrators were not agitating against the Minister of Agriculture, who was also president of the NFU. They marched to give him support. But when the anger erupted in 1965 it was a direct result of a squeeze on farmers' income and it was not London but Saffron Walden where the main action occurred.

For many years farmers talked sympathetically about the Labour Party. The legacy of Minister Tom Williams remained bright in their memories. They voted Conservative but still harked back to the immediate post-war years and the security which the Agriculture Act 1947 had brought them.

It was when the next Labour Government came to power, and imposed a harsh settle-ment at the Annual Price Review that farmers became disillusioned with Labour policies.

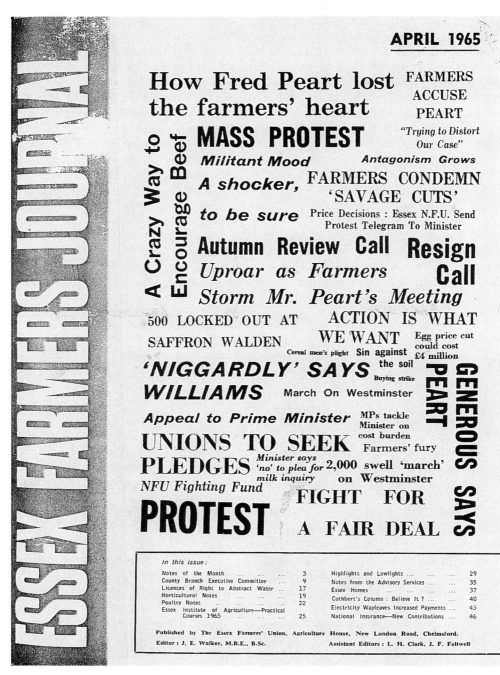

APRIL 1965

ESSEX FARMERS JOURNAL

How Fred Peart lost the farmers' heart

FARMERS ACCUSE PEART

"Trying to Distort Our Case"

A Crazy Way to Encourage Beef

MASS PROTEST

Militant Mood

A shocker,

to be sure

Antagonism Grows

FARMERS CONDEMN 'SAVAGE CUTS'

Price Decisions : Essex N.F.U. Send Protest Telegram To Minister

Autumn Review Call

Uproar as Farmers

Storm Mr. Peart's Meeting

Resign Call

500 LOCKED OUT AT SAFFRON WALDEN

ACTION IS WHAT WE WANT

Cereal men's plight Sin against the soil

Egg price cut could cost £4 million

'NIGGARDLY' SAYS WILLIAMS

Buying strike

March On Westminster

Appeal to Prime Minister

MPs tackle Minister on cost burden

Farmers' fury

UNIONS TO SEEK PLEDGES

Minister says 'no' to plea for milk inquiry

2,000 swell 'march' on Westminster

NFU Fighting Fund

GENEROUS PEART SAYS

FIGHT FOR A FAIR DEAL

PROTEST

Published by The Essex Farmers' Union, Agriculture House, New London Road, Chelmsford.

Editor: J. E. Walker, M.B.E., B.Sc.   Assistant Editors: L. H. Clark, J. F. Feltwell

113 Farmers angry. Front cover Essex Farmers Journal. '500 locked out at Saffron Walden'.

The sitting MP, the popular R.A. Butler, had retired and in the by-election the Labour Minister, Fred Peart, was scheduled to support the Labour candidate at the eve-of-poll rally. An event normally supported by a hard core of activists. It became a farmers' rally against Peart and it was estimated that 600 farmers crowded into the Town Hall. "All day on Monday the telephone messages sped across the county; Bring a car full. Be there by 7.0 o'clock; at least an hour early. Bring tins with stones in, rattles, whistles – anything to make a noise", said the Essex County Standard.[4] The problem area was dairying. Peart finally escaped via a side door but Saffron Walden had never seen a night like it.

Throughout the summer, posters proclaiming the farmers' anger were displayed along every lane. They came down in August but the campaign continued and a rally of Land Rovers was organised, meeting at Buckhurst Hill where 50-odd vehicles paraded in a convoy through Woodford, to Gates Corner, and thence to Gants Hill. Leaflets were distributed and local farmers interviewed on the TV. An Essex 'Action' committee was formed.

It was at the end of Labour's six-year term that anger was again displayed in January 1970. Despite annual increments from the Government costs were increasing faster. Barley was 13% lower in 1970 than it had been a decade earlier. Wheat was down 2%. The price of a loaf of bread had doubled, wages had gone up 75% and tractors from £600 to £1.200. "I know of at least five farmers who are about to be forced to sell up and leave

114 1965 Saffron Walden. A farmer's Land Rover pushes the message. Left centre - Victor Gray, Chairman of Essex Farmers Union.

115 Three men from Essex who served as national president of the Country Landowners' Association. John Norris (centre), of Mountnessing Hall, Brentwood, Sir Nigel Strutt (right), branch president, and Sir John Ruggles Brise, his predecessor in that post.

their farms".[5] In other counties farmers were taking more militant action. Roads were jammed with tractors. The following month Essex farmers paraded through London carrying banners. The largest banner read 'Fair deal for Essex farmers'. Three hundred had travelled to support others from all over the country.

In February the streets of Maldon, Colchester and Chelmsford saw farm tractors and trailers parading with large posters emphasising the farmers' plight. The Labour Government lost the election in June 1970 and measures were introduced to alleviate the farmers' plight.

In February 1974 Fred Peart returned to MAFF as an old hand. But he faced a simmering legacy from his Conservative predecessor and livestock farmers were not happy. Beef prices were £5 per cwt down and were loosing £40 per beast. Pig farmers were loosing £4 per pig. Whilst cereal growers were seeing their prices rise, albeit other costs were escalating, it was livestock farmers who faced the greatest problems. As each successive wave of unprofitability occurred some farmers forsook livestock, by ploughing up more land and increasing their commitment to arable crops. These factors were influential in the swing away from livestock which was a permanent feature of the second half of the century.

The farmers convergence upon London had brought 8,000 onto the streets in 1970. The 1998 'Countryside March', attracted a quarter of a million people but was not a farmers' march. Many who joined it, ostensibly to support the continuance of hunting, were anti-hunt men. They felt that the countryside, and farmers in particular, were being attacked by another new Labour Government. The sunshine from Tom Williams had long since disappeared.

Forces of Nature

Flooded farmland in England was not an unusual occurrence. Flooded land by salt water, such as the East Coast Floods in 1953 was extremely unfortunate, and Essex bore the brunt of this climatic phenomena. 41,760 acres of good farmland was encroached and flooded with purile salt water, 7,000a had been autumn sown with cereals. 779 tons of grain were spoilt and unsaleable, 141 stacks of hay and straw were written off as a total loss, unthreshed stacks of wheat and barley began steaming within a few days and many were lost. 286 tons of animal food was lost, 288 tons of potatoes, 144 tons of artificial fertiliser and 3,033 tons of farmyard manure. Posts, fencing, gates, farm buildings, glass houses, pig styes – 155 in all were ruined. 258 cattle lost their lives in the flood with 64 of these at Oxenham, Great Wakering. 1,008 sheep, 478 pigs, of which 249 were on Foulness and 150 on Canvey Island, six horses, 7,177 poultry.

15,075a of the flooded land was arable. The area stretched from Mistley on the Stour round to Harwich, along the coast leaving a gap where the cliffs of Walton, Frinton, Clacton held it back, and spread inland along the Blackwater, Crouch, Roach, flooded the seven Essex islands at the Thames estuary, missed a small area around Southend but there was further flooding along the inner reaches of the Thames. The whole area was covered for two days, 10,000a was under salt water for at least a week and a month after the disaster 10,000a was still covered. There was, fortunately, a wet summer in 1953 which helped to wash-through the saline content of the soil but only 2% of the flooded arable land produced a crop that year. 119 people lost their lives and the livestock casualties quoted did not include those animals that died later as a result of their sufferings. The final toll was never confirmed.

A farmer at Foulness told his story; "I called to my foreman, who lived just by the yards. As he could not hear anything of them he looked from a bedroom and saw that the eighteen cattle in one yard were drowned".[6] At Alresford John Pilkington, was luckier; "arriving at Brightlingsea Hall we found that the stock were all safe in the yards, but by the dishevelled looks of many of them I think they must have swum out".[7] In total 371 farms were affected.

There had been floods before, notably in 1897 and in 1949 when 2,000a was covered but the scale of the 1953 disaster made it the most dramatic of the century. Lessons had been learnt from the past and gypsum was supplied by the Government and applied with greater scientific knowledge than the previous disaster. The land was producing good crops five years later. In 1897 it had taken 15 years.

With shades of the wartime Red Cross sales the EFU organised gift sales in aid of the Lord Mayor's Fund. Eight Farmers Union branches in the county raised £16,000. It was a substantial sum but was a long way short of the sums raised during the war. The greatest help came from the 4,000 workers, students and farmers who were deployed daily to repair the breached walls. David Macaulay, Birch farmer and chairman of the Essex A.E.C. immediately promised a volunteer force of 2,000. In the event this figure was exceeded, but the A.E.C. was responsible for the deployment and targeted the breaches which were the most catastrophic. An unexpected result of the coastal flooding

116 1953 February. Southminster, Middlewick. Volunteers and soldiers stemming the breach.

was the excessive river flooding which occurred when the Wid met the seawater and backed-up. Areas around Chelmsford saw major floods although the water was not saline.

The Greatest Storm of the Century

There were many climatic extremities during the century. The 1921 drought was one, and there were always wet harvests, and dry ones, but the Great Storm on Friday 5 September 1958 was the most disastrous for Essex farmers. The fields were saturated due to heavy summer rainfall. The harvest was already under threat and in 1958 combines were antiquated and grain dryers were rare. Those that had predicted that combines had no future felt fully vindicated by the events of that summer. The final deluge on 5 September ultimately resulted in carol singing around bedraggled combines at Christmas. Many crops were abandoned.

The Essex Farmers Journal reported the event.[8]

> "At Writtle, the Institute's rain gauge measured 2.2in. in an hour and a half. At one farm near Wickford 3.27in. were measured in 90 minutes, and we've heard one suggestion of 3½ in. To get it into any sort of perspective you have to think of a month's normal rainfall in Essex coming down within an hour".

A vast stretch of farmland in South Essex from the outskirts of London to Romford with flooding between Bulphan and Upminster, through the valley of the Wid. There were several miles of land between Battlesbridge and Chay's Hill. Barns were flooded, corn that had been threshed became wet, stacks stood in 3ft. of water, potatoes were washed out of the ground and poultry losses were considerable.

Farmers faced ruin and unploughable fields cast grave doubts about a harvest in 1959. A Claas Bogmaster used in paddy fields was hurridly imported from Germany. The first arrived in Essex but it was mid-October before two more arrived. The harvest had become a salvage operation. Said the Essex Farmers Journal [9], "thus the Bogmaster began its two months work of necessity and mercy, only to be terminated by the New Year Snow". The heavy clay south of Colchester, that had gone derelict in the 1920s, was one of the worst spots in the county. From Abberton, Layer Marney to Dunmow and "so to Bovills Hall, Little Clacton on December 22nd, happily the long night following the shortest day was graced by moonlight which permitted the machine to finish the job in one shift". At Cann Hall, Great Clacton, this monster was traversing the fields on Christmas Eve. Economically the crop was a write-off. It took nearly three hours to cut an acre!

The Essex Broad Red Clover Seed was a total failure. Local strains had been developed over many years and the county had acquired a commensurate reputation. There had been no dilution of purity since 1939 but the only way to provide Red Clover Seed for UK farmers the following year was by granting import licences. In the Dengie peninsular many farmers did not crop their fields in 1959. The fallow fields amounted to 35,000a, more than twice the average when fallowing was considered an integral part of the rotation. It was also the highest fallow area for 22 years. On some farms there were no crops at all and 1959 was a hot, dry season which burnt up those on other soil types. 1960 was wet, but not as wet as '58 and it was into the '60s before farmers had recouped the losses which they incurred in these two succeeding years.

Far from putting the brake onto the expansion of combine harvesting – it acted as a spur. Manufacturers provided larger tyres to give greater floatation and grain dryers came to be considered as part of this new era of mechanisation.

There was government encouragement to lay tile drains in fields and Essex farmers took advantage of these grants. Eight years after the storm which ravaged the crops, 14% of the total U.K. schemes for field drainage were completed in Essex. In one year (1971) over 19,000a was drained. During war-time, in five years only 128,000a were drained in England and Wales. It was only just over the area drained in Essex between 1964/72. The Essex Land Drainage Officer, Ernest Barker, estimated that only one third of the land which would benefit had been drained.[10]

Contrary to the programme of relieving water-logging was the expansion of irrigation reservoirs being built on many farms with the resultant picturesque sprays of water during the summer months. The extreme drought years 1975/6, the latter being recorded as the 'drought of the century', put more encouragement upon farmers to install an irrigation system to grow potatoes.

A decade earlier Lord Rayleighs Farms built a 15a reservoir holding 100m gallons of water in an old valley of the River Ter at Leez. Some of the water was used at Leez Lodge and Priory Farms as well as on the remainder of the Terling Estate. It involved nine miles of pipe work. In 1997, Guy Smith at St Osyth acquired the dubious accolade of an entry in the Guiness Book of Records, with a rainfall which bordered on the Sahara Desert. Irrigation was also used to prevent a late frost on blackcurrants and other fruits. By this time they were triggered off by thermostats and electronic mechanisms.

Hail and Hurricanes

There was a hail storm in 1898 named 'The Essex Tornado' and another in 1913 which had its epicentre at Great Yeldham. It lasted eight minutes but glass houses and barn roofs were smashed. After the 1898 hail storm Rev'd F.A. Adams of Doddinghurst said "such storms as these can only come occasionally in a century".

In 1985 a swarth of farms were hit in a one mile wide, 15 miles long area which hit 100 farmers north and west of Chelmsford. At Good Easter, Tommy Matthews kept some hailstones in his refrigerator. They were the size of eggs. He described his fields; "looking as if they had been under artillery bombardment".[11] Wheat crops were stripped of their ears, potatoes lost their leaves, peas were pulverized, barley was decimated. There was no insurance. Farmers had always taken the vagaries of the weather, accepting that it could be their friend, or their enemy. They helped each other by contributing to a, 'Hail Fund'.

In 1987 the Essex County Standard reported: "As North Essex suffers the wettest summer this century and flood waters rise threateningly, farmers face disastrous harvest losses of up to £40m".[12] A brief hail storm that year cost Mr. Cheeseman of Foxash Nurseries £30,000.

The hurricane which swept across southern England in October 1987 created a vista a destruction which took many years to recover. No part of the county was unaffected. Every lane was blocked by fallen trees and debris, Elizabethan barns were flattened. It was mainly farm buildings which suffered – and farmers discovered with horror that their insurance did not cover hurricanes.

The fields were already flooded from an exceptionally wet autumn when 12in. of rain fell during the three preceding months. Dedham Vale was awash like a lake. Little autumn drilling had been done. Many potatoes still lay in the ground.

Salt spray spread many miles inland, as the wind battered the hedgerows, already covered with salt. They turned black on one side, and remained green on the other. Farms were cut off for several days, telephone were lost, electricity supplies prevented cows being milked and both pig and poultry enterprises suffered.

Poplar trees had the tops ripped out of them, many came tumbling down. Willows were split, Scots pine were uprooted. The already soggy soil conditions made the oaks vulnerable and many fell with their unearthed roots beside a crater. Many had substantial branches broken. It was estimated that the task of clearing the dead trees might take several months. In the event it was nearly five years before the last of the evidence was removed. It was firmly predicted that hurricanes would only come once in a century. Yet 26 months later in January 1990 another storm smashed farm buildings which had just been repaired. The damage was not as extensive but it was classified as a hurricane.

In the early 1990s a series of hot summers and dry winters caused depletion of the water supply for the public, the winter refilling of farm reservoirs was not accomplished and as the subsoil dried out, many 100 year old cottages and houses, mainly brick built with insufficient foundations, were so severely cracked that subsidence went in to the vocabulary of the insurance companies. There was cover for this type of disaster but many properties had to be rebuilt completely. The older timber-framed cottages were more flexible and did not suffer to the same degree. The modern steel-framed, asbestos clad buildings were largely unaffected. The strength of the foundations had been subjected to greater scientific input.

A hailstorm scythed across Essex in April 1994 whipping out salad and apple crops and Doug McIntyre, Marketing Manager of Foxash Growers said "the band of hail cut clean through the co-operative. I would say we lost 160,000 to 170,000 speciality lettuces – they are the popular lettuces used as salad garnishes. They are worth £60,000 to £70,000".[13]

The second 50 years produced more climatic disruption than the first half. In some ways farmers were better equipped to deal with wet and delayed harvests, but, despite these advances, there were occasional reminders that the weather could still deliver unpleasant shocks.

Pests and Diseases
In other areas farmers were hit. There was a succession of animal diseases throughout this period. Some, like Foot and Mouth Disease became less common as the measures to control them were more successful. New diseases also appeared.

Newcastle Disease, or Fowl Pest, an old one, occurred with severity in January 1959 when 44 cases were confirmed in Essex. Laying flocks were affected and the origins, although never proven, were traced in the carcasses from the 1958 Christmas period. London swill was used extensively to feed both pigs and poultry. The disease spread with rapidity. In 1959 there were 12 outbreaks in the last two months. Restrictions of movement helped to curtail the epidemic and the total number of chickens on Essex

117 1962 Dunmow. John Salmon potato harvester. Fordson Super Major on harvester, Ferguson 35 on trailer

farms rose by over 700,000 birds between 1958-60. North Essex was declared a 'Fowl Pest black spot'.

In 1964 the blame was attributed to the reluctance of some poultry farmers to have their stock vaccinated. At that time 25% were unvaccinated. The 1964 epidemic was centred around Colchester, Halstead and Witham areas with one outbreak at Tollesbury. Two years later poultry respiratory diseases swept through 80% of the large flocks in the county. Essex was second only to Norfolk in the eastern region for poultry density and the egg packing stations in the county reported that "they had never had to deal with so many second quality eggs".[14] In 1970 a serious outbreak of Fowl Pest occurred again and the efficiency of the vaccination programme was questioned.

David Cannon, Watercress Hall, Fordham, lost thousands of birds and claimed that on farms with unvaccinated stock there was "a huge booster station for the disease".[15] Rev'd. Philip Wright said later "because Essex was the starting point of the outbreak, the county is permanently linked with the virulent form of virus. It is even officially known as Essex 70!"[16] Salmonella was another problem for poultry farmers although the major force of the epidemic was not centred in the county.

Pigs suffered from a series of disease problems. Transmittable gastro-enteritis (TGE) occurred in 1957/8 and in 1965. Within three weeks it had spread from Saffron Walden to the Thames. In 1972 a new disease was spotted in Britain, Swine Vesicular disease and in 1974 Essex became part of a large area over which movement restrictions were imposed. Store pig markets were closed and those for immediate slaughter had to be licenced. A slaughtering policy was invoked and the pig population dropped by just over 37,000 between 1973/5. The incidence of BSE amongst Essex herds was not high but Government directives caused animals to be slaughtered. It contributed to the already sharply declining numbers of cows and cattle in the county.

All these animal diseases caught the public imagination. The problems in plants was less noticeable. Rhizomania, a virus that attacked sugar beet crops resulted in a field near Bury St Edmunds being cordoned off by the MAFF but only a small number of Essex fields were affected.

Two more diseases appeared after 1950 which had a profound effect They were both, in different ways, beneficial. The first was Myxomatosis and the second Dutch Elm Disease.

The decimation of the rabbit population was an unexpected bonus. Pre-war, rabbits had affected the crops on many farms whilst fields adjacent to woodland were planted regularly, but never harvested. The rabbits ate the ground bare and there had been a concerted effort during the war to reduce the damage. These efforts had wiped out tens of thousands of rabbits but had hardly altered the problem. In 1953 Myxomatosis swept across the countryside killing 97% of them and after the first outbreak a network of Rabbit Clearance Societies was created to co-ordinate the efforts and eradicate the last remaining immune ones.

A year later it reappeared in the autumn, to the east of Colchester and in the Maldon and Witham areas. There were fewer outbreaks in the south and west, "but the main spread still comes from the original 'outbreaks' on the East Coast and they, like Foot-and-Mouth 'outbreaks', just came."[17] Farmers were accused of deliberately transporting infected rabbits from one farm to another.

After the disease had done its work they lost enthusiasm to support the RCSs hoping that the disease would keep them in check. This was partially achieved and it became rare to find rabbit damage of great severity. But the rabbits never disappeared and 25 years later there were still thousands of wild rabbits in the countryside. In succeeding years the disease reappeared – but never eradicated the last rabbit. The Clearance Societies transformed themselves into commercial enterprises. The West Essex Rabbit Clearance Society Ltd., based at Hall Wood Common, Epping, serving nearly half the county offered contract controls for rats, mice, sparrows and moles.

The magnificent skyline of indigenous elms had been the inspiration for painters and artists as well as a home for rooks and crows. The Essex countryside predominated with stately elms. Despite its slow start the elm population was insidiously decimated.

Dutch Elm Disease caused by a fungus *ceratocystis ulmi* produced a toxic substance which caused a form of thrombosis exacerbated by the movement of the elm bark beetles. Its appearance in Essex was, and remained, a mystery. Although it had swept across Canada in the 1920s it was previously unknown in Britain.

In September 1972 the ECC inspectors calculated that 21,810 trees had been affected and although there were regulations which insisted upon felling, at that date only 54% had been cut down. "Of all the trees inspected only about 20% have been found to be affected, which gives hope that the county will not become denuded of elm trees". It was a pious hope and new saplings succumbed before they could reach a significant size. Each autumn the leaves turned prematurely brown and withered away. Far from the artist's image the skyline became dominated by skeletal trees. All areas of the county, excepting Epping Forest and Hainault which were mainly oak, were affected.

Farmers were tree-conscious planters but preferred to create plantations in odd corners or refurbish woodland. Large hedgerow elms cast significant shadows which resulted in green corn when the remainder was mature. There were significant losses to cereal crops, fewer to grassland where the cows rested in the shade of the leaves or sheltered during storms, but the roots extracted moisture from a wide area affecting the crops.

Essex Farming and Wildlife Advisory Group

As the movement away from food production to countryside conservation gained momentum the public criticism of modern farming methods became more vocal, and farmers set out to defend themselves. The awareness and needs of conservation became apparent. In 1969 a conference at Silsoe highlighted the need for farmers to put their own house in order. In Essex FWAG was formed and its first chairman, Jeremy Dillon-Robinson, set out a model on his own farm which became known as the 'Widdington Exercise'. It was an organised attempt to combine good husbandry, and profitable farming without destroying the natural habitat of many wildlife animals.

FWAG was created as an advisory organisation composed basically of 1/3 representatives of statutory bodies and 1/3 voluntary bodies. The ECC was strongly represented and the long established Essex Naturalists Trust, which became the Essex Wildlife Trust also co-operated. Until 1982 restricted funds prevented advice on a regular basis. The Countryside Commission was empowered to provide 'start-up' money but each county matched the contributions and the Essex FWAG was being supported by the ECC, some District Councils and by enthusiastic farmers.

A full-time advisor, Lawrence Jones-Walters, was recruited and replaced by Fiona

118 1978 Feering. Hurst's new Research and Trial grounds at Gt. Domsey Farm. Top shows Marks Tey Kelvedon portion of A12.

Hall in 1989. In the previous five years over 300 farmers had requested and received detailed advice. "Many of the farmers who have taken advice from Fiona are delighted to discover that, on many occasions little is needed to enhance the landscape and wildlife value of their farms".[19] Later the advice became more embracing and whole-farm plans, called 'Landwise' were drawn up to assess the cropping regime "and devise the way to make the farm a complete habitat – not just jewels in a desert".[20]

It did not adopt a lobbying role and avoided a high profile stance although its patent sincerity gave it an authoritative voice. An annual award was instituted with a trophy donated by Essex chemical manufacturer, May & Baker, later taken over by Rhone Poulenc. Fiona Hall advocated that "conservation can save money. It does not always involve expenditure"[19] and Savills published a survey of Mark Thomasin-Foster's Great Leighs farm, giving two valuations, one based on a denuded countryside and the other on a balanced wildlife/farmland combination. The result showed an enhanced value for the second option. Potential farm buyers were patently not Philistines!

The objectives of FWAG were to convince farmers of the importance of a balanced countryside set against an ever increasing county population, and other demands on land. "FWAG would hope that in 50 years time the land that is left after the domestic, industrial and transport appetites have been satisfied will show farmers continuing their commitment to the environment".[21]

Conserving Wildlife

Another body which was successful in preserving flora, fauna and wildlife in a practical manner,and also acquired 7,000a, mainly but not exclusively around the coastal marshland, was the *Essex Wildlife Trust* (hereafter EWT). With 15,000 dedicated members participating in restoring ponds, clearing scrubland, replanting woods, creating nature trails and providing bird hides the EWT, a registered charity, claimed to be the largest organisation of its kind in Essex. Over 1,000 volunteers gave active support. 27,000 children were given practical lessons and demonstrations to educate them in the natural heritage of the county in 1997. In that year they spent over £1m and had set-up an organisation with its HQ at Fingringhoe Wick and three other visitor centres at Abberton Reservoir, Langdon and Thorndon, and 14 local groups organising a full annual programme designed to encourage and promote wildlife appreciation.

EWT started in 1959 with 110 members. Its first success was to focus awareness that development to the Naze at Walton would be detrimental. The application was refused and the Naze remained protected. One year after its formation, and with only £214 in the bank the EWT offered the owners of Fingringhoe Wick; Brightlingsea Aggregates Ltd., £3,500 for 100a. Such was its success at attracting funds that the money was repaid within two years. They still had a cash balance of £301. The gravel working equipment was removed and a warden, Clifford Owen, was appointed. When an Open Day was arranged in 1962, 900 people attended. A fire spread into the Reserve during the hot summer of 1976 but natural regeneration was allowed to repair the damage. It revealed a galaxy of plant life and demonstrated the benefits of clearance, albeit it was considered a severe blow at the time.

The EWT touched a chord in the minds of townspeople who discovered, many for the first time, the delights of nature. Most of the 7,000a was purchased by the Trust. E.W.T. bought the 601a Blue House Farm, North Fambridge in 1998, and received a grant from the Heritage Lottery Fund of £825,000. In addition many private charitable Trusts made substantial donations. Its work was considered exemplary and it set out to become a guardian of the county, scrutinising over 200 planning applications in 1997, and commenting upon nearly 60 of them. They organised campaigns highlighting threats such as pollution, developments and road schemes. Its popularity was demonstrated when 200,000 visitors went to the five conservation centres in one year alone. They also had management arrangements on three *National Trust* (hereafter N.T.) properties. Danbury and Lingwood Common, 244a of common land acquired by the N.T. in 1953. Blakes Wood, Little Baddow 108a acquired in 1956 where the majority of the woodland was pre-1600 ('ancient'). It was here that the 1987 hurricane caused considerable damage and a policy of leaving it to regenerage was observed. The third N.T. property was Ray Island, Peldon, 100a of salt marsh with a small area of higher land at the centre.

It was acquired by the N.T. in 1970 and was originally earmarked as a summer venue for the Boy Scouts.

Side-by-side with the EWT, the County Council was purchasing suitable areas, such as Chalkney Wood and Cudmore Grove, East Mersea. The Forestry Commission granted public access to its woods at Coggeshall and Gosfield.

The National Trust acquired 2,724a in Essex starting with 1,040a of medieval war hunting forest at Hatfield and Takeley in 1924. Northey Island 286a in the Blackwater bought in 1978 and South House Farm on the landward approach to Northey, the site of the Battle of Maldon 991AD acquired in the same year. Bridges Farm and Lower Barn Farms in Dedham Vale 332a, mainly grassland and considered of great landscape importance with its association with John Constable, the grazing let to tenant farmers. Copt Hall Farm and 400a of salt marsh at Little Wigborough bought in 1989 and the farmland let to a tenant. The N.T. also acquired the second most famous barn in Essex. The most impressive being the Cressing Temple Tithe Barn. Second in importance, Grange Barn, Coggeshall reputed to be the oldest surviving timber framed barn in Europe dating from the 12th century and originally part of a Cistercian Monastery. It was dismantled and restored using the ancient craft techniques in the early 1980s by the Grange Barn Trust, Braintree D.C. and E.C.C.

The Forestry Commission in Essex

The first land acquired in Essex by the Commission was Rowney Wood, near Saffron Walden, in 1950. This was bought freehold for £6/acre. The last was Thrift Wood on the Markshall Estate (leasehold) in 1959 for an annual rent of £5 (12½ p/acre). At its peak the total holding in the country was approximately 2,646a. This was managed as three separate units namely: Navestock, Walden and Honeywood, each with its own office, forester and workforce. The majority of these sites were planted with conifer and broadleaf mixtures.

The 1980s saw a large number of woods sold off as part of the Commission's disposal programme. This period also saw a series of amalgamations and redundancies resulting in the estate being managed on a day to day basis by a foreman with all work being carried out by contractors.

In 1999 Forest Enterprise held 1,170a. In addition an Underlease on timber at the Markshall Estate and 300a of Hainault Forest on behalf of the Woodland Trust. Policy was to revert all woods to site native species as markets allowed via natural regeneration. The average production was approximately 4,000 tonnes/year. The products being sawn timber, fencing, pulp, firewood and charcoal.

CHAPTER 27

The Markets Close

In 1900 there were 13 weekly markets in the County. There were others which held annual shows and those which dealt in vegetables and other produce. By 1999 there were only two left; Chelmsford and Colchester. The markets were always a two-way trade. Butchers bought fatstock for slaughter, and farmers replenished their farms with stores and weaners. It was also a convivial meeting place where valuable exchanges were made. There had been 18 regular markets half a century earlier but the depression in farming had reduced them.

Purpose built Corn Exchanges were a 19th century invention. The Braintree Exchange cost £3,000 in 1839, and had to be enlarged. A new Corn Exchange was built in Colchester in 1845, complete with an Ionic Colonnade surmounted by a group of sculpture. It cost £4,000 and at Saffron Walden an Exchange in the Italianite theme was built in 1848. "This is one of the largest corn markets in Essex", said Whites directory.[1]

Market day was a highlight of the week for the townspeople. Frank White recorded his memories of Romford, and said "we children would pressure our parents to visit the town, so that we could watch the drovers driving the cattle onto the weighbridge". This was 1926 when a bursting town like Romford could boast that it was still "very much a county market town...it was a local market served by local people".[2]

Romford market received its Charter in 1247AD and there were others such as Colchester which could boast an ancient lineage. A market Charter was revered as an accolade of importance and there was a rule which determined that markets should have a six mile catchment area. In the 19th century this rule fell into abeyance. Each town had its own prescribed market day to avoid clashing. The markets in 1900 were; Billericay, Dunmow, Southminster, Waltham Abbey, Halstead and Harwich on Tuesdays, which seems to have been a popular day of the week. Braintree and Romford were on Wednesdays. Rochford on Thursdays. Chelmsford and Epping on Fridays and Colchester and Saffron Walden on Saturdays.

This coverage balanced supply and demand. The changes became more pronounced after 1900. A rising population, and the increasing availability of motorised transport eroded the pattern. By 1912 Billericay and Harwich markets had closed. The 70,000 head of cattle which had been regularly arriving at 'the cattle landing', at Tilbury was reduced and finally ceased as steam ships and new facilities were opened further up the Thames. Harwich had never been a natural centre for a country market but had been involved in the importation of live cattle from the continental ports. There were overnight cattle pens and lairage. As two markets closed two more opened. A regular cattle market was established at Thaxted and in 1908 a Great Bentley farmer, James Cordy, opened a market for cattle, sheep and pigs at Thorpe-le-Soken. It was developed by his son, Bernard who cycled around the local villages persuading farmers to send their animals to Thorpe rather than to Colchester.

The Stanford family were prominent farmers in the Tendring Hundred. Charles

Maurice Stanford became an auctioneer in Colchester and it was his son, Gerald, who, in 1913 established another market at Thorpe selling farm animals, eggs, vegetables and butter. "The drovers used to drive the animals to market from the farms, the butchers bought them, then they were driven to the slaughterhouses".[3] Thorpe was never a large market and in one week in 1955 there were only 14 cattle, eight lambs and 69 fat pigs.[4] This demonstrated the reduction in farm animals in a predominantly arable corner of the county. By contrast in 1919 26,668 horses, cattle, sheep and pigs passed through Colchester Cattle Market.[5]

The Maldon market had only operated on the first Thursday in May and September when cattle, either yarded, or off the marshes in September, were sold. There was no regular market at Southminster in 1890 but by 1900 a weekly stock market had opened. A market was established at Stanford-le-Hope by Offin & Rumsey. A.W. Offin ran the Wickford and Romford markets. G.B. Hilliard & Son auctioned stock every Friday at Chelmsford with horse sales on the first Friday of each month. Richard Hilliard ran weekly sales at Romford on a Wednesday. Balls & Balls (Est.1846) had a market at Braintree and Saffron Walden run by Alan Nott. Ernest Gale ran the Southminster market and Fred Taylor and Co., official auctioneers to the Essex Pig Society (1924) had stock sales at Chelmsford every Friday.

J.F. Benson held weekly sales of fat and store stock, poultry and produce every Monday in a small market at Great Yeldham, although this was never a major business centre. Other firms which were committed to agricultural trade were Cheffins, Saffron Walden, Fenn Wright at Colchester who, in conjunction with Stanfords, held a rival market in a different part of the market place on the same day. Woodward & Priday also held an active auction of rabbits, poultry and eggs on a nearby site. Woodward & Priday had four auctions; Saffron Walden, Bishop's Stortford, Braintree and Colchester where they conducted sales of poultry, eggs and rabbits with turkeys a major selling line at Christmas. Kemsley at Romford, Surridge at Coggeshall and J.M. Welch & Son at Dunmow were other auctioneers.

Bishop's Stortford

The old market premises were extended to provide separate attested accommodation at the end of meat rationing on 1 July 1954. Periodic sales of store cattle were held in the new premises particularly in the spring. Lairage at the railway station disappeared in the mid-1950s but transport by rail except for the odd consignment of north country cattle was virtually non-existent by then. In the early '70s there were 70 cattle, up to 150 pigs and perhaps 100 sheep. All these figures depend on the time of year and refer to finished stock. The Cattle Market in Northgate End closed just before Christmas in 1982. By this time there were about five cattle, three or four pens of sheep and 20 to 30 pigs per week. The main auctioneer from the early 1930s was Robert Trigg. His son, Peter, ran that side of the business until his untimely death in August 1982.

Chelmsford

Markets were always situated in the centres of their towns. But in the second half of the century it became inconvenient to have the market day disruption with lorries, other traffic, animals and people jostling into crowded streets. Colchester market had been removed from the High Street down to the bottom of North Hill in the 19th century.

119 1980 Chelmsford Market. (L-R) Christopher Clarke, Michael Spear and Nigel Nott. (James Abbott Partnership). The market was later taken over by Tom Whirledge and Nigel Nott. Chelmsford market moved twice. 12 markets in Essex closed between 1950-80.

Chelmsford remained in the centre of the town until 1962 when its site was taken over for a multistory car park, and a produce market with other stall holders on the ground level. The market was removed to a purpose built modern edifice in Victoria Road in 1962, at a cost of £300,000. Markets were controlled by local councils and the premises leased to the auctioneers. Chelmsford council, like others, decided that a town centre site was too valuable for a cattle market.

The new market in Victoria Road had the facilities of permanent buildings and adequate car and lorry parks. It existed for 27 years and was replaced by a Homebase store. A new market was built at Springfield where the horse auction area was later transformed into a thriving car auction.

In the larger centres there were often three or more auctioneers with segregated parts of the trade. There were three in Chelmsford. Darby's ran a pig auction but later developed into a furniture sale room. Hilliards sold fat cattle and calves. Offin & Rumsey sold store cattle and sheep. There was a poultry market but with egg rationing during the war they were sold through packing stations and never went back through the markets when they were derationed.

Hilliards survived the longest but succumbed and the market was taken over by some of the erstwhile partners who, with others from Colchester, created the James Abbott Partnership. There was no Mr. Abbott. The partners thought that Abbotts would always be at the top of any alphabetical directory. In 1987 there were changes and Tom Whirledge, a partner in Abbotts and Nigel Nott, who had been with Offin & Rumsey created 'Whirledge & Nott' to run the Chelmsford market.

120 1950s Chelmsford Corn Exchange on a Friday afternoon when considerable business was being done.

Kelly's Directory in 1900 said "the market is held on a Friday and, with regard to corn, is one of the largest in the county. A cattle and horse market was laid out in the rear of the Corn Exchange in 1880". A far cry from these times was the Springfield market. The third site in less than a century – but Chelmsford market survived and became important when others had closed.

Colchester
In 1970 when Colchester Corporation wished to redevelop the site at Middleborough, the market moved to Severalls Industrial Estate. The auctioneers amalgamated their market interests into Colchester Market Auctions and at the same time changed the traditional market day from Saturday to Thursday. When Ipswich market merged the market day transferred to Tuesday. Fenn Wright relinquished their involvement in the market when they sold out those interests to W.H. Brown who at that time had taken over Stanfords. Stanfords later bought themselves out of the Brown group. The through-put at market dropped from 200 cattle a week to 50, from about 1,000 sheep per week in the busy season to 3/400, and that changed from the higher through-put when lambs were marketed from stubble turnips. Fat pigs declined from about 1,000 a week to 100.

121 1909 Colchester Market. Buyers, drovers and boys appraise a long horned - probably Shorthorn cow.

Dunmow

The firm of J.M. Welch & Sons was founded by Col. Joseph Marsh Welch, the son of Thomas H. Welch of the Folly Farm, Great Dunmow. Early in 1886 he set up in business as an Auctioneer, Valuer and Estate Agent, with offices at 11 High Street, Lloyds Bank later replaced it. J.George Cole ran a fortnightly Fatstock Sale at a Saleyard adjoining the G.E. Railway Yard. On Tuesday 6 July 1886 J.M. Welch opened his Saleyard in a field adjoining the Saracen's Head. His Fatstock Sale was held on the first Tuesday in every month.

"On 13 July 1886 J.M. Welch held his first Auction Sale of Land, comprising 7 Building Plots in the High Street of Dunmow. By Christmas 1888 J.M. Welch was holding fortnightly Fatstock Sales. After this date J.George Cole ceased to advertise in the Essex Weekly News or Essex Chronicle, so it is likely that he ceased trading."[6]

The Livestock Market closed in 1968 and the buildings were converted into furniture salerooms. In January 1976 the business was purchased by Hamptons.

Saffron Walden

The livestock market in Saffron Walden during the 20th century occupied two locations. The main Cattle Market was in Market Street and was owned by Henry Joshua Cheffins. The Pig Market was on land owned by Saffron Walden Borough Council, and situated in Hill Street. The Borough Pig Market was notable for its portico archway adjacent to which was built a Gent's public lavatory, one of the earliest public conveniences erected in Essex. The portico entrance survived being incorporated in the shop development and the inscription 'Erected by Subscription – Anno Domini – 1831'.

122 *1905 Waltham Abbey Market. Sheep penned, cattle tethered.*

Both the Cattle and Pig markets were operated by Mr. Cheffins and represented a relatively small town market until the post war restrictions were lifted in 1955. At that time, Thomas Chalk and Bob Arnold were the two senior partners of Cheffins, and they had interests in the partnership of the Cambridge based auctioneers Grain & Chalk. By the end of the 1950s and into the 1960s the throughput of the market had grown significantly with upwards of 300 fat cattle, 200 sheep and 300 pigs being sold on any Tuesday. The Christmas Fatstock Shows were an event for the whole town with many dignitaries of national status attending the lunches held in the Town Hall.

Saffron Walden Livestock Market had received Royal patronage on an intermittent basis both before and after the Second World War and King George V was awarded a First Prize in the Sheep Classes at the 1937 Fatstock Show. R.A. Butler, MP for Saffron Walden, persuaded the Sandringham Estate to enter stock for the Fatstock Shows at that time. Rarely did His Majesty receive a major prize mainly because the standard of competition was so high! At this time the cattle market site was re-modernised with new steel penning to replace the old wooden ones. Saffron Walden became a major livestock centre for East Anglia with buyers regularly attending from the Midlands, Wales and beyond. The rapid decline of livestock farming in the region during the 1970s was the beginning of the demise of Saffron Walden Market which was closed at the 1982 Fatstock Show, the same time that Bishop's Stortford closed, when the partners of Cheffins Grain & Chalk transferred the livestock auction business to their other market based in Cambridge.

Witham

It is probable that there was a market at the pre-conquest settlement at Chipping Hill in the tenth and eleventh centuries. During the twelfth century the manor was given by King Stephen to the Knights Templars, who, in 1212 were granted a charter for a new market at 1a Neweland – now Newland Street. For a time there were two markets, one at

Chipping Hill on Tuesdays (having been altered in 1219 from Sundays), and one at Newland on Thursdays. The Chipping Hill market ceased some time before 1307.

The market continued until the second half of the 19th century. White's Directory of Essex for both 1848 and 1863 refers to Witham as having "a small market every Tuesday for corn, cattle etc." Kelly's Directory for 1866 makes no mention of a market, whilst that of 1870 refers to the market as discontinued.

In 1894 a Maldon auctioneer, E.E. Clear, established a fortnightly sale of fat and store stock "in the meadow adjoining the Railway Bridge". These sales were advertised as "Central Stock Sales". A syndicate of local farmers, after acquiring the site, developed it by installing penning, cattle standings and a weighbridge. They erected a single storey timber building as a corn exchange. Clear continued as auctioneer until he was fatally injured by a hunting accident in 1905. He was succeeded by Hugh Page. In 1909 the same syndicate of farmers formed themselves into a limited company known as Witham Stock Sale and Cattle Market Ltd. They were: Philip Hutley, Powers Hall, Witham. Charles Brown, The Maltings, Witham. John Polley, Springholds, Rivenhall. Thomas Speakman, Hill Farm, Faulkbourne. Edwin Fairhead, Stock Street Farm, Coggeshall. Praed William Wood, Sparrows Farm, Terling. Hugh Page, Collingwood Road, Witham (Auctioneer).

The market operated at first fortnightly but then weekly, on Tuesdays throughout the first half of the century, Mr. Page continuing as auctioneer until his retirement in 1946. During the Second World War the market operated under the Ministry of Food as a collecting and grading centre, animals for slaughter being allocated to different abattoirs throughout south-east England. Until 1950 it was not unusual for bunches of thirty or forty cattle to be driven from the market via Collingwood Road and Newland Street to the abattoir off Guithavon Street.

When meat rationing ended and marketing returned to private enterprise, the throughput of stock at Witham was insufficient to justify the exenditure then considered necessary to improve facilities. In 1955 the directors decided to close the market. The site was sold and later became the local Labour Party Club. The tradition of a market at Witham was revived soon afterwards by the Council establishing a stall market off Collingwood Road.

The Glory That Went

The Ministry of Agriculture figures in 1991 showed that Essex farmers reared and sold for slaughter the fourth highest numbers of steers and heifers in the country with 79,400 head slaughtered. There were 7,000 cows and bulls, very few calves, sheep and lambs, but 425,200 pigs including sows and boars.

Despite these impressive numbers the system of marketing had radically changed. More animals went directly to abattoirs and meat processing premises. The principal end buyers (supermarket chains) were not prepared to stand at an auction ring and bid for individual cattle. They wanted identical portions, packaged and delivered. It changed the whole essence of marketing, a process that had started with the bacon factories and was stimulated by the meat distribution system.

But it destroyed the conviviality which existed amongst the farming fraternity. It did not disappear completely but in 1900 nearly every farmer went to market once a week. At the end of the century only about one in ten farmers ever went near a market. Stockless farms now predominated and they had no need to attend. A valuable meeting place was lost.

CHAPTER 28

Progress With Pride

After 100 years farmers could look back with pride at the achievements which they had made. Despite the almost engulfing tide of urban development farming remained the predominant industry in the county, occupied the largest area and had acquitted itself in two world wars to feed the nation. There was a feeling that the county had been well served by its farmers and they were regarded as amongst the most progressive in the United Kingdom. Many of the changes which had overtaken the whole country had been stimulated on the test-bed of Essex acres. Other counties looked towards Essex with envy. Its farmers were always ahead of their times.

Essex grown seeds were grown widely throughout the world. They were always considered 'quality'. Essex had supplied leaders of national farming organisations which were unheard of in 1900. They had grasped the nettle and leadership emerged from the yeomen stock of the county.

There had been considerable changes and the power base of local politics had changed. It is trite to suggest that the land owning aristocracy and gentry had been usurped and that the land owning classes no longer held sway. This is to deny the fact that the power had moved from the long established county families to the erstwhile middle class of farmers who, by the end of the century, had become the landowners. It gave a greater freedom to plan and to execute radical changes in their farming systems. It allowed policy making on the hoof – but it quickly became apparent, against a tide of beaurocratic government, that instant decision making was more effective, and more satisfying.

In county affairs the Vice Lord Lieutenant was a farmer, an unusual appointment in 1900 but accepted with alacrity a century later. Amongst the membership of the Essex County Council the agricultural representation had moved from the old families to the new farmers, and despite the advances of urbanisation and the population explosion, the farming voice was still heard in approximately the same percentage. At the lower levels of government a majority of the parish council chairmen were leading local farmers. Their involvement in parish affairs was both respected and admired. They brought to the job an inherent belief in the traditions of village life and a love and respect to preserve the better aspects of parish affairs.

The conflict between town and country was mitigated by the pattern of behaviour which the farming community adopted. No longer did the farmers' wagons, cattle and motorcars take over such places as Colchester and Chelmsford on market days. Whilst one half of the populace welcomed them as traders, the other sector regarded the weekly invasion with suspicion and annoyance. The only two markets remaining were both situated on the outskirts of their towns. There was no traffic disruption by farmers blocking every pavement.

With mechanical hedge cutters, farmers kept the countryside tidy. Country lanes unsuited for motorised transport, and definitely unsafe, were improved by farmers'

*123 Pre-1917. Ford tractor with cylindrical radiator. One of more than 50 experimental models built
in the USA. The forerunner of the Essex built tractors.*

actions. Such events as blocked roads after heavy snowfall, were quickly cleared by farm
machinery and in particular when the county was brought to a standstill after the
hurricane in October 1987 it was chain saws and tractors which cleared the roads. The
public spirited attitude of the agricultural community was recognised and despite the
occasional pin pricks particularly over straw burning which was later banned, there
remained a general sympathy for the problems of farmers, countered perhaps by less
knowledge of farming practices than their forbears would have known.

When the Public Inquiry system was introduced it was the NFU and the CLA which
sought to protect the valuable and beautiful countryside from the despoilation of
concrete. With new housing inevitable and Industrial Parks popular, it was the farming
organisations which directed the thoughts of the Planning Officers towards alternative
sites, or a well planned community such as the Notley Garden Village. Farmers could be
proud that they were the guardians and custodians of incomparable countryside.

Farming practice changed beyond belief and as manual tasks were taken over by
machinery the traditional workers were left to occupy their cottages for life. Twenty-five
percent of the farmland was lost to agriculture – but the production went up. Substantial
increases in crop yields were only achieved by adopting scientific and research-led
developments. The relative prosperity of agricultural incomes financed the transfer from
labour to tractors and combines. This money, and also income from sales of development
land (usually village in-filling), was vital to enable the march of progress to be achieved.
Farmers insisted upon reinvesting everything in their farms and since most farmers had

become the owners of their land there was a feeling of personal achievement for the future.

Others were attracted in, and money men from the City bought farms where they discovered that their property had an insatiable appetite for reinvestment. Many did not continue into the second generation, but they left behind farms that had new cottages, new barns, and modernised farm houses. Concrete roads to the fields supplanted muddy tracks and under-drainage immeasurably improved the productivity of the fields.

During the 19th century the railways had carved their way across the county. Many of the smaller branch lines were abandoned after the Beeching Axe and reverted back to land from which they had originally been taken. The motorways and general road improvements consumed large amounts of land. Although most of the new by-passes were carved across virgin land, their impact was less than might have been expected, and productivity did not decline as scientific influence was promoting greater yields.

Contrasting the appearance of farmsteads from 1900 farmers had become tidier. No longer was the farm yard littered with tumbrils and pieces of iron machinery with stinging nettles and a profusion of skeletal trees. Concrete yards which were necessary for the 25 ton lorries which took away the farm produce, and which could not have approached most farms without being bogged down, were now given the facility to collect their loads.

It could be argued that it was the increase in lorry weights, the adoption of rubber tyres on tractors, and the width of combine harvesters which made farmers embark upon easier access. But it is also debatable that these changes were stimulated by the introduction of ready-mixed concrete and the realisation by individual farmers that their businesses would not succeed if they could not achieve quicker transport of machinery around their fields.

The countryside presented a well ordered and neat appearance. No longer did high hedges and overhanging boughs impede movement. Although field sizes grew they were only reverting to their appearance before the fussy Victorian patchwork emerged. Great swaths of highly productive crops looked magnificent and as the machinery trundled across them it was self evident that the land was in a better state of fertility than it had been a century earlier.

Tree planting went on apace. The traditional willow industry in Essex continued to supply the wood for Test Matches. There were no great stretches of coniferous forest, which adorned many of the northern counties of England and Scotland. The Essex tree planting programme, instituted by individual farmers, sought to recreate the county into a giant 18th century country park with clumps of trees interspersed by open farmland. Farmers proved they were not Philistines. There might have been less woods – but there were more trees. They were in different places although, towards the end of the century and aided by government grants, many areas were replanted where they had been taken out in earlier times.

Thatched buildings and pantiles were replaced by concrete blocks and asbestos but the blinding white colour was soon mitigated by weathering and they began to nestle into the vista as neatly as the timber buildings of yore. There were less farmsteads as the centres of operations were concentrated into neater, well planned blocks, rather than haphazardly dotted around incongruous locations.

The impact of the motorways and road widening schemes still left large untouched areas and Essex became a favourite location for TV films where there were plenty of sites without the intrusion of pylons and poles.

The livestock was decimated. Essex had always struggled to be a livestock producing county. It had supplied the needs of its own populace. Milk had been produced for the same reasons, but as transportation increased Essex could revert to its more natural role as a grain, seed and root growing county.

Wet summers caused more disruption than the opposite, yet although farmers could combat the inclement seasons with grain dryers and more powerful machinery, they attempted also to combat the drought years by the installation of on-farm water reservoirs and irrigation systems. This applied particularly to fruit, vegetables and market garden production which maintained its tenuous hold but could not increase its importance when freshly picked produce could be transported around the world in a few hours. The organic movement gained little in the county. The demand was satisfied, but the demand was small and most farmers disregarded organic farming as a serious large-scale operation.

Farms got larger. This removed the small under capitalised men who were often pursuing outdated practices as neighbours were swept up into the corporate umbrella of their larger and more dominating entrepreneurs. Farmers were managing large enterprises when their forbears had found difficulty in maintaining units of fractional size.

The cows went and some of the grassland. With modern techniques the unproductive marshland areas along the east coast, and the Thames Estuary, low lying, ill drained and unkempt, were under drained and produced magnificent crops, Wallasea Island being a prime example but there were many others. The cold, wet farms on the eastern seaboard became as neat and productive as those of the upland areas.

There was only one farmer in 1999, for every two in 1900. There was only one worker for every 10! Yet the forward thinking initiatives of Essex farmers made the practice of tilling the land a faster operation. Timeliness was achieved with greater ease. The peasant image of a straw sucking, pipe smoking, unshaven, lean figure with his smock and gaiters was a total caricature of the past, even if it was a predominant image. The agri-businessman took his place with his Range Rover, his 'mobile' and his ability to command the business knowledge and acumen of an industrialist.

Farmers integrated into the community to a wider degree. In many counties in England they still preserved a social mafia which revolved around the markets. In Essex the farming community offered an open hand to the newcomers who bought up the redundant farm houses and settled in the villages. There was a social interchange that had not been previously apparent. This resulted in a two-way movement. Many of the new parishioners acquired a greater knowledge and respect for the travails of the farmer, and often the business ethics and rules of the newcomers gave imagination to the farmers in their quest for progress.

The class divisions which had been important were muted, and in most cases disappeared. Rotary clubs in every town had their farmer members. Farmers and professional men mixed with ease. If the definitions of class could be bracketed by income levels there was little to choose between them. The peasant status of farmers was abolished and they could become confident members of an integrated society structure.

The workers had their own cars, many lived in farm cottages, but many did not. The workers' children went to universities and the workers had a creditable knowledge of the complicated, and often confusing requirements for the precise setting of combines and

124 1900 Heybridge. Bentalls was well established

tractors for greater productivity. The workers became more independent, in greater partnership with their employers and completely disregarded the erstwhile image of a servile, forelock touching, humble servant. It was another step in the levelling out of the class system. The farmers usurped the upper class of landowners and aristocrats, but did not ape them. The historic families turned their hands to active farming and in a sense lowered themselves into trade. Thus from either direction the sharp class divisions of earlier days were blunted and mitigated.

The 20th century was a time in which nothing was sacrosanct. There were severe misgivings when Essex farmers started to grow continuous wheat crops. The pundits foresaw the impoverishment of the soil, and the spread of plant diseases. In practise the soil became more productive and the concerns were proved to be unfounded. The soil of Essex, at the end of the century was in better heart than it had ever been before. The viability of farms was subject to international events and currency fluctuations, but there was an aura of continuity, and an inbuilt confidence which was coupled and supported by the resilience of farmers to change – when change was required! Farming had also extended its wings.

Almost half the farmers in Essex developed sidelines ancillary perhaps to their main business. Some had developed considerable industrial parks, such as at Earls Colne and at many locations in the south of the county but beyond this there had been a break down in the 'pureness' of farming under which the men of old had eschewed anything that was not strictly within the bounds of animal and crop husbandry. There was a degree of arrogance in this attitude but it was swept away as Essex farmers led the vanguard by enthusiastically accepting sideline activities which were remunerative. Some created equestrian establishments which became as important as the farm income. Others developed storage facilities, boat building, civil contracting; the list was endless and the inventiveness of Essex farmers was unbounded.

The question can be legitimately asked; "why were Essex farmers in the vanguard of progress?" It is a valid examination. Undoubtedly the influx of enterprising Scottish settlers brought new blood into the county and this was a contributory factor. But this invasion took place in the early part of the century and by the end these families had not simply been assimilated into the county but had become natives. Many were in the 3rd/4th generation and had lost contact with their roots.

The proximity of London, and the spread of new ideas was another factor. The introduction of town and city-based men rubbing shoulders with farmers undoubtedly assisted this process. It was often said that progress in England was like throwing a stone into Essex and watching the ripples spread. If this was true there must have been a considerable tradition of enterprise. Men of initiative, such as Tom Harvey of Coggeshall and Ernest Doe of Ulting. There were others who were inventors and entrepreneurs. The spread of agricultural knowledge was promoted by communication but farming practice, coupled to an inbuilt suspicion against change, was only accepted when it was proven. Like the pond ripples, one innovative farmer in a district was soon copied by those who looked over the hedge. There were no secrets in farming and mistakes as well as successes were very public.

Essex was supported by an infrastructure of enterprising corn merchants, who quickly grasped the export opportunities through the county ports. This stimulated demand, which stimulated production. There was support from the scientific arm with such organisations as the Perry Foundation aiding research projects. The University of Essex, the par excellence of Writtle College as a beacon of light, even amongst the academia of agricultural universities.

The enterprise and co-operation between farmers was another highlight. In many parts of Britain farmers were loathe to share their experiences. They would talk in the Market Tavern and around the cattle rings but were often tight-lipped about their personal affairs. Essex farmers did not have this reserve. They were highly independent but the prolification of 'Open Days' when farmers let other farmers (their competitors) view their farms and discuss the crops was a welcome innovation. No longer did they make their mistakes in private. The E.A.S. instituted an annual, "Best Farm" competition, as also did the Thorpe Discussion Group. Such establishments as Throws Farm, Dunmow with its multitude of crop trials, the enterprise of the Nicholls family with Kings of Coggeshall, the research farm of May & Baker at Ongar, the Animal Health Trust at Stock and many other similar centres provided a leadership that was unequalled in any other county.

The answer to the question must be contained in the happy co-operation between all sides of the industry, from making tractors to producing seed crops, from the open minded attitude of the enterprising farmers and from the influence of the metropolis. Some of the more remote, and perhaps more rural counties of England did not achieve this degree of progress – but Essex did and it was a record of which Essex farmers could be justifiably proud. It was a century of change, an exciting century, and above all a century of transition which was accompanied by success.

God speed the plough, and God save the farmer. The next century will be another challenge.

Crop and Stock Tables

Table 1

CROPS (ACRES)						
Year	Farmed Area	Fallow	P.Pastures Heath (inc. Rough Grazings	Wheat	Barley	Oats
1900	801,768	32,812	271,907	113,722	84,050	62,336
1901	802,216	32,930	269,940	110,826	82,679	59,894
1902	797,969	20,256	267,383	109,227	83,432	66,448
1903	796,398	32,261	277,621	100,693	80,752	68,099
1904	793,722	45,540	283,214	79,678	82,727	79,020
1905	793,262	36,452	285,924	114,868	71,021	65,778
1906	793,185	31,402	286,492	112,020	68,321	68,095
1907	811,397	23,083	284,101	105,630	69,643	73,392
1908	793,395	25,711	286,945	112,042	61,166	71,309
1909	793,893	26,206	28,381	123,770	60,411	67,243
1910	793,453	36,920	286,729	117,836	63,111	69,680
1911	799,829	31,303	290,804	136,899	52,275	66,257
1912	791,420	29,187	284,148	136,344	55,639	64,826
1913	798,878	27,840	290,065	128,324	61,012	63,004
1914	791,203	29,561	284,610	133,070	61,681	59,400
1915	789,599	24,273	282,565	162,201	42,698	67,622
1916	789,755	41,087	280,779	133,697	53,683	66,280
1917	789,508	41,098	278,196	135,307	65,999	72,303
1918	787,539	45,683	259,166	155,707	56,920	67,927
1919	783,367	59,517	256,616	128,307	59,653	70,700
1920	786,266	42,912	266,283	131,796	64,272	68,145
1921	779,720	40,170	270,610	137,380	63,690	63,080
1922	778,112	35,501	275,197	135,742	73,516	65,497
1923	777,534	32,812	279,169	112,098	69,072	62,978
1924	774,572	28,194	286,079	105,851	77,379	63,028
1925	770,237	40,490	293,769	96,435	79,636	57,036
1926	767,457	43,053	299,823	103,001	71,252	55,313
1927	765,986	44,746	312,757	110,144	57,382	52,005
1928	763,434	46,856	320,597	97,383	66,977	53,592
1929	762,355	32,835	330,124	90,101	67,462	58,446
1930	759,000	26,900	336,396	91,130	60,110	53,580
1931	754,986	29,832	346,070	77,471	66,077	45,347
1932	751,910	32,670	354,070	84,790	62,620	42,390
1933	751,138	37,170	357,114	109,048	49,932	40,974
1934	747,100	28,600	353,400	104,200	62,300	36,200
1935	742,700	23,100	343,500	106,600	59,900	37,100
1936	732,400	26,300	344,800	105,100	60,200	37,300
1937	734,800	42,000	346,700	106,600	55,700	29,000
1938	730,909	25,996	345,251	115,129	60,664	36,645
1939	728,806	23,543	341,780	107,747	63,888	35,537
1940	724,666	23,853	309,797	83,079	85,002	52,770
1941	730,912	17,304	264,626	113,578	83,178	62,201
1942	728,014	17,500	238,797	113,449	81,130	56,132
1943	725,235	12,217	209,992	144,085	82,130	50,605
1944	723,432	8,862	194,764	135,294	91,806	54,603
1945	725,102	16,984	197,776	97,495	116,764	57,982
1946	724,172	12,415	193,999	99,515	117,783	55,540
1947	723,410	25,254	196,407	110,198	106,684	51,160
1948	725,918	11,518	190,197	111,938	113,540	55,995
1949	723,319	15,625	188,827	98,254	111,396	56,992

Table 1

CROPS (ACRES)						
Year	Farmed Area	Fallow	P.Pastures Heath (inc. Rough Grazings	Wheat	Barley	Oats
1950	722,677	15,773	182,910	126,422	98,036	52,719
1951	724,126	20,894	186,089	122,226	103,017	45,863
1952	721,858	20,376	179,565	113,046	125,637	48,132
1953	721,805	10,870	176,668	121,693	120,000	47,000
1954	720,092	13,850	164,834	141,988	110,887	39,391
1955	718,714	16,731	168,388	137,959	119,268	37,454
1956	716,698	14,673	168,023	151,103	118,947	38,606
1957	716,355	22,000	170,650	140,600	126,423	33,745
1958	715,738	16,099	166,880	150,485	130,266	31,107
1959	712,718	35,160	168,588	121,757	148,642	25,784
1960	710,773	13,460	162,569	152,626	155,316	25,565
1961	690,802	27,992	163,061	110,464	184,500	21,836
1962	690,079	12,943	159,653	153,473	167,583	17,928
1963	686,193	15,406	154,927	136,709	191,179	13,295
1964	684,766	16,905	149,171	150,606	193,130	10,690
1965	683,181	10,548	140,726	178,294	191,271	10,042
1966	688,246	13,620	130,502	165,674	213,132	9,844
1967	684,697	13,794	110,690	160,222	217,743	12,147
1968	676,619	10,582	115,209	116,223	204,420	13,251
1969	669,619	14,877	110,691	143,444	221,876	13,943
1970	674,748	12,962	104,302	171,992	193,776	12,969
1971	679,095	9,059	107,775	191,724	186,798	15,263
1972	651,395	9,139	130,262	203,305	178,457	14,923
1973	673,520	6,555	104,431	209,346	170,005	12,987
1974	675,701	7,183	104,685	217,631	139,392	10,798
1975	673,667	26,201	97,960	189,177	173,547	9,838
1976	674,090	8,672	96,826	232,076	145,436	10,307
1977	631,566	7,222	116,393	213,294	167,293	9,603
1978	631,107	6,281	115,544	237,075	151,848	6,708
1979	630,697	6,488	107,605	255,276	146,226	4,917
1980	666,712	5,703	89,646	259,745	142,686	5,748
1981	667,482	5,787	87,425	274,604	134,076	5,238
1982	665,067	5,332	82,189	281,184	131,485	4,631
1983	666,240	9,398	78,696	282,642	127,224	3,719
1984	666,218	4,297	78,726	307,702	111,641	3,445
1985	662,523	3,443	76,481	294,374	116,944	4,423
1986	634,019	3,275	75,665	304,970	105,407	3,304
1987	663,866	3,275	75,171	304,970	105,407	3,299
1988	663,049	5,626	95,510	264,457	113,229	N/A (1)
1989	661,843	5,137	96,369	294,705	92,227	2,865
1990	659,749	3,450	97,453	284,978	89,591	2,267
1991	657,924	3,196	99,150	274,770	82,764	2,193
1992	658,551	2,712	74,156	275,123	77,022	2,472
1993	659,282	3,462	73,312	231,179	66,793	1,879
1994	657,027	2,541	73,035	246,387	58,375	3,072
1995	651,321	2,887	71,138	249,400	63,911	2,524
1996	647,703	2,131	70,096	262,059	64,306	2,242
1997		1,368		268,936	70,854	1,963

(1) 3,697 appears in this entry but includes mixed corn and rye.

Table 2

CROPS (ACRES)					
Year	Peas	Clover & Grasses	Linseed & Flax	Beans	Lucerne
1900	17,362	97,543	56	24,240	
1901	*18,071	102,735	82	23,600	
1902	19,984	95,430	73	23,241	
1903	20,190	93,842	51	22,611	
1904	19,386	85,856	3	24,388	
1905	20,828	72,279	80	26,495	13,408
1906	19,422	75,819		30,480	14,483
1907	20,635	78,688		33,018	16,644
1908	21,126	78,966		33,193	18,067
1909	23,408	67,242		33,670	18,554
1910	22,525	70,248		26,483	15,923
1911	21,316	63,454		33,090	13,662
1912	24,634	59,615		31,496	14,285
1913	25,059	70,190		29,986	14,721
1914	24,811	64,261		31,620	14,183
1915	22,151	63,510		30,725	13,675
1916	18,974	80,717		26,989	14,043
1917	19,208	70,362		19,261	12,569
1918	17,450	64,535		25,517	10,203
1919	20,068	72,171		30,899	8,798
1920	22,632	66,558	3,256	27,704	10,204
1921	21,620	70,840	1,120	24,940	11,150
1922	26,204	42,327	1,079	28,409	11,891
1923		75,787	1,137	24,754	14,325
1924	28,009	63,846	835	23,916	16,737
1925	19,855	73,919	721	19,358	13,809
1926	19,673	66,858	696	20,058	11,551
1927	18,724	62,291	601	18,955	10,223
1928	18,167	64,456	815	15,257	8,327
1929	20,291	62,576	675	14,988	8,291
1930	18,630	71,770	790	16,180	9,220
1931	15,785	78,683	597	14,607	10,138
1932	16,540	65,670	260	12,800	8,700
1933	16,704	39,381	229	14,338	7,554
1934	17,100	45,200	100	14,300	7,500
1935	15,700	57,200		10,600	7,600
1936	15,100	52,400	200	9,700	7,900
1937	10,900	58,600		8,300	6,500
1938	14,149	40,933		10,528	5,370
1939	*3,715	46,164	568	12,627	5,645
1940	*3,286	56,446	3,549	5,957	5,694
1941	*4,835	43,555	7,111	17,199	5,005
1942	*6,132	61,545	5,392	17,006	5,440
1943	*8,052	66,638	2,951	21,351	See Clover
1944	*4,928	78,775	2,628	24,174	& Grasses
1945	4,822	87,326	2,776	16,153	See Clover
1946	3,591	94,326	2,344	13,359	& Grasses
1947	3,765	90,825	5,412	4,967	See Clover
1948	5,030	80,289	9,565	4,185	& Grasses
1949	*4,478	93,582	8,348	4,858	

Crown Copyright ©

Note: Beans 1961-1981 includes peas.
* Peas for stockfeeding.

Table 2

CROPS (ACRES)					
Year	Peas	Clover & Grasses	Linseed & Flax	Beans	Lucerne
1950	5,398	68,562	7,040	5,688	See Clover
1951	4,416	81,524	5,471	6,474	& Grasses
1952	4,432	73,657	3,280	6,980	16,725
1953		65,726	1,260	8,531	14,141
1954	5,736	71,721	1,244	7,146	14,918
1955	3,531	74,949	809	6,836	13,950
1956	3,148	70,622	46	7,722	13,530
1957	2,340	80,710		8,209	12,122
1958	2,864	74,532		10,254	10,206
1959	1,930	81,708		8,638	7,767
1960	2,076	69,626		10,372	6,634
1961	See beans	87,125		11,432	6,518
1962	See beans	80,366		12,268	5,468
1963	See beans	78,172		11,570	5,460
1964	See beans	68,939		14,724	4,893
1965	See beans	56,357		20,104	3,997
1966	See beans	45,854		22,811	3,033
1967	See beans	40,776		28,344	2,264
1968	5,298	40,259		42,502	
1969	See beans	37,079		40,883	2,279
1970	See beans	37,293		32,920	2,332
1971	See beans	35,423		27,239	2,942
1972	See beans			23,884	
1973	See beans	34,792		29,152	3,618
1974	See beans	33,087		30,207	3,388
1975	See beans	38,771		19,216	3,527
1976	See beans	34,750		21,451	3,924
1977	See beans			17,774	
1978	14,330			17,314	3,502
1979				19,451	
1980		25,166		20,661	
1981		25,821		18,749	
1982	11,821	22,852		14,679	
1983	6,646	22,459		12,179	
1984	8,983	18,826		10,309	
1985	13,379	18,495		11,421	
1986	20,629			16,180	
1987	20,629	17,835		18,786	
1988	22,462			28,607	
1989	19,638			21,407	
1990				19,792	
1991	12,587			18,154	
1992	13,345	61,411		16,867	
1993	14,580	21,343		21,987	
1994	14,528	20,174		23,818	
1995	14,303	18,618		23,304	
1996	14,886	19,401		20,399	
1997	17,386			19,048	

Note: Beans 1961-1981 includes peas.
* Peas for stockfeeding.

Table 3

CROPS (ACRES)							
Year	Small Fruits	Orchards	Potatoes	Turnips Swedes	Mangolds	Sugar Beet	Oilseed Rape
1900	1,996		9,629	20,276	26,325		
1901	1,983	2,501	9,975	18,080	27,441		
1902	2,065		9,975	18,080	27,441		
1903	1,991		9,474	17,248	25,612		
1904	2,061		8,828	17,803	24,349		
1905	2,018		10,549	17,855	26,036		
1906	2,058		10,285	17,620	27,078		
1907	1,994	2,797	10,205	15,105	27,327		
1908	2,150		10,885	15,402	26,588		
1909	2,229		11,643	16,257	28,066		
1910	2,148		10,701	16,122	27,886		
1911	2,187	2,903	11,765	16,395	28,368		
1912	2,048		12,811	14,137	28,326		
1913	2,014	1,775	12,659	12,694	26,180	158	
1914	2,134		13,770	13,266	26,825		
1915	2,094		13,773	10,460	22,204		
1916	2,262	3,399	12,537	10,930	18,642		
1917	2,194		13,208	14,349	18,876		
1918	1,945		20,586	11,849	20,690		
1919	1,813		13,333	11,732	18,438		
1920	1,579		16,728	11,009	19,138		
1921	2,070		19,300	8,810	18,030		
1922	2,088		18,273	7,365	19,040		
1923	1,818		15,378	9,203	19,712		
1924	2,489		13,371	7,449	17,974	214	
1925	2,600		15,469	6,870	16,031	1,631	
1926	2,699		15,088	6,761	12,552	5,598	
1927	2,854		17,595	6,241	10,631	9,925	
1928	2,803	4,513	16,540	6,755	10,377	5,254	
1929	2,784		16,475	6,573	10,723	7,873	
1930	2,970		12,170	5,380	11,090	12,190	
1931	2,949		13,438	4,627	9,349	10,365	
1932	2,600	5,122	17,660	4,470	8,390	10,670	
1933	2,829	5,800	19,358	4,011	8,295	15,568	
1934	2,900	6,500	17,400	3,500	8,000	15,800	
1935	2,800	6,800	16,200	3,500	8,600	15,100	
1936	2,900	7,300	15,200	3,000	7,400	14,200	
1937	2,700	7,900	15,900	3,200	6,200	10,900	
1938	2,596	7,416	17,268	2,744	6,119	12,436	
1939	2,469	7,921	13,708	2,264	6,326	12,820	
1940	2,475	8,252	16,107	3,647	6,872	13,997	
1941	2,247	8,583	19,261	3,200	9,128	15,396	
1942	2,112	8,382	21,703	2,955	8,932	19,913	
1943	1,864	8,341	22,902	1,809	9,969	20,302	
1944	1,869	8,384	23,829	1,819	10,112	21,330	
1945	1,410	9,185	28,113	1,881	9,690	19,967	
1946	1,805	9,604	29,424	1,850	9,082	21,087	
1947	1,941	10,166	28,601	1,776	7,626	18,999	
1948	2,229	10,714	35,733	1,937	8,386	21,191	
1949							

Table 3

CROPS (ACRES)							
Year	Small Fruits	Orchards	Potatoes	Turnips Swedes	Mangolds	Sugar Beet	Oilseed Rape
1950	3,032	12,145	31,390	720	7,659	21,695	
1951	2,959	12,838	28,202	1,159	7,011	21,112	
1952	2,577	13,273	26,834	917	5,145	20,760	
1953	3,041	12,891		696	4,417	21,330	
1954	2,404	13,371	28,321	544	3,870	22,394	
1955	2,272	13,392	29,981	586	3,739	21,506	
1956	2,153	13,392	32,330	736	3,243	21,352	
1957	2,109	13,080	30,000	686	2,838	20,824	
1958	2,159	13,080	33,009	491	2,437	22,085	
1959	2,145	12,889	30,819	773	2,174	21,072	
1960	2,345	12,586	31,010	798	1,840	21,244	
1961	2,218	12,502	24,352	342	1,386	20,688	
1962	2,209	12,266	26,679	312	1,185	20,263	
1963	2,212	12,226	27,382	337	916	19,375	
1964	2,097	11,504	27,425	278	697	19,540	
1965	1,943	11,121	25,792	235	478	20,280	
1966	1,761	9,927	21,664	189	341	20,741	
1967	1,645	9,702	23,285	168	284	21,627	
1968	1,652	9,571	23,750	124	234	22,086	148
1969	1,683	9,560	22,142	136	178	21,807	32
1970	1,723	9,388	24,829	105	131	21,941	78
1971	1,521	9,024	24,264	155	165	21,976	112
1972	1,647	8,941	22,805	345		21,802	182
1973	1,695	7,744	22,215	198	143	22,245	865
1974	1,583	7,146	28,839	139	164	21,823	2,185
1975	1,620	6,792	19,290	328	140	20,473	4,433
1976	1,854	6,575	19,332	368	212	21,350	6,333
1977	1,770	6,372	18,747	452	113	16,502	7,987
1978	1,901	6,036	17,299	323	91	16,225	10,650
1979	1,928	6,120	15,684	229	83	15,612	13,300
1980	2,232	5,705	14,854	276	113	15,412	17,635
1981	2,151	5,374	13,538	192		13,933	24,030
1982	2,146	5,033	13,431	217		12,606	32,616
1983	1,938	4,974	13,777	251	81	11,571	39,119
1984	1,872	4,638	13,431	135	116	10,554	43,857
1985	1,763	4,633	13,002	148	155	10,734	45,163
1986	1,778	4,609	12,367	79	167	10,907	42,518
1987	1,778	4,507	12,367	79	167	10,907	42,518
1988	1,684	4,322	12,522	79		10,413	52,643
1989	1,714	4,310	12,703			10,420	50,580
1990	1,659	4,161	12,965	86		10,793	56,239
1991	1,827	4,050	12,248	59		10,339	64,941
1992	1,637	3,996	13,496	54		10,487	63,560
1993	1,598	4,006	12,779	79		10,196	50,938
1994	1,506	4,068	11,737	113		10,423	44,627
1995	1,462	2,872	12,174			10,596	44,264
1996	1,383	2,699	12,957			10,680	46,688
1997	1,217	2,791	12,191			10,707	58,329

Table 4

		LIVESTOCK				
Year	Horses	Cows in Milk/Calf	Bulls	Other Cattle	Pigs	Sheep
1900	30,729	35,636			80,866	295,334
1901	39,285	34,575		51,522	67,824	265,096
1902	30,088	33,984			73,288	254,220
1903	31,179	33,917			89,263	235,364
1904	31,917	37,588			100,932	221,926
1905	31,101	39,415			82,777	212,975
1906	30,987	42,156			71,897	220,633
1907	39,160	42,886		51,813	83,689	219,888
1908	31,205	32,266			94,034	251,933
1909	31,760	32,943			81,339	269,583
1910	32,287	33,660			77,901	245,045
1911	30,626	46,095		56,944	91,693	227,185
1912	30,013	33,435			85,404	194,774
1913	26,685	42,023		50,117	70,571	184,168
1914	26,233	33,440			81,570	172,352
1915	23,894	43,595		57,148	77,484	160,870
1916	24,829	31,256			77,484	170,559
1917	25,309	31,256			63,919	161,014
1918	25,384	29,626			54,418	141,221
1919	25,472	30,250			57,966	136,699
1920	24,224	40,052		48,231	65,290	111,381
1921	24,530	41,750		44,410	90,620	105,320
1922	24,004	43,848		49,159	87,370	93,045
1923	29,913	47,841		49,042	96,100	108,931
1924	23,399	49,153		47,183	126,565	113,578
1925	23,072	49,883		51,630	101,775	140,226
1926	22,780	51,925		54,008	79,010	150,717
1927	22,158	53,372		52,528	95,987	149,130
1928	21,566	52,168		45,246	107,031	152,307
1929	20,235	52,884		45,392	82,691	151,810
1930	19,456	51,200		44,800	74,400	146,100
1931	18,541	54,640		48,070	84,110	182,600
1932	17,990	56,813		53,204	102,344	223,250
1933	17,500	59,800		60,000	110,400	213,500
1934	16,100	62,700		55,800	114,000	176,400
1935	15,600	61,100		51,600	122,800	159,300
1936	14,800	60,800		50,300	132,400	160,600
1937	14,200	58,900			131,300	164,500
1938	13,848	56,488	2,594	51,446	137,145	170,061
1939	13,200	59,659	2,732	50,288	135,765	165,485
1940	12,863	62,141	2,996	56,680	126,207	169,106
1941	13,423	62,815	3,054	52,742	80,660	126,935
1942	11,358	65,627	3,556	55,773	62,087	101,192
1943	12,390	66,106	3,533	58,877	50,920	77,034
1944	11,430	63,905	3,340	58,772	52,920	61,512
1945	N/A	40,118	2,132	60,500	60,029	59,494
1946	N/A	39,267	2,066		58,517	58,261
1947	N/A	38,884	2,050		44,894	51,120
1948	N/A	39,938	2,086		60,716	47,309
1949	7,075	40,556	1,995		85,594	41,243

Table 4

LIVESTOCK						
Year	Horses	Cows in Milk/Calf	Bulls	Other Cattle	Pigs	Sheep
1950	8,625	41,619	1,803		93,138	38,261
1951	7,517	40,520	1,653		135,689	41,554
1952	6,583	40,018	1,470		168,421	42,972
1953	5,621	55,396	1,765	62,301	166,000	35,000
1954	4,955	37,581	1,177		198,441	41,180
1955	4,624	37,791	1,152		198,708	57,411
1956	3,993	38,500	1,030		189,320	61,461
1957	3,616	54,600	999	57,355	197,523	71,000
1958	3,271	37,562	876		206,882	80,702
1959		35,814	819		184,904	91,935
1960		32,662	815		177,779	90,320
1961	2,938	52,721	797	77,899	178,975	93,687
1962		51,286	733	72,708	195,836	97,036
1963		48,944	646	70,765	194,181	94,415
1964		46,079	793	71,797	213,859	95,794
1965		40,860	751	70,991	234,813	87,038
1966		26,663	740		230,813	81,053
1967		26,202	769		237,424	73,183
1968		25,752	517		246,913	63,351
1969		25,122	700		246,477	81,535
1970		25,093	710		260,313	54,220
1971		24,663	500		275,455	49,590
1972		27,359		65,197	276,445	46,816
1973		25,133	542		286,787	49,438
1974		24,962	517		278,475	
1975		23,885	546		249,712	48,065
1976		22,660	485		257,510	40,487
1977		24,535		103,727	269,267	42,557
1978		22,123	435		258,848	47,456
1979	48	23,092	586	100,217	253,375	50,677
1980		18,953	357		224,842	52,918
1981		16,725	347		214,893	57,127
1982		16,114	296		206,611	61,956
1983		16,553	324		186,666	63,490
1984		16,107	284	47,483	186,622	64,456
1985		14,790	256	46,221	186,666	69,039
1986		14,288			180,040	77,286
1987		14,219	250		169,186	76,444
1988		13,582	221	46,134	157,135	82,196
1989			225		169,186	76,444
1990		11,329	254	35,419	135,969	87,464
1991		10,680	255	42,007	128,751	83,639
1992		9,464	246	50,563	136,180	87,069
1993		8,742	248	47,484	132,252	82,747
1994		8,646	256	46,894	132,042	78,710
1995		8,563	258	46,578	122,726	79,323
1996		9,506	271		111,923	76,083
1997		9,703	289	42,168	118,011	76,815

Table 5

Livestock			
Year	Chickens	Ducks	Turkeys	Geese
1900				
1901				
1902				
1903				
1904				
1905				
1906				
1907				
1908				
1909				
1910				
1911				
1912				
1913	738,820	45,686	18,329	6,607
1914				
1915				
1916				
1917				
1918				
1919				
1920				
1921	694,810	59,286	13,246	9,046
1922				
1923				
1924				
1925				
1926				
1927				
1928				
1929				
1930	1.695m	43,209	25,254	
1931	1.921m	46,550	21,032	
1932	2.285m	50,895	21,202	
1933	2.395m	49,107	31,220	
1934	2.365m	40,000	30,000	
1935	2.249m	42,000	29,000	
1936	2.240m	42,300	30,700	
1937	1.907m	34,900	28,900	6,500
1938	1.960m	35,444	34,391	
1939	1.971m	33,746	40,149	
1940	2.005m	39,716	31,212	
1941	1.408m	40,150	20,429	
1942	1.160m	49,469	16,539	
1943	.855m	48,112	11,875	
1944	.981m	51,569	13,405	
1945	1.222m	53,171	17,961	16,505
1946	1.310m	50,641	18,497	15,336
1947	1.395m	50,997	18,982	15,953
1948	1.802m	61,353	28,477	19,605
1949				

Table 5

Livestock			
Year	Chickens	Ducks	Turkeys	Geese
1950	2.175m	59,136	30,687	14,408
1951	2.267m	43,653	32,038	11,093
1952	2.296m	51,271	34,299	11,569
1953	2.200m	41,820	41,680	
1954	2.173m	26,502	42,911	10,421
1955	2.383m	20,588	44,604	8,623
1956	2.473m	22,329	83,605	8,340
1957	2.500m	16,606	81,145	6,967
1958	2.553m	15,979	87,038	6,041
1959	2.787m	15,462	99,726	5,287
1960	3.313m	15,325	109,957	5,054
1961	3.229m	14,410	191,155	
1962	3.208m	9,797	162,002	
1963	3.458m	8,315	166,415	
1964	3.322m	6,167	200,392	
1965	3.807m	6,361	147,017	Plus EL GL
1966	3.553m	10,129	163,457	2,923
1967	4.002m	9,750	157,265	3,175
1968	3.890m	8,832	207,615	2,321
1969	4.402m	9,143	126,702	1,931
1970	4.468m	7,881	134,430	1,897
1971	3.640m	8,258	73,589	2,186
1972	2.378m			
1973	4,098m	3,930	91,994	2,014
1974				
1975				
1976				
1977	3.150m			
1978	4.107m	5,231	58,562	2,313
1979	3.865m	6,441	68,412	
1980				
1981				
1982				
1983				
1984	3.184m	8,625	43,680	2,178
1985	3.178m	9,602	53,461	2,602
1986	3.055m	8,570		
1987				
1988	3.285m			
1989	3.569m	10,200	35,106	2,877
1990	3.718m	20,040		2,783
1991	3.636m	25,050		3,049
1992	3.744m	22,300		3,004
1993	3.692m	32,514		3,532
1994	3.615m	34,815		2,937
1995	2.953m	40,108		2,523
1996				
1997				

317

Footnotes

ABBREVIATIONS USED IN FOOTNOTES

1. EADT   East Anglian Daily Times
2. ECS   Essex County Standard
3. EFJ   Essex Farmers Journal

4. ERO   Essex Records Office
5. EYFJ   Essex Young Farmers Journal
6. VCH   Victoria County History

A TRULY RURAL LANDSCAPE
1. 'General View of Agriculture of the County of Essex' Vol.1 p.194
2. V.C.H. vol. 2 p.445
3. Martin, John Wesley 'The Ruin of Rural England' 1901, North End Place, Ford End, Felsted, p.14.
4. E.R.O. DU251/89, Joseph Page Diaries.
5. Hussey, Stephen, 'The Changing Face of the Essex Countryside 1900-1950'. The Kenneth Newton Lecture, Chelmsford Cathedral 30 October 1997.
6. Made at Peasenhall in Suffolk.
7. 'General View of Agriculture of the County of Essex' Vol.1 p.44.
8. 'The Great Landowners of Great Britain and Ireland' 1876 by John Bateman who was Squire of Brightlingsea Hall.

BEFORE THE WAR 1900–1914
1. Owner of the Orsett Estate. Father of (Sir) Francis Whitmore whose son, John, sold the remainder of the estate in 1968.
2. Collins, Dr.E.J.T., *The History of the Orsett Estate 1743–1914*
3. Martin, John Wesley, *The Ruin of Rural England* (1901)
4. Hussey, Dr.Stephen, *The Changing Face of the Essex Countryside 1900–1950* Kenneth Newton Lecture, Chelmsford Cathedral, 30 October 1997.
5. *English Farming Past and Present* (1912) (R.E.Prothero later Lord Ernle).
6. ECS 31 May 1902.
7. Rider Haggard,H. *Rural England (1906)*.
8. ECS 19 April 1902.
9. Curtis, Gerald, *The Story of the Sampfords* (1981),p.231.
10. ECS 11 January 1902, Field Marshall (farming correspondent) the pseudonym of Thomas Pertwee, a Langenhoe farmer.
11. Agricultural Correspondent, The Times 1911.
12. Curtis, Gerald, *The Story of the Sampfords* (1981),p.233.
13. Sometimes spelt Roothing, the 8 contiguous parishes; High, Leaden, Margaret, Abbess, White, Beauchamp, Aythorpe and Berners. Approx 11,862 acres which Kelly's directories considered 'very fruitful'.
14. Orsett Hall Collection quoted by Dr.E.J.T.Collins, Thurrock Local History Society No.9, 1965.
15. ECS 15 March 1902.
16. Minutes of First Business Meeting, ECF 17 May 1904, Chairman E.J.Cheney.

THE WARTIME BOOM
1. E.F.J. February 1929. J.A.Venn, Gilbey Lecturer in Agricultural Economics, Cambridge University speaking to the Essex Farmers Union 4 February 1929 at the East Anglian Institute of Agriculture, Chelmsford.
2. Whetham, Edith H. *Beef, Cattle and Sheep 1910–1940* University of Cambridge, Department of Land Economy pub. 1976.
3. Curtis, Gerald C. *The Story of the Samfords* (1981) p.234.
4. Gavin, Sir William, *Ninety Years of Family Farming* (1967) p.169.
5. Rowland Prothero was the author of 'English Farming Past and Present' pub.1912 and considered one of the best agricultural histories written. Prothero's tome resulted from an article which he wrote in *The Quarterly Review* in 1885, later expanded into a book in 1888. Finalised in its major form in 1912 and resulted in various editions up to 1961.
6. E.F.J. May 1942. Oldershaw, A.W. *Farming In 1914–18* p.26.
7. Watson, John *Savills, a Family and a Firm, 1652–1977* pub.1977 p.97.
8. The Herts. and Essex Observer 3 March 1917.
9. IBID 28 July 1917.
10. E.F.J. May 1942, Oldershaw, A.W., *Farming In 1914–18* p.26.

11. E.C.S. 12 June 1920.
12. IBID 3 January 1920.

THE BLACK SPOT OF THE CENTURY
1. Watt, Hew, *Changes in Agriculture in Thurrock 1880/1965* pub. Thurrock Local History Society (1965), p.22.
2. Brown, William. Taped interview with Andrew Phillips 1995.
3. Cooper, Ashley *The Long Furrow*, Bulmer Historical Society (1982), p.170.
4. Pertwee, Norman, *Not Roses all the Way 1924–1980* pub.1980 p.8.
5. Gavin, Sir William, *Ninety Years of Farming* (1967), p.72.
6. Essex Farmers Union Handbook 1930, p.163.
7. E.C.S. 26 June 1920.
8. Essex Farmers Union Handbook 1930, p.273.
9. Private papers of Alfred Blomfield donated to the Farmers Club, Whitehall Place, London, by his daughter, Helen Blomfield in 1997.
10. Essex Farmers Union Handbook 1927, p.115 et seq.
11. E.F.J. February 1929, p.562.
12. IBID November 1937 *Farming Losses in the Eastern Counties.*
13. Cooper, Ashley, *The Long Furrow* (1982) p.169.
14. Sadler, Ralph Newman, *Sunshine and Showers* (1988) p.52.
15. Cooper, Ashley, *The Long Furrow* (1982) p.168.
16. Hawkeswell, John, Son-in-Law of Mrs.Judges who bought Langenhoe Hall. Privately printed and distributed. Hawkeswell later emigrated to Canada.
17. Mr.Venn, *The Gilby Lecture to Essex Farmers.*
18. E.F.J. 1929, P.560.
19. IBID June 1938.
20. IBID January 1939.
21. IBID October 1938, p.51

A LAND OF MILK AND MONEY
1. Watt, Hew, Essex Countryside, March 1996, *Scottish Links.*
2. Young, Arthur *General View of the Agriculture of the County of Essex* 1807 p.63.
3. Fussell, G.E. F.R.Hist.S. E.F.J. June 1950, *A Scotsman on Essex Farming in 1825.*
4. Collins, E.J.T. *The Great Agricultural Depression in South Essex*, Thurrock Local History Society No.9 Spring 1965.
5. Cooper, Ashley, *Our Mother Earth; of the Furrow Born*, Bulmer Historical Society, November 1998.
6. E.F.J. August 1947, Note by Mr. David Gemmill to an article "The Invasion" by G.L. Waring.
7. McConnell, Primrose, Jour.R.A.S.E. 1891, p.311 *Experiences of a Scotsman on the Essex Clays,*
8. IBID
9. Brown, William, Interview by Andrew Phillips 29 October 1995 Tape deposited in Essex Audio History Library.
10. Dunlop, James, Kilmarnock Standard, 4 July 1924, *Scotsmen Farming in England.*
11. McConnell, Primrose, Jour.R.A.S.E. 1891, *Experiences of a Scotsman on the Essex Clays.* p.315.
12. Halstead Gazette 19 March 1938.
13. Dunlop, James, *Scotsmen Farming in England*, Series of articles printed in the 'Kilmarnock Standard' from 4 July 1924 and succeeding issues. The Glasgow Herald published an article under the title 'Southward Ho!" in December 1890 with the emphasis upon the parishes from which the Essex settlers had come.
14. Kilmarnock Standard 18 November 1916.
15. Filby née Young, Kathleen *The Annals of the Young family During Three Generations of Farming in Essex*, 1896–1995.

SAVED – BY THE WAR
1. Watt, Hew, *Changes in Agriculture in Thurrock from 1880 1965* Local History Society 1965 p.22.
2. EFJ December 1940, p.21.
3. IBID June 1940 p.187.
4. Finch, Peter, *Warmen Courageous*, Burrows, 1957.
5. Curtis, Gerald, The Sampfords in War and Peace, 1900–50 (1981) p.263.
6. EFJ December 1939 p.499.
7. IBID December 1939 p.543.
8. IBID June 1940, p.12.
9. IBID December 1941, p.9.
10. IBID February 1943. Report by Mrs. Solly-Flood.

11. Clive Beale & Geoff Owen, *Writtle College. The First Hundred Years 1893–1993* p.34.
12. EFJ May 1943 p.11.
13. National Farm Survey of England and Wales. A Summary Report HMSO 1946.
14. The returns were quarterly until 20 years after the war when they became annual with a 'sample' taken quarterly to alert trends.

THE RED CROSS SALES
 1. EFJ March 1942.
 2. IBID May 1943.
 3. Letter from Mrs. Churchill 2 June 1942 in author's collection.
 4. EFJ December 1943.
 5. IBID June 1944.
 6. IBID March 1946.

THE WAR AG – VITAL OR VICIOUS
 1. Sadler, Ralph Newman, *Sunshine and Showers* (1988) Chapter 10 describes his work during the war.
 2. Wentworth-Day, James *Harvest Adventure* (1946) p.278.
 3. Winnifrith, Sir John, *The Ministry of Agriculture Fisheries and Foods, New Whitehall Series No.11* (1962) p.28. Winnifrith was the Permanent Secretary to MAFF 1959/67.
 4. Sadler, Ralph Newman, *Sunshine and Showers* (1988) p.60.
 5. Sworn statement by Mrs.Ellie Brown to E.P. Algar, J.P. 13 September 1943.
 6. Wentworth-Day, James *A Farming Adventure* p.141.
 7. The Ministry of Food existed as a separate entity until 1955, by which time food rationing had been abolished. It's Minister became known for his "Woolton Pies" and received many photographs from thankful mothers which were captioned "One of Lord Woolton's Babies". He was considered a genial and successful Minister of Food.
 8. Sadler, Ralph Newman, *Sunshine and Showers* (1988) p.71.
 9. Trist, P.J.O. *A Brief Account of the Undeveloped Building Land in Essex* (1948) chap.7.
10. E.F.J. November 1943 p.17. Comment by 'Observer'.
11. Trist, P.J.O. *A Brief Account of the Undeveloped Building Land in Essex* (1948) p.92.
12. IBID
13. EFJ *Food Production Campaign*. June 1942.
14. IBID
15. Sadler, Ralph Newman, *Sunshine and Showers* (1988) p.69.
16. Wentworth-Day, James, *Harvest Adventure* (1946).
17. IBID p.272
18. J.R.Wilson, Rector of Peldon 1939/48 recalled "the Home Guard keeping watch from the church tower". *A Short History of The Parish Church of St.Mary the Virgin* Rev.Anthony Gough (1970).
19. Wentworth-Day, James, *Harvest Adventure* (1946) p.271.
20. IBID p.275.
21. IBID p.273.
22. IBID.
23. EYFJ, The Aerodrome, (February 1948)

THE GREAT ESTATES
 1. Newby, Howard, *Green and Pleasant Land*, 1979. Newby was at Essex University when this book was written.
 2. John Bateman, The Squire of Brightlingsea Hall, analysed and published the results of the 1873 Landowners Survey in 1880.
 3. Spurrier, Felice, *The Maynards of Easton Lodge*, 1987.
 4. Ward, John T, "Farm Sale Prices Over a Hundred Years", Estates Gazette, 3 May 1958.
 5. Thompson, F.M.L., *English Landed Society in the 19th Century*, 1963, p.124.
 6. Gavin, Sir William, *Ninety Years of Family Farming*, p.106.
 7. IBID p.107.

NEW OWNERS – SKY HIGH PRICES
 1. EFJ February 19.4, p.312.
 2. ECS 29 September 1963.
 3. IBID 29 May 1964.
 4. Firmin, Joe, ECS 2 August 1968.
 5. EFJ July 1972.
 6. Wright, Michael, speaking at NFU Annual Dinner, Marks Tey, December 1972.

7. ECS 11 May 1979.
8. IBID "Countrywise", 5 January 1979.
9. IBID "Countrywise", 6 June 1986.
10. IBID "In The Country", 7 February 1992.

THE COUNTY SHOW
1. Street, A.G., *Farmers Weekly*, 9 June 1961
2. Walker, John, *A History of the Essex Show*. Insert in 1969 show catalogue
3. EFJ January 1944, AGM of the EAS 7 January 1944 chairman Charles Round (Birch Hall)
4. *The Essex Weekly News*, 21 January 1944
5. ECS 4 June 1965
6. IBID 10 December 1965
7. IBID 4 June 1965
8. IBID 4 June 1965, D. Burns MD Colchester Tillage Ltd
9. IBID December 1948
10. Thom, James,EYF Magazine, *Golden Grain*, Vol.1 No.1 March 1955
11. ECS 25 May 1956, Farming notes by Pioneer
12. ECS 16 June 1966
13. EFU Committee Minutes 24 June 1966, Mr.Victor Gray in the Chair. Meeting at the Institute of Agriculture, Writtle
14. Crisp, N.V., *A Standholder's Viewpoint*, EFJ June 1948 P.21

THE ESSEX FARMERS UNION
1. ECS 15 February 1839. An observation by John Conyers, Copped, Epping, who was the current president and chairman. He commented "to that rule he had strictly adhered".
2. Baker, Stanley, *Milk to Market*, 1973 Chap.4, 'The Dark Ages' p.57.
3. EFJ April 1970, 'Fifty Years in Chelmsford Branch 1919–1969', Fred Smith.
4. IBID December 1969 p.9.
5. Taped conversation with author, March 1998.
6. EFJ 1947, Yeomans, Miss E.C. 'The Early Years', p.17
7. IBID October 1938, Obituary of John Gill by S.L. Bensusan, p.494
8. IBID 1977 p.1
9. IBID 1947, Yeomans, Miss E.C. 'The Early Years'

ESSEX YOUNG FARMERS
1. EFJ February 1925, p.313
2. IBID November 1930, p.384
3. IBID April 1931
4. IBID June 1931
5. IBID February 1932
6. IBID November 1934
7. IBID April 1936
8. IBID October 1936
9. IBID July 1934
10. IBID July 1936. Address by the Principal at the Annual Prize Distribution at Mid-Essex Technical College and School of Art, Chelmsford. The Institute of Agriculture remained in the centre of Chelmsford until 1939
11. Later claims have been made that the Federation was formed in 1943. The first annual report was reported in the Essex Farmers Journal in March 1945 and claimed that the Federation was one year old
12. EFJ March 1945
13. EYFJ Vol.1 No.1, November 1947
14. IBID February 1946, p.19
15. IBID 1978
16. IBID March 1984
17. IBID March/April 1998
18. EFJ August 1936, p.323
19. IBID June 1946
20. IBID September 1945
21. Beale, Clive and Owen, Geoff, *Writtle College, The First Hundred Years*, 1993, p.69.

THE DECLINE OF FARMWORKERS
1. VCH Vol.2 p.357.

2. Clouting, H.W., "The Agricultural Worker", Essex Farmers Handbook 1930,p.21.
3. Brown, A.F.J, "Meagre Harvest", E.R.O. 1990, p.228.
4. Essex Chronicle, 28 July 1933.
5. ECS 28 February 1975.
6. EFJ "Essex Farm", December 1953, p.17.
7. IBID October 1950.
8. ECS 11 January 1902.
9. EFU Handbook 1923 p.246.
10. IBID "Tractors" 1923, p.188.
11. EFJ "Machinery on Farm Land", March 1925, p.8.
12. EFU 1928 p.362.
13. IBID May 1933, p.132.

THE GRANARY OF ENGLAND
1. Walker, J.E., Statement of Objections to Development on behalf of the EFU. Walker was county secretary 1938–67.
2. EFJ May 1949, p.6.
3. EFU Handbook 1924 'Cereal Crops 1923', W.Hasler p.211.
4. IBID p.221.
5. ECS 1 January, 1910.
6. EFJ July 1931, p.221.
7. ECS 1 December, 1967.
8. IBID 10 February, 1989.
9. IBID 18 November 1966. Desmond Bird, PRO for the Compound Animal Feedstuffs Manufacturers Association, speaking to Maldon farmers.
10. IBID 19 November 1971.
11. IBID 18 February 1972.
12. Ward, Gladys, 'Essex Farming in 1801', *Essex Archeological Transactions*, Third Series, Vol.185 p.192.

OLD CROPS AND NEW ONES
1. ECS 20 August 1965.
2. IBID 11 April 1968
3. IBID 11 February 1972 'Essex Growers Show Grain Maize is .here to Stay', Roger Freeman.
4. IBID 19 May 1972.
5. IBID 5 April 1991 'In the Country'
6. IBID 6 February 1976.
7. Essex Chronicle 17 September 1982.
8. Interview with author July 1998.
9. ECS 28 August 1970.
10. IBID 3 November 1969.

SPUDS, SUGAR AND MANGEL WORZELS
1. ECS 8 January 1910.
2. IBID 15 October 1910.
3. Gavin, Sir William, *Ninety Years of Family Farming* p.103.
4. EFJ February 1924.
5. IBID November 1949, 'Twenty-Five Years of Sugar Beet'. Walker, John, p.35.
6. Essex Weekly News, 1 October 1926, Rev'd. W.J. House.
7. EFJ August 1949.
8. EFJ November 1930.
9. IBID October 1936.
10. IBID February 1928, p.560.
11. IBID August 1954, p.15.
12. ECS 18 September 1970.
13. Young, Arthur, *A Six Weeks' Tour through the Southern Counties of England and Wales*. 1768.
14. Griggs, Messrs. *Board of Agriculture, General View of the Agriculture of Essex, With Observations on the Means of it's Improvement*. 1794.
15. VCH Vol.2, p.475.
16. A Small farm in Paglesham, *Essex Within Living Memory*, pub. Federation of Essex Womens Institutes 1995. The Authorship of this particular memory is not ascribed.
17. VCH Vol.2, p.476.

18. Young, Arthur, 'General View of the agriculture of the county of Essex drawn up for the consideration of The Board of Agriculture and Internal Improvement'(1807).
19. Caird, James *English Agriculture in 1850/51* p.139.
20. Gavin, Sir William, *Ninety Years of Family Farming*, 1967 p.100.

APPLES AND ORCHARDS
1. EFU Handbook *Fruit Production* 1930, p.263.
2. EYFJ May/June 1951.
3. EFU Handbook , 1927, p.332.
4. EFJ November 1947, p.18.
5. IBID December 1949.
6. IBID Clark, Leslie, *The Horticultural Show at Boreham* November 1950, p.18.
7. IBID August 1937.
8. IBID April 1943.
9. ECS *Foxash Tenants are Beating the Dutch at their Own Game* 8 May 1970.
10. IBID 22 May 1920.
11. Benham, Maura *The Story of Tiptree Jam, The First Hundred Years*, 1885-1985
12. Letter from W.E.Gladstone 23 January 1886 to A.C. Wilkin.
13. Haggard, H.Rider Rural England 1906.
14. Mingay, G.E. *Rural Life in Victorian England*, 1976.
15. VCH, Vol.2 p.482.
16. Brewster, Harold *Seabrooks; A History in Fruit Growing*, Boreham, History Tales and Memories of an Essex Village, Edited by Elinor Burgess and Mary Rance.
17. ECS 19 April 1973.
18. IBID 25 January 1974. Speaking at a conference at Agriculture House, Knightsbridge, to 40 delegates from every EEC country.
19. IBID *Countrywise*, 2 May 1980.
20. IBID *In the Country*, 16 June, 1995.

LEA; THE VALLEY OF THE SEA OF GLASS
1. V.C.H. Vol.2 (1907) p.474.
2. Brown, A.J.F. *Meagre Harvest ERO*, (1990), p.226.
3. Rooke, Peter, 'The Lea Valley Nursery Industry', *Hertfordshire's Past*, 42 p.2.
4. Collins, E.F.J. *Thurrock Local History Society* No.9 (1965) p.18.
5. Ernle, Lord, *British Agriculture Past and Present* (1912)
6. EYFJ. May 1949, Gunary, G. 'Market Gardening'.
7. Stevenson, R.A. *The Glasshouse Industry of the Lea Valley. A Brief Outline of its History and its Present State* (1993).R.A. Stevenson secretary of the Lea Valley Branch of the NFU.
8. Rook, Peter, 'The Lea Valley Nursery Industry, *Hertfordshire's Past*, p.12.
9. Coppock, J.T. *An Agricultural Geography of Britain*, p.279.

THE IMPORTANCE OF COWS
1. ECS 15 March 1902.
2. EFJ February 1976.
3. Gavin, Sir William, *Ninety Years of Family Farming 1876–1966* pub.1967, p.217.
4. IBID
5. McConnell, Primrose, RASE Journal 1891.
6. VCH Vol.2 p.341.
7. EFJ July 1926, p.191.
8. EFJ 'Milk Clubs' by J.C. Leslie, p.435.
9. ECS 3 August 1984.

BEEF AND SHEEP IN A DRY COUNTRY
1. Young, Arthur, *General View of the Agriculture of the County of Essex, 1807*. Vol.2 p.303
2. ECS, 12 December 1958, "Beef Cattle is the Farmers Best Bet at the Moment.
3. IBID 25 March 1958
4. IBID 15 December 1967
5. IBID 1 June 1990
6. VCH Vol 2, p.380
7. IBID, Round, J.H. *The Domesday Survey* Vol 1, p.371
8. EFJ, Hill, Alfred, *Domesday Book*, August 1928, p.264

9.   Trow-Smith, Robert, *A History of British Livestock Husbandry 1700–1900*, pub.1959, p.24
10. The calculation used by the EEC for computing animal stocking levels when the Dairyherds Conversion Scheme was introduced in 1973.
11. EFJ, October 1953
12. Trow-Smith, Robert, *A History of British Livestock Husbandry 1700–1900* pub.1959, p.278

THE ESSEX PIG
1.   Young, Arthur, *General View of the Agriculture of the County of Essex, 1807*, Vol. 2 p.340
2.   Astor and Rowntree, *British Agriculture, The Principles of Future Policy*, 1938, p.228
3.   Trow-Smith, Robert, *A History of British Livestock Husbandry 1700–1900* (1959), p.292
4.   Wilson, R. M., *The History of the Essex Pig Society*, December 1949.
5.   McLean, Donald, "Who Killed the Essex Pig?' *Essex Countryside*, January 1978, Vol. 26, p.252.

CHICKENS – FROM SCAVENGERS TO BIG BUSINESS
1.   Young, Arthur, *General View of the Agriculture of the County of Essex*, Vol.2, p.361
2.   Ernle, Lord, ([R. E. Prothero]) *English Farming Past and Present*, 1912, p.390
3.   Astor, Viscount and Rowntree, Seebohn, *British Agriculture* 1938
4.   EFJ *Essex Farms*, May 1953
5.   IBID *The Poultry Industry in Essex*, 1946
6.   Cooper, Ashley, *The Long Furrow*, p.232
7.   EFU Annual Handbook 1927
8.   EFJ May 1931, p.112
9.   ECS 'Countrywise' 2 August 1985
10. IBID 'Farming Notes' 27 September 1957
11. EFJ December 1953 p.15

FROM WINDMILLS TO MERGERS
1.   VCH Vol.1 pp 426–698.
2.   IBID Vol.2 p.447.
3.   Essex Review "The History of Corn Milling In Essex", Marriage & Smith.
4.   ECS 13 June 1969.
5.   Pertwee, Norman, *Not Roses all the Way 1924–1980*, pub.1980
6.   Roper, Eleanor, M.C. *Seedtime – The History of Essex Seeds 1989* p.192.
7.   Gavin, Sir William, *Ninety Years of Family Farming*. p.2.
8.   Lewis, Bernard, L. *The Story of Cornard Mills*, Hugh Baker 1994. p.35.
9.   Brooks, John, Letter to author 15 December 1997.
10. EFJ 1953.
11. ECS 7 April 1977.
12. Roper, Eleanor, M.C. Seedtime – *The History of Essex Seeds 1989* p.208.
13. Press Conference 1977.
14. Kelly's Directory 1929.
15. EFJ February 1925.

MERCHANTS WHO CAME AND WENT
1.   ECS 10 March 1967.
2.   Pertwee, Norman, *Not Roses All The Way*, 1924–1980, p.66.
3.   IBID p.54
4.   IBID p.91.
5.   ECS 22 April 1988.
6.   IBID 22 August 1983. Letter to the Editor.
7.   Lewis, Bernard L, *Green Flour Mills Ltd. From 1896–1989*, pub. 1994.
8.   ECS 26 November 1971 "Countrywise".
9.   IBID 6 July 1979.
10. EFU Handbook 1924, p.399

THE MACHINERY PEOPLE
1.   Kelly's Directory, 1902.
2.   EFJ February 1933, p.541.
3.   Kemp, Lt.Cdr. P.K. *The Bentall Story*, 1805–1955.
4.   Brigden, Roy, *The Agricultural Engineers*, 1986, p.173.
5.   Corder-Birch, Adrian *A History of Great Yeldham*, 1994.

6.   Tyler, Colin, *Digging By Steam* 1977, p.37.
7.   EFJ Sydney E. Darby "65 Years of Remembrances", December 1947, p.27.
8.   Haining, John and Tyler, Colin, *Ploughing By Steam* 1970, p.90.
9.   EFJ August 1928.
10. VCH Vol.2, p.497.
11. Kelly's Directory 1890, p.42.
12. IBID 1929.
13. ECS 15 January 1971, "New Beet Harvester Shines in Sticky Essex Clay", Roger Freeman.
14. Gibbard, S. *Ford Tractor Conversions* 1995, p.113.
15. IBID p.126.
16. IBID p.132
17. IBID p.132
18. ECS 13 February 1976, "Doe Show Hits a New Record", Freeman, Roger.
19. IBID 26 October 1975.
20. Gibbard, Stanley, *Tractors at Work*, Vol.2, 1995.
21. "The Perry Foundation", Golden Jubilee Brochure 1937-87.
22. Onslow, Richard, *A History of The Animal Health Trust*.
23. Ninth Annual Report AHT 1956/7.
24. The Times, 19 June 1956.

1950–2000
1.   Matthews, Joe, *Essex its Farming and Horticulture*, published by Barclays Bank plc and EFU.
2.   Sadler, R.N., *Sunshine and Showers*, p.59.
3.   Daily Mail 2 February 1939.
4.   ECS 26 March 1965.
5.   IBID 9 January 1970, "Land at Work".
6.   Smith, J.R. "Foulness", ERO 1970, p.33. The farmer's name is not mentioned but the farm is Rugwood.
7.   EYF Magazine, "Golden Grain", Vol.1, No.1, March 1953, "Just Water", John Pilkington, Arlesford Lodge.
8.   EFJ September, 1958.
9.   IBID January, 1959.
10. ECS 21 April, 1972.
11. Currie, Davison, Ogley, "Essex Weather Book", Froglet Publications, 1992, p.133.
12. ECS 28 August, 1987.
13. IBID 5 April, 1944.
14. IBID 4 February 1966, Comments of Annie Ironside, Regional Poultry Officer.
15. IBID 9 October 1970.
16. Essex Countryside, "Fowl Pest in Essex" January 1972, Vol.2, (issue 180), p.4.
17. EFJ September 1954. Comment by EFU Sec. John Walker, p.11.
18. ECS 22 October, 1972.
19. ECS 24 February 1989, "Countrywise".
20. Squier, Jeremy, Letter to author 1998.
21. EADT "Conservation Work Eventually Accepted", Slater, John, 18 July 1998.

THE MARKETS CLOSE
1.   White's Directory of Essex, 1863, p.678.
2.   Romford Recorder Souvenir 1997, p.17.
3.   Londsdale, Pearl *Changes in an Essex Village*, 1994, p.76.
4.   East Essex Gazette, 7 January 1955.
5.   Report to Estate and Cattle Market Committee. Colchester Town Council. Reported in Essex County Standard, 7 February, 1920.
6.   The Dunmow Centenary Book 1894-1994, p.12.

Index

Chelmsford, Colchester, Dunmow, Maldon, Saffron Walden are not listed as they appear with regularity.